Mastering and Managing the FDA Maze

Mastering and Managing the FDA Maze

Medical Device Overview

A Training and Management Desk Reference
for Manufacturers Regulated
by the Food and Drug Administration

Gordon Harnack

ASQ Quality Press
Milwaukee, Wisconsin

DISCLAIMER OF IMPLIED WARRANTIES

This desk reference is intended to provide a simple source for a portion of any device manufacturer's FDA regulatory training and managing requirements and many of FDA's inspectional expectations. Each medical device manufacturer is wholly and totally responsible for their Quality System's compliance with federal laws and FDA regulations.

Neither the author, the American Society for Quality, nor any distributor of this desk reference makes any claim that it provides a complete reference or that it contains all the information necessary for any device manufacturer's complete FDA medical device regulatory compliance.

The author, the American Society for Quality, and all distributors hereby disclaim, with respect to any services or obligations of this desk reference, all implied warranties to the maximum extent allowable by law. The author, the American Society for Quality, and all distributors shall have no liability for special or consequential damages, including lost profits, of any reader or medical device manufacturer.

The reader and medical device manufacturer agree that the maximum of the author's, the American Society for Quality's, and all distributors' liability and indemnification available under any conditions shall be the documented cost of this desk reference.

Mastering and Managing the FDA Maze
Gordon Harnack

Library of Congress Cataloging-in-Publication Data

Harnack, Gordon, 1939–
    Mastering and managing the FDA maze : medical device overview : a
training and management desk reference for manufacturers regulated
by the Food and Drug Administration / Gordon Harnack
        p.   cm.
    Includes Index.
    ISBN 0-87389-455-3 (alk. paper)
    1. Medical instruments and apparatus—Safety regulations—United
States.   2. United States.   Food and Drug Administration—Rules and
practice.   I. Title.
KF3827.M4H37   1999
344.73'042—dc21   99–19229
                                                              CIP

10 9 8 7 6 5 4 3 2

ISBN 0-87389-455-3

Acquisitions Editor: Ken Zielske
Project Editor: Annemieke Koudstaal
Production Coordinator: Shawn Dohogne

ASQ Mission: The American Society for Quality advances individual and organizational performance excellence worldwide by providing opportunities for learning, quality improvement, and knowledge exchange.

Attention: Bookstores, Wholesalers, Schools and Corporations:
ASQ Quality Press books, videotapes, audiotapes, and software are available at quantity discounts with bulk purchases for business, educational, or instructional use. For information, please contact ASQ Quality Press at 800-248-1946, or write to ASQ Quality Press, P.O. Box 3005, Milwaukee, WI 53201-3005.

To place orders or to request a free copy of the ASQ Quality Press Publications Catalog, including ASQ membership information, call 800-248-1946. Visit our web site at http://www.asq.org.

Printed in the United States of America

∞   Printed on acid-free paper

American Society for Quality

☒ASQ ™

Quality Press
611 East Wisconsin Avenue
Milwaukee, Wisconsin 53202
Call toll free 800-248-1946
http://www.asq.org

CONTENTS

FIGURES

ACKNOWLEDGMENTS

The writing of this book was catalyzed by a consulting requirement to provide medical device manufacturers with a documented training resource on Food and Drug Administration medical device regulatory affairs. The author, both in his consulting practice and work on this book, has been encouraged and assisted by a number of individuals who need to be thanked and acknowledged. They are, in alphabetical order:

Karen White Becker, who provided needed editing and suggestions, making this a better book.

Robert "Bob" Brookman, President, Business Systems Architects, Los Gatos, CA, who gave support and advice early in my consulting career.

Cézanne Marie Harnack, daughter and cheerleader.

H. Andrew Harnack, brother and coauthor of *"The Internet Guide for Students and Writers,"* St. Martin's Griffin, New York, who provided support and advice.

Lynne Namka (Harnack), Ed.D., psychologist, wife, author, and cheerleader.

Any and all errors in this book are the responsibility of the author.

How to Use This Training and Managing Desk Reference

Writing anything requires making decisions. Writing a desk reference about the Food and Drug Administration's (FDA) medical device regulatory "maze" requires deciding who is the target audience is. The target audiences for this desk reference include the following:

- Regulatory professionals, who know their responsibility to keep their firm's employees trained and competent on FDA device regulations and who need a preliminary desk reference that can be used throughout their enterprise to help train and ensure compliance
- Neophytes, who know nothing about FDA but need a resource that provides both broad and specific information in sufficient detail to be useful
- Beginners, who know a little about FDA and need to know more and have a reference tool to be more effective and productive in their job
- Intermediates, who knows enough about FDA to know they need to know more and need a reference tool that provides them with both more basics and executable detail
- Busy managers, who need to know regulatory requirements and FDA expectations in order to manage compliance in their specific activity
- Busy executives (CEOs, COOs, and operations managers, whom FDA holds responsible for all regulatory compliance), who also need a desk reference with specific information to quickly assess regulatory compliance, identify noncompliance, and review corrective, preventive, and compliance actions

Except for the casual observer, one quickly learns that there is a lot of "stuff" whenever you deal with FDA. Understanding this is the first part of dealing successfully with the FDA's information maze.

Next you need to decide how much of that information you **need** to know. That is different from how much of it you **want** to know. Very few people get deeply involved with FDA rules and regulations because they want to know it. Deciding how much you need to know is difficult to assess. What FDA stuff you need to know will depend upon your job and FDA's expectations.

Now comes the hard part: You need to decide where you can get the FDA information you need to know. There is a mountain of information related to FDA regulations and compliance. The task is daunting, and very few busy manufacturers are regulatory mountain climbers. Reading the regulations provides only a small part of the picture. Understanding of *what they mean* and *how compliance can be achieved in your environment* is the key.

Because the number of FDA rules and regulations is staggering and their content is boring and because you need insight and limited detail, **Mastering and Managing the FDA Maze: Medical Device Overview, A Training and Management Desk Reference** was written.

For the neophyte, beginner, intermediate, busy manager, and busy executive, reading the **Introduction** (How to Use This Training and Management Desk Reference) and the first two chapters, **FDA Laws and Regulations** and **FDA Inspections** should be required. Neophytes, beginners, and intermediates should then review the **Introduction, Scope,** and **Definitions** of the remaining chapters to decide whether they need to know what those chapters contain. The firm's regulatory professional can help identify chapters of special interest to individuals and activities within their own enterprise.

Managers, executives, and individuals requiring a deeper understanding of the larger FDA regulatory picture, should read Chapter 3, **Quality System and Management Responsibilities.**

They should then minimally review the **Introduction, Scope, Definitions,** and the information associated with the **Procedures, Documents and Records Icon,** and the **FDA Investigator Icon** (discussed below) for the remaining chapters.

Obviously, most material dealing with FDA is not exciting, which makes it difficult to teach and more difficult to learn. This presents problems for both the teacher and the student and a challenge for any firm's regulatory professional or consultant. Because of the way this desk reference was designed, readers will become aware of repetition of concepts. Not all repetition is bad, and some will help reinforce thoughts, thus improving their chance of being retained by the reader and appropriately implemented when and where required.

This desk reference attempts, through the use of graphical **icons,** to provide "eye candy" for the reader, make boring FDA stuff more appealing, easier to learn, master, and manage. What is meant by eye candy? The desk reference's eye candy includes a group of graphical icons, such as the **Definitions icon,** illustrated below, which highlight definitions specific to each chapter's subject.

Definitions   **Definitions icon** provides a visual aid to the definitions of terms and words associated with that chapter. Definitions are always printed in 10 point type.

Each chapter may be read as an isolated chapter, and chapters may be read days, weeks, or months apart. This means that definitions specific to a chapter may be repeated in later chapters should their use be required, without the reader having to looking back to those earlier chapters. In the back of the desk reference there is a **Glossary** of all of the words and terms used with the **Definitions icon.**

Also in the back of the desk reference is a list of **Abbreviations,** not all of which are used in the desk reference but which may be encountered by reading other FDA regulatory materials.

Wherever appropriate, the **Regulation icon,** illustrated below, highlights a part of or a complete regulation specific to that chapter's subject.

What the   This is the **Regulation icon,** identifying a section or all of the regulation specific to the
regulation states   chapter's subject. Lengthy or complex regulations are broken down into individual parts. Regulations are always printed in 10 point type.

After each **Regulation icon** are discussions of what that regulation means. These discussions use more eye candy icons to illustrate important concepts and information or to identify procedures, documents, or records required for regulatory compliance.

For example:

Remember!   The **Remember icon** identifies an important concept or thought.

Don't forget!   The **Don't Forget icon** identifies a different important concept or thought.

Something to note!   The **Something to Note icon** identifies yet another important concept or thought.

Under each **Regulation icon** is usually a **Required Procedures, Documents, and Records icon,** illustrated below:

Required procedure(s), document(s), and record(s)   The **Required Procedure(s), Document(s), and Record(s) icon** identifies specific procedures, documents, and records required by the regulation or that section of the regulation. In many cases, lists or tables are provided with brief but specific detail. Procedures, documents, and records information is always printed within rules.

Some chapters contain references to **EXHIBITS,** which are at the end of the chapter and contain one or more individually numbered **Figures.** A list of **FIGURES** can be found on pages *vii* and *viii.* Because the Design Control regulations, § 820.30, are new, emphasis has been placed on providing examples of documents and checklists that might be associated with general device manufacturing design control. Figures are provided to provide insight into how regulatory compliance might be attempted; they are general and only begin to scratch the surface of FDA complete procedure, document, or record compliance.

Applicable chapters also end with an **FDA Investigator icon,** illustrated below:

What the FDA Investigator wants to see during an inspection   The **FDA Investigator icon** provides a discussion of what FDA Investigators are trained to review, expect manufacturers to "establish and maintain," and what consequences may result from noncompliance or nonconformities. These sections are especially helpful to busy managers, executives, and regulatory professionals to help them quickly focus on key issues. FDA Investigator information is always printed within rules.

We would welcome your comments and suggestions on how to make future editions of **Mastering and Managing the FDA Maze: Medical Device Overview** a better desk reference. To assist you in making comments and providing corrections, please use the **"Comment and Corrections Form"** on the inside back cover of this desk reference. Please feel free to make copies of this form and forward your comments and/or corrections to our offices by FAX or mail:

Oracle Consulting Group
5398 Golder Ranch Road., Suite. 1
Tucson, AZ 85739
(520) 825-0556 FAX
(520) 825-0555 Voice

Comments and corrections can also be sent by e-mail to:

<author@fdamaze.com>

1

FDA Laws, Regulations, and Medical Device Oversight

INTRODUCTION

This chapter of **Mastering and Managing the FDA Maze: Medical Device Overview Training and Management Desk Reference** discusses FDA laws, regulations, and medical device oversight.

SCOPE

The goal of Chapter 1 is to provide an overview of FDA laws, regulations, and FDA oversight affecting medical device manufacturers. Significant detail has been omitted, and readers are advised to undertake further training to ensure proficiency and understanding to the level required for FDA compliance.

Chapter 1 discusses the backbone of FDA compliance (that is, the applicable U.S. federal law and FDA regulations) and outlines the activities and structure of FDA's medical device oversight. Subsequent chapters provide additional overview material on FDA inspections, specific elements of the Quality System Regulation (QS Regulation), and other applicable regulations.

Although this discussion is specific to *medical device* manufacturing establishments, it does not deal with establishment's manufacturing foods, drugs, or biologics. Each of these regulatory environments has its own specific FDA laws, regulations, and inspections, which are beyond the scope of this training.

Compliance with FDA laws and regulations requires both understanding and use of the regulatory language of the FDA. Readers and students should integrate these FDA regulatory terms and their meanings into applicable parts of their regulatory activities.

This chapter provides applicable definitions. Readers should understand these definitions, all of which, unless followed with an asterisk, are quoted from FDA's Quality System Regulations.

FDA LAWS

Definitions

Act means the Federal Food, Drug, and Cosmetic Act, as amended (secs. 201–903, 52 Stat. 1040 *et seq.*, as amended (21 U.S.C. 321–394)). Note: Also referred to as the FD&C act.

Device means an instrument, apparatus, implement, machine, contrivance, implant, in vitro reagent, or other similar or related article, including any component, part, or accessory, which is:

(1) Recognized in the official National Formulary, or the United States Pharmacopoeia, or any supplement to them
(2) Intended for use in the diagnosis of disease or other conditions, or in the cure, mitigation, treatment, or prevention of disease, in man or other animals, or
(3) Intended to affect the structure or any function of the body of man or other animals, and which does not achieve its primary intended purposes through chemical action within or on the body of man or other animals and which is not dependent upon being metabolized for the achievement of its primary intended purposes.* [Title 21, USC, Section 201 (h)]

Class I medical devices are subject only to FDA's general controls because they are the least complicated and present the least risk. FDA's general controls are thought to provide reasonable assurance of the safe and effective use of these devices.*

Class II medical devices are more complicated and present greater risks than Class I devices. Class II devices are subject to FDA's general controls. Furthermore, because those controls do not provide reasonable assurance of the devices' safety and effectiveness, these devices are also subject to any specific performance standard, postmarket surveillance, patient registry, guidelines, and premarket notification requirements promulgated by FDA. See Premarket Notification.*

Class III medical devices are devices that cannot be classified as Class I or Class II because (1) general and special controls do not provide reasonable assurance of their safety and effectiveness, (2) the device is to be used in supporting or sustaining human life, and (3) the device presents a potential unreasonable risk of illness or injury. See Premarket Approval.*

General controls include (1) an establishment's FDA registration (Form FDA 2891), (2) a product listing (Form FDA 2892), (3) compliance with FDA's good manufacturing practice regulations, now called Quality System Regulations, and (4) adverse event reporting or FDA's Medical Device Reporting regulations.*

Intended use is the objective intent of the manufacturer or person(s) legally responsible for the labeling of devices and includes labeling claims, advertising matter, and oral or written statements by such firms or their representatives.*

Manufacturer means any person who designs, manufactures, fabricates, assembles, or processes a finished device. Manufacturer includes but is not limited to those who perform the functions of contract sterilization, installation, relabeling, remanufacturing, repacking, or specification development, and initial distributors of foreign entities performing these functions.

Premarket notification or 510(k) is a process by which a submitter notifies the FDA at least 90 days prior to the submitter's introduction of any appropriate device (some Class I and most Class II devices) into interstate commerce. The submission must include a product classification based on safety and effectiveness. Based on the information and data submitted, the FDA determines whether the product is substantially equivalent to a legally marketed predicate device. When FDA makes that finding, the submitter is notified and may market the device. These submissions are called 510(k)s because the report submission requirement is identified in the Act under section 510(k).*

Premarket approval (PMA) is a process by which Class III medical devices are approved to enter into interstate commerce. Typically, a PMA requires detailed labeling identifying the intended use of the device, clinical and nonclinical studies documenting safety and effectiveness, and a detailed summary of the medical device's design, development, verification, validation, manufacturing, and distribution.*

Predicate device is a medical device legally marketed prior to May 28, 1976, the date of The Medical Device Amendments of 1976 enactment. A predicate device is required for all Class I or Class II medical devices.*

Major Medical Device Amendments

The Medical Device Amendments of 1976
The Safe Medical Devices Act of 1990
The FDA Export Reform and Enhancement Act of 1996
The Food and Drug Administration Modernization Act of 1997

Law Discussion

Background

The FDA is one of a dozen or so federal agencies under the direction and control of the Department of Health and Human Services. The FDA is mandated by the federal government to enforce Title 21 of the United States Code, typically referred to as 21 U.S.C., as amended. The FDA consists of a variety of departments or centers charged with the oversight of specific activities, including foods, human and animal drugs, biologics, cosmetics, and medical devices. The center responsible for medical devices is the Center for Devices and Radiological Health (CDRH). Its responsibilities and organization are discussed later in this chapter.

Something to note!

The FDA is a Federal agency with about 9,000 employees, an almost $1-billion budget, and oversight over one in every four dollars spent by American consumers. The products FDA oversees are worth over $1 trillion. FDA management costs each American approximately $3.00 per year.

Early Laws

In 1906 Congress enacted the Food and Drugs Act of 1906, which prohibited the interstate commerce of misbranded and adulterated food, drinks, and drugs.

Congress enacted the Federal Food, Drug, and Cosmetic Act of 1938, referred to as the Act, to ensure that (1) foods are safe to consume and are produced under sanitary conditions; (2) drugs and devices are safe and effective for their intended use; (3) cosmetics are safe and made from appropriate ingredients; and (4) labeling and packaging is truthful, informative, and not deceptive.

This Act initiated federal control over medical devices.

The Medical Device Amendments of 1976

Remember!

In 1976 Congress amended the Act with The Medical Device Amendments of 1976 to ensure the safety and effectiveness of medical devices.

The 1976 Amendments introduced the concept of premarket notifications and approvals, predicate devices, and performance standards.

The Safe Medical Devices Act of 1990 (SMDA of 1990)

The SMDA of 1990 established new standards for devices whose use cause or contribute to the death, serious illness, or injury of a patient.

The FDA Export Reform and Enhancement Act of 1996 (Export Reform Act)

The Export Reform Act provided for the legal export of medical devices that are not legally marketed in the United States, provided that a series of requirements is met, including an approval in one of 24 "Tier 1" countries known to have well-developed product clearance systems. Tier 1 countries include Australia, Canada, Israel, Japan, and the European Union.

The Food and Drug Administration Modernization Act of 1997 (FDAMA of '97)

Remember!

FDAMA of '97 establishes a framework for efficient premarket review and fine-tunes FDA's authority. This act's implementations included changes in FDA's oversight of device tracking, reporting, PMAs, and 510(k)s, required the agency to identify recognized standards, and instituted new approaches to labeling claims and intended uses.

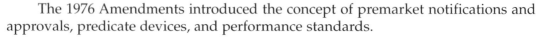

FDA REGULATIONS

Definitions *Federal Register* is the legal newspaper published every business day by the National Archives and Records Administration (NARA). It contains federal agency regulations; proposed rules and notices; and executive orders, proclamations, and other presidential documents. The *Federal Register* informs citizens of their rights and obligations and provides access to a wide range of federal benefits and opportunities for funding. NARA's Office of the Federal Register prepares the *Federal Register* for publication in partnership with the Government Printing Office (GPO), which distributes it in paper, on microfiche, and on the worldwide web.*

Regulations are the FDA's implementation of federal law. Regulations require preannouncement, publishing in the *Federal Register,* a public comment period, and review of any comments prior to finalization.*

Title 21 Food and Drugs of the Code of Federal Regulations is printed and available from the Superintendent of Documents, Box 371954, Pittsburgh, PA 15250–7954. Chapter I of Title 21 is composed of parts 1–1299, which are specific to the Food and Drug Administration and published in eight volumes.

Specific FDA Regulations That Apply to Medical Device Manufacturers (among others)

Code of Federal Regulations (CFR), Title 21, Part 7—Enforcement Policy and specifically
    Subpart C—Recalls
CFR, Title 21, Part 11—Electronic Records; Electronic Signatures
CFR, Title 21, Parts 800–1299 and specifically 21 CFR 801 Labeling
CFR, Title 21, Parts 800–1299 and specifically 21 CFR 803 Medical Device Reporting
CFR, Title 21, Parts 800–1299 and specifically 21 CFR Part 806 Medical Devices; Reports of
    Corrections and Removals
CFR, Title 21, Parts 800–1299 and specifically 21 CFR 807 Establishment Registration and Device
    Listing for Manufacturers and Distributors of Devices
CFR, Title 21, Parts 800–1299 and specifically 21 CFR 814 Premarket Approval of Medical Devices
CFR, Title 21, Parts 800–1299 and specifically 21 CFR 820 Quality System Regulations
CFR, Title 21, Parts 800–1299 and specifically 21 CFR 821 Medical Device Tracking Requirements
CFR, Title 21, Parts 800–1299 and specifically 21 CFR 860 Medical Device Classification
    Procedures
CFR, Title 21, Parts 800–1299 and specifically 21 CFR 861 Procedures for Performance Standards
    Development
CFR, Title 21, Parts 800–1299 and specifically 21 CFR 892 Radiological Devices
CFR, Title 21, Parts 800–1299 and specifically 21 CFR 895 Banned Devices
CFR, Title 21, Parts 800–1299 and specifically 21 CFR 1010–1050 Performance Standards for
    Electronic Products

Discussion

Overview of Applicable Regulations

CFR, Title 21, Part 7–Enforcement Policy and specifically Subpart C–Recalls
These regulations implement FDA's responsibilities and authority to require the recall of failed, defective, adulterated, or misbranded medical devices.

Based on FDA assessment, this regulation empowers the agency with significant powers to remove, through a variety of recall actions, devices the agency feels require removal from the marketplace.

CFR, Title 21, Part 11—Electronic Records; Electronic Signatures

These regulations implement FDA's criteria for and authority over the use of electronic records and electronic and handwritten signatures executed in electronic records. FDA requires such uses to be trustworthy, reliable, and generally equivalent to paper records and handwritten signatures executed on paper. Any computer systems, both hardware and software controls, and documentation maintained under Part 11 must be readily available for and subject to FDA inspection.

Don't forget!

CFR, Title 21, Parts 800–1299 and specifically 21 CFR 801 Labeling

These regulations implement FDA's responsibilities for and authority over each medical device's labeling.

Labeling includes all labels and other written, printed, or graphic matter on any device or its containers or wrappers or accompanying such devices and includes advertising matter and oral or written statements made by manufacturers or their representatives.

Remember!

CFR, Title 21, Parts 800–1299 and specifically 21 CFR 803 Medical Device Reporting

These regulations implement FDA's responsibilities and authority requiring manufacturers, users and distributors to report health-related medical device failures and their corrections or removals from the market. 21 CFR 803 is an important regulation for devices that may have health-related failures.

CFR, Title 21, Parts 800–1299 and specifically 21 CFR Part 806 Medical Devices; Reports of Corrections and Removals

These regulations implement FDA's responsibilities and authority concerning the reports of corrections and removals provisions of the Safe Medical Devices Act of 1990 (the SMDA). FDA implements that responsibility and authority by requiring that manufacturers, importers, and distributors report promptly to FDA any corrections or removals of a device undertaken to reduce a risk to health posed by the device or to remedy a violation of the Act caused by the device that may present a risk to health.

Corrections and removal-reporting regulations became effective May 17, 1998, and manufacturer's compliance will be high on FDA Investigator's checklist during inspections.

Something to note!

CFR, Title 21, Parts 800–1299 and specifically 21 CFR 807 Establishment Registration and Device Listing for Manufacturers and Distributors of Devices

These regulations implement FDA's responsibilities and authority requiring manufacturers to (1) register initially on Form FDA 2891 and update annually thereafter on an agency-supplied form and (2) to list manufactured devices on Form FDA 2892 and to update this list annually. This is the regulation that initiates FDA oversight of medical device manufacturers.

CFR, Title 21, Parts 800–1299 and specifically 21 CFR 814 Premarket Approval of Medical Devices

These regulations implement FDA's responsibilities and authority over Class III devices and the manufacturer's requirement to submit PMAs on appropriate devices.

Don't forget! *CFR, Title 21, Parts 800–1299 and specifically 21 CFR 820 Quality System Regulations*
These regulations implement FDA's responsibilities and authority over medical device manufacturers' management, design, development, verification, manufacture, validation, distribution, installation, support, quality assurance, and records for each new or listed device.

This regulation is the major regulatory thrust of day-to-day FDA oversight of device manufacturers and the focus of this book. Most of the remaining chapters are specific to the Quality System Regulations, which were finalized October 7, 1996, and, except for Subpart C—Design Controls, were effective June 1, 1997. Subpart C—Design Controls was effective one year later on June 1, 1998. These regulations are also the agency's attempt to harmonize medical device regulation with international quality standards, specifically ISO 9000.

Quality System Regulation Subparts and Sections

The Quality System Regulation consists of the following subparts and sections:

Subpart A—General Provisions
820.1 Scope
820.3 Definitions
820.5 Quality system

Subpart B—Quality System Requirements
820.20 Management responsibility
820.22 Quality audit
820.25 Personnel

Subpart C—Design Controls
820.30 Design controls

Subpart D—Document Controls
820.40 Document controls

Subpart E—Purchasing Controls
820.50 Purchasing controls

Subpart F—Identification and Traceability
820.60 Identification
820.65 Traceability

Subpart G—Production and Process Controls
820.70 Production and process controls
820.72 Inspection, measuring, and test
    equipment
820.75 Process validation

Subpart H—Acceptance Activities
820.80 Receiving, in-process, and finished
    device acceptance
820.86 Acceptance status

Subpart I—Nonconforming Product
820.90 Nonconforming product

Subpart J—Corrective and Preventive Action
820.100 Corrective and preventive action

Subpart K—Labeling and Packaging Control
820.120 Device labeling
820.130 Device packaging

Subpart L—Handling, Storage, Distribution, and Installation
820.140 Handling
820.150 Storage
820.160 Distribution
820.170 Installation

Subpart M—Records
820.180 General requirements
820.181 Device master record
820.184 Device history record
820.186 Quality system record
820.198 Complaint files

Subpart N—Servicing
820.200 Servicing

Subpart O—Statistical Techniques
820.250 Statistical techniques

Don't forget!

The Quality System Regulations are philosophically simple:
Comply with the regulations.
Say what you do.
Do what you say.
Document that you have done what you say.

As FDA regulations say time after time: "[E]stablish and maintain written procedures that . . ." are current, reviewed, approved, accurate, and documented with records that clearly illustrate that the procedures are being followed.

This book endeavors to inform readers of their responsibilities and the required procedures, documents, and records that FDA Investigators will look for during inspections.

Regulatory Oversight in the World Community

Something to note!

The new Quality System Regulations are FDA's attempt to harmonize its oversight of medical device design, development, and manufacturing with the voluntary international quality standards, especially the twenty ISO 9000 quality elements. See "FDA Regulations and ISO 9000" at the end of this chapter.

CFR, Title 21, Parts 800–1299 and specifically 21 CFR 821 Medical Device Tracking Requirements

These regulations implement FDA's responsibilities and authority over (1) medical devices that are permanently implanted or life sustaining or life supporting or (2) any other device that the agency may designate.

The FDA Modernization Act (FDAMA) of 1997, among other changes, removed the mandatory tracking requirements and limited FDA's discretionary authority to require tracking to only Class II and III devices that are:

- reasonably likely to have serious adverse health consequences upon failure of the device, or
- intended to be implanted for over one year, or
- life sustaining or life supporting and intended for use outside a device user facility.

CFR, Title 21, Parts 800–1299 and specifically 21 CFR 860 Medical Device Classification Procedures

These regulations implement FDA's responsibilities and authority over the classification and reclassification of medical devices. See Class I, Class II, and Class III definitions, pages 2–3.

CFR, Title 21, Parts 800–1299 and specifically 21 CFR 861 Procedures for Performance Standards Development

These regulations implement FDA's responsibilities and authority over the establishment, amendment, and revocation of performance standards for medical devices. Congress intended performance standards to be a means of establishing generic premarket review of devices by defining requirements for devices that, when met, would reasonably assure safe and effective devices.

For a variety of reasons, FDA has issued few performance standards. Subsequent legislation altered performance standard development from a mandatory to a discretionary status.

CFR, Title 21, Parts 800–1299 and specifically 21 CFR 892 Radiological Devices

These regulations implement FDA's responsibilities and authority over radiological medical devices.

CFR, Title 21, Parts 800–1299 and specifically 21 CFR 895 Banned Devices

These regulations implement FDA's responsibilities and authority over devices identified by FDA that present substantial deception or an unreasonable and substantial risk of illness or injury.

CFR, Title 21, Parts 800–1299 and specifically 21 CFR 1010–1050 Performance Standards for Electronic Products

These regulations implement FDA's responsibilities and authority to control electronic products. Manufacturers of applicable medical products are required to certify that the product conforms to all applicable standards.

FDA MEDICAL DEVICE OVERSIGHT

Definitions

Federal Register is the legal newspaper published every business day by the National Archives and Records Administration (NARA). It contains federal agency regulations; proposed rules and notices; and executive orders, proclamations, and other presidential documents. The *Federal Register* informs citizens of their rights and obligations and provides access to a wide range of federal benefits and opportunities for funding. NARA's Office of the *Federal Register* prepares the *Federal Register* for publication in partnership with the Government Printing Office (GPO), which distributes it in paper, on microfiche, and on the worldwide web.*

All federal bureaucracies operate under one or more federal laws and regulations specific to that bureaucracy. The preceding discussion identified federal laws and FDA regulations specific to medical device oversight and illustrates the detail and depth of regulations governing medical devices.

FDA Organization

The FDA is a highly organized bureaucracy. A Commissioner and the Office of the Commissioner control the agency. Other organizational elements include the Office of Policy, Office of External Affairs, Office of Management and Systems, and Office of Operations. (See Figure 1.1, FDA Oversight of Medical Devices, page 10.)

Remember!

Most individuals or firms affected by FDA interact with either the Office of External Affairs or the Office of Operations. The Office of External Affairs operates a variety of offices that interact with manufacturers, consumers, federal and state governments, and international contacts.

The Office of Operations operates nine offices that deal with regulatory oversight of biologics, drugs, devices, food, animal health, toxicological research, "orphan products development," regulatory affairs, and science.

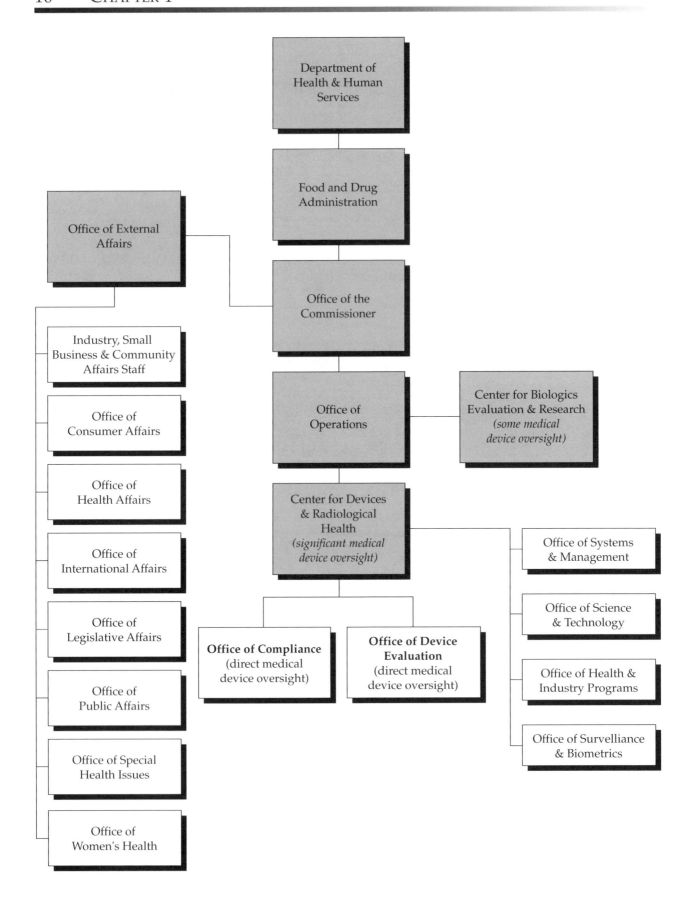

Figure 1.1. FDA Oversight of Medical Devices

Center for Devices and Radiological Health

Something to note!

The organization charged with most medical device oversight is the Center for Devices and Radiological Health (CDRH) under the Office of Operations. CDRH's website (http://www.fda.gov/overview.html) provides an overview of its responsibilities and states that it "is responsible for ensuring the safety and effectiveness of medical devices and eliminating unnecessary human exposure to man-made radiation from medical, occupational and consumer products." A limited number of devices fall under the oversight of the Center for Biologics Evaluation and Research (CBER), which is also under the Office of Operations.

CDRH accomplishes its mission by:

- Reviewing requests to research or market medical devices.
- Collecting, analyzing, and acting on information about deaths and injuries in the use of medical devices.
- Establishing and enforcing good manufacturing practices and regulation and performance standards for medical devices.
- Monitoring compliance and surveillance programs for medical devices.
- Providing technical and other assistance to small manufacturers of medical devices.

Figure 1.1, FDA Oversight of Medical Devices, page 10, provides a diagram of the various "offices" that constitute the CDRH. They include the following:

Office of Systems and Management

Advises CDRH's director on all administrative management matters; plans, develops, and implements Center management policies and programs concerning financial and human resource, contracts and grants, and conferences. Provides communication, coordination, training, and implementation of ethics issues within the Center.

Office of Compliance

Advises CDRH's Director and other FDA officials on legal, administrative, and regulatory programs and policies concerning FDA's compliance responsibilities relating to medical devices. Develops, directs, coordinates, evaluates, and monitors compliance and surveillance programs of regulated device manufacturers and users. Conducts field tests and inspections and evaluates industry quality assurance and testing programs to ensure regulatory compliance. Designs, develops, and implements CDRH's activities to register device manufacturers and list their products. Enforces federal law as it relates to medical device promotion and advertising. Develops regulations and guidelines for the control of restricted devices, health fraud, and promotion of devices pending premarket clearance. Reviews and monitors trade and professional meetings, promotional materials, and professional journals to determine compliance. Coordinates activities with National Association of Attorneys General.

Office of Device Evaluation

Advises CDRH's Director and other agency officials on all premarket notification submissions (519(k)s), premarket approval (PMA) applications, product development protocols (PDPs), device classifications, and investigational device exemptions (IDEs). Plans, conducts, and coordinates CDRH's actions regarding (1) approval, denial, and withdrawal of approval of PMAs, PDPs, and IDEs; (2) makes substantially equivalent determinations for 510(k)s; and (3) monitors sponsors' conformance with requirements of all programs. Conducts ongoing review, surveillance, and medical evaluation of the labeling, clinical experience, and required reports by sponsors of approval applications. Develops and interprets regulations and guidelines regarding classification, PDPs, IDEs, PMAs, and 510(k)s.

Office of Science and Technology

Provides scientific support and laboratory analysis in response to the program needs of CDRH and other FDA components. Provides scientific and engineering support in the review of regulatory documents, the development of regulatory decisions, and the analysis of postmarket surveillance issues. Participates in the development of national and international consensus standards and voluntary guidelines.

Office of Health and Industry Programs

Analyzes medical device user-related problems and conducts research. Applies systems analysis and human factors strategies to problem identification and solutions. Implements and evaluates user-related solution strategies. Conducts and evaluates programs to provide technical and other assistance to small manufacturers of medical devices to promote their understanding of medical device regulatory compliance.

Office of Surveillance and Biometrics

Advises, coordinates with, and provides consultation to the Director and other FDA officials concerning premarket review activities, postmarket management activities, surveillance, and biometrics programs and activities for medical products. Establishes policy for surveillance programs. Identifies and analyzes device problems. Develops solution strategies to those problems and tracks programs or solution implementations.

Office of Regulatory Affairs

Also under the Office of Operations is the Office of Regulatory Affairs (ORA), charged with ensuring that FDA-regulated products comply with applicable federal laws and FDA regulations. With its headquarters in Rockville, MD, ORA operates 21 district offices throughout the United States and its territories. The FDA also maintains local offices in over 145 additional cities across the country.

Don't forget!   ORA's mission is to achieve effective and efficient compliance of regulated products in the marketplace through active and aggressive oversight that ensures a high level of consumer protection. ORA's Investigators visit more than 15,000 facilities each year. ORA's activities include medical device import oversight to prevent the entry of noncompliant products and ensure the removal of any noncompliant products already in commerce.

ORA's inspections and import oversight results in the collection of over 80,000 product samples for further examination and labeling assessments. Import oversight results in the detention at port of entry of over 25,000 import shipments annually. ORA is the FDA office that is charged with surveying and inspecting the regulated industry for compliance with federal law and FDA regulations. ORA's compliance activities include pursuing appropriate legal remedies, including injunction, seizure, and prosecution. Typically, about 3,000 products a year are found to be unfit for consumers and are withdrawn from the marketplace.

FDA Documents Discussion

The FDA's website, <http://www.fda.gov>, lists over 30,000 documents, many of which have been developed to flesh out federal laws and FDA regulations the agency has produced. A significant number of these documents are related to medical devices. The FDA has produced a significant number of guidelines—documents that guide their staff and provide the establishments they regulate with details and insight on regulatory compliance.

Remember!

Guidelines are controlled documents that require a significant investment to produce and that ensure appropriateness, completeness, and scientific accuracy. The FDA publishes announcements of draft guideline availability for review and comment in the *Federal Register.*

21 CFR 10.90 (b)(1) Food and Drug Administration regulations, guidelines, recommendations, and agreements states:

Guidelines establish principles or practices of general applicability and do not include decisions or advice on particular situations. Guidelines relate to performance characteristics, pre-clinical and clinical test procedures, manufacturing practices, product standards, scientific protocols, compliance criteria, ingredient specifications, labeling, or other technical or policy criteria. Guidelines state procedures or standards of general applicability that are not legal requirements but are acceptable to FDA for a subject matter which falls within the laws administered by the Commissioner.

Something to note!

21 CFR 10.90 (b)(1) (i) states: "A person may rely upon a guideline with assurance that it is acceptable to FDA, or may follow different procedures or standards. When different procedures or standards are chosen, a person may, but is not required to, discuss the matter in advance with FDA to prevent the expenditure of money and effort on activity that may later be determined to be unacceptable."

Remember!

21 CFR 10.90 further states that the use of FDA testing guidelines "assures acceptance of a test as scientifically valid, if properly conducted, but does not assure approval of any ingredient or product so tested. Test results or other available information may require disapproval or additional testing." It also states that "the Commissioner may not recommend legal action against a person or product with respect to an action taken in conformity with a guideline issued under this section that has not been amended or revoked."

FDA REGULATIONS AND ISO 9000

Definitions

ISO The International Organization for Standardization (ISO) is based in Geneva, Switzerland. ISO is a created acronym taken from the Greek word *isos,* meaning "equal."*

ISO 9000 A group of generic international standards for quality management, quality assurance, and implementation of a quality system.*

ISO 9001 A specific generic international conformance standard to which a firm involved with design, development, production, installation and servicing may comply and be found compliant.*

There are several major differences between ISO 9000 and FDA's Quality System Regulations:

- FDA's regulations are backed by U.S. Code. They are federal law!
- ISO 9000 consists of voluntary quality standards, which manufacturers comply and document compliance with periodic internal and external auditing of their selected registrar.
- FDA's management responsibility, management representative, management review, design controls, and complaint regulations (among others) are more prescriptive and specific than ISO 9000.
- ISO 9000 has no failure-reporting requirement, recall requirement, and, in fact, no safety and effectiveness requirement.
- On the other hand, FDA has limited control over personnel, largely personnel assessment, approval for their position, and training requirements. ISO 9000 expects the personnel department to be fully controlled.
- FDA has no control over a manufacturer's financial department, assuming it is not the purchasing arm of the firm. Again, ISO 9000 expects the financial department to be fully controlled.
- FDA has little oversight over marketing and sales, except for client lists during recalls and any labeling activity, whereas ISO 9000 expects both sales and marketing departments to be fully controlled.

Don't forget!

For manufacturers who must deal with *both* FDA and ISO 9000, logical compliance efforts call for establishing a single quality system that fulfills FDA regulatory requirements and appropriate ISO 9000 elements without duplication of effort. Because of FDA's regulatory and legal implications, FDA compliance will always overshadow voluntary ISO 9001 certification expectations.

2

FDA Inspections

INTRODUCTION

This chapter of **Mastering and Managing the FDA Maze: Medical Device Overview Training and Management Desk Reference** discusses FDA inspections.

SCOPE

The goal of this chapter is to provide an overview of FDA inspections of medical device manufacturers. Significant detail has been omitted, and readers are advised to undertake further training to ensure proficiency and understanding to the level required for FDA compliance.

This chapter discusses the enforcement of FDA laws and regulations through FDA's inspection of medical device manufacturing establishments for compliance. Subsequent chapters provide an additional synopsis of specific elements of the Quality System Regulation (QS Regulation) and other applicable regulations.

Readers should note that this discussion is specific to *medical device* manufacturing establishments; it does not deal with establishments that manufacture foods, drugs, or biologics. Each of these regulatory environments has different specific FDA laws, regulations, and inspections and are beyond the scope of this training.

This chapter provides applicable definitions. Readers should understand these definitions, all of which, unless followed with an asterisk, are quoted from the FDA's Quality System Regulations.

FDA INSPECTIONS

Definitions

Bottom-up inspection was FDA's standard inspection process for routine good manufacturing practice (GMP) inspections prior to 1998. Investigators were taught to start inspections by investigating one or more instances of quality problems, such as complaints or recalls, as a strategy to evaluate each manufacturer's GMP compliance.*

Comprehensive inspection is an inspection performed on all elements of a firm's quality system, subject to FDA jurisdiction, to assess the firm's compliance status.*

Directed inspection is an inspection performed on specific elements of a firm's quality system, subject to FDA jurisdiction, as identified by agency manuals, assignments, or officials to assess those elements' compliance status or technological characteristics.*

Establishment Inspection Report (EIR) is the report completed by the FDA Investigators after an inspection is completed and forwarded to their district office. This report is lengthy and provides details of the firm, its management, products, the inspection, Investigator's findings, and concerns related to the "objectionable conditions or practices" that were identified in the 483 as "observations."*

Form FDA 482, Notice of Inspection is the form FDA presents to firms immediately prior to an inspection. Typically, the form is presented to the senior management individual available at the firm.*

Form FDA 483, Inspectional Observations is the form FDA presents to inspected firms at the end of each inspection. Typically, the form is presented to the senior management individual available at the firm.*

Quality System Inspection Technique (QSIT) is FDA's current inspection strategy. QSIT involves what FDA calls "top-down" inspections of the four major subsystems of each device manufacturer's quality system, for example, their management controls, design controls, corrective and preventive actions, and production and process controls.*

Table-Top Inspection is an inspection strategy of reviewing a firm's written procedures and, perhaps, records, from a fixed location, such as an office or table-top, and not performing audits of practices and records at the location in which they were created or implemented.*

Top-Down Inspection is FDA's newest inspection strategy. Inspectors are taught to (1) evaluate device manufacturers' "quality systems," starting with the firm's quality policy, quality system procedures, and quality plan and to (2) "touch bottom" by sampling each firm's quality system records.*

Track I Inspection is a limited inspection of a manufacturer's quality system performed by FDA every two years.*

Track II Inspection is a complete audit of a manufacturer's quality system performed by FDA every four years.*

Situation I conditions are those conditions that provide evidence "that the manufacturing process is producing nonconforming and/or defective finished devices." Under these conditions, inspectors identify "systemwide deficiencies" and are instructed to terminate the routine inspection and issue an FDA Form 483 list of observations. These inspections usually result in a Warning Letter.*

Situation II conditions are those conditions that do not meet the description of Situation I conditions. Inspectors are instructed to complete the inspection and issue an FDA Form 483 list of observations.*

Warning Letter is an administrative action typically issued to firms with Situation I conditions identified on their Form FDA 483 observations. Warning Letters require a written response from the firm within 15 working days.*

FDA Inspection Information Specific to Quality System Regulation

Something to note!

At the end of each chapter of an element of FDA Quality System Regulation are discussions of the documents and records FDA Investigators typically will want to see and copy. This information will be valuable in preparing for inspections.

FDA Inspections

FDA inspections are typically performed by local or regional Investigators reporting to the Office of Compliance. FDA's inspectional approach has been that of a federal agency's "official," careful, and critical examination of a regulated medical device manufacturer. Most often these are comprehensive inspections performed to assess the firm's compliance with federal laws and regulations administered by the agency. A few are directed inspections, performed to obtain evidence to support other administrative or legal actions when violations are suspected or found. Even fewer directed inspections are performed to investigate and learn about new technologies.

The breadth and depth of any inspection will depend upon the assessment process and outcome of the inspection and will include the following:

- The current agency compliance program focus
- The nature of the assignment, that is, comprehensive or directed inspection
- The Investigator's knowledge of the firm's devices and their marketplace
- The Investigator's knowledge of the firm's previous quality system problems
- The Investigator's observations of the firm's quality system conditions during the inspection

Remember!   The FDA's authority to inspect any medical device manufacturer is based on federal statutes. The agency is required to follow a number of obligations to the firms they inspect. Investigators must do the following:

- Display their credentials to the top management of the firm
- Issue an original, properly executed, and signed Form FDA 482, Notice of Inspection (see Figure 2.1, pages 19–20).
- Provide top management with original copies of Form FDA 484, Receipt of Samples identifying any samples obtained during the inspection
- Upon completion of the inspection and prior to leaving the premises, provide the highest management representative available with the Investigator's findings on Form FDA 483, Inspectional Observations

Firms should recognize that FDA Investigators are not authorized to do the following:

- Sign any waivers exempting the firm from any responsibility or liability should the Investigator be injured on the firm's premises
- Sign any forms that control access to or release confidential company information
- Sign any forms or provide any documents that request information

Additionally, Investigators are precluded by the Food, Drug and Cosmetic Act (FD&C Act), as amended, from making any determination of medical device appropriateness, safety, or effectiveness. However, Investigators can be expected to note any such findings in their Establishment Inspection Report (EIR) for possible additional investigations.

Investigators are expected to comply with a firm's good sanitation or good manufacturing practices, particularly where such practices are required by written procedures in the quality system.

For medical device firms with numerous devices or process- or technologically complex devices, inspections often involve a team inspection. Typically, teams are composed of two or more individuals who have different areas of expertise or technical backgrounds appropriate to the firm's medical devices. One of the Investigators will be designated the team leader and will be responsible for the overall inspection.

During inspections, it is not unusual for Investigators to call field regional and national experts and engineers for technical assistance. These consultations are almost always performed away from the firm's premises.

Prior to 1998, FDA's routine good manufacturing practice (GMP) inspectional strategy was characterized as a "bottom-up" inspection. FDA Investigators were taught to start their inspections with a review of a firm's quality system failures, which might include complaints, recalls, and corrective and preventive actions. Investigators assessed these records for quality failures and then followed the firm's paper trail or the lack thereof to failures of procedures, processes, systems, and, when appropriate, management.

This strategy often led to long, drawn-out inspections as Investigators followed up numerous instances of real, imagined, or potential quality failures. Form FDA 483 observations would often list all minor deviations encountered (see Figure 2.2, pages 21–22). The Investigator's report easily turned into pages of minor deviations without any assessment of the firm's broader manufacturing, production, and/or process control.

Complicating this situation were the pre-1997 GMP regulations that imposed limitations on the FDA's ability to evaluate device manufacturers' design controls. Those regulations largely limited the agency's access to design controls on only those products that were changed after their final approval. In 1997, after years of development and review, the FDA finalized its revision of 21 CFR 820, with the Quality System Regulations. These regulations provided FDA with oversight of each device manufacturer's complete design and development process for all finished medical devices.

DEPARTMENT OF HEALTH AND HUMAN SERVICES PUBLIC HEALTH SERVICE FOOD AND DRUG ADMINISTRATION	1. DISTRICT ADDRESS & PHONE NO.

TO

2. NAME AND TITLE OF INDIVIDUAL
VOID

3. DATE
VOID

4. FIRM NAME
VOID

VOID

5. HOUR — VOID a.m.

6. NUMBER AND STREET
VOID

VOID p.m.

7. CITY AND STATE & ZIP CODE
VOID

8. PHONE # & AREA CODE
VOID

Notice of Inspection is hereby given pursuant to Section 704(a)(1) of the Federal Food, Drug, and Cosmetic Act [21 U.S.C. 374(1)][1] and/or Part F or G, Title III of the Public Health Service Act [42 U.S.C. 262-264][2]

9. SIGNATURE *(Food and Drug Administration Employee(s))*
VOID

10. TYPE OR PRINT NAME AND TITLE *(FDA Employee(s))*
VOID

Applicable to portions of Section 704 and other Sections of the Federal Food, Drug, and Cosmetic Act [21 U.S.C. 374] are quoted below:

[1]Sec. 704. (a)(1) For purposes of enforcement of this Chapter, officers or employees duly designated by the Secretary, upon presenting appropriate credentials and a written notice to the owner, operator, or agent in charge, are authorized (A) to enter, at reasonable times, any factory, warehouse, or establishment in which food, drugs, devices, or cosmetics are manufactured, processed, packed, or held, for introduction into interstate commerce or after such introduction, or to enter any vehicle being used to transport or hold such food, drugs, devices, or cosmetics in interstate commerce; and (B) to inspect , at reasonable times and within reasonable limits and in a reasonable manner, such factory, warehouse, establishment, or vehicle and all pertinent equipment, finished and unfinished materials, containers and labeling therein. In the case of any factory, warehouse, establishment, or consulting laboratory in which prescription drugs or restricted devices are manufactured, processed, packed, or held, the inspection shall extend to all things therein (including records, files, papers, processes, controls, and facilities) bearing on whether prescription drugs or restricted devices which are adulterated or misbranded within the meaning of this Chapter, or which may not be manufactured, introduced into interstate commerce, or sold, or offered for sale by reason of any provision of this Chapter , have been or are being manufactured, processed, packed, transported, or held in any such place, or otherwise bearing on violation of this Chapter. No inspection authorized by the preceding sentence or by paragraph (3) shall extend to financial data, sales data other then shipment data, pricing data, personnel data (other than data as to qualifications of technical and professional personnel performing functions subject to this Act), and research data (other than data, relating to new drugs, antibiotic drugs and devices and, subject to reporting and inspection under regulations lawfully issued pursuant to section 505(i) or (k), section 507(d) or (g), section 519, or 520(g), and data relating to other drugs or devices which in the case of a new drug would be subject to reporting or inspection under lawful regulations issued pursuant to section 505(k) of the title. A separate notice shall be given for each such inspection, but a notice shall not be required for each entry made during the period covered by the inspection. Each such inspection shall be commenced and completed with reasonable promptness.

Sec. 704(e) Every person required under section 519 or 520(g) to maintain records and every person who is in charge or custody of such records shall, upon request of an officer or employee designated by the Secretary, permit such officer or employee at all reasonable times to have access to and to copy and verify, such records.

Section 512 (l)(1) In the case of any new animal drug for which an approval of an application filed pursuant to subsection (b) is in effect, the applicant shall establish and maintain such records, and make such reports to the Secretary, of data relating to experience and other data or information, received or otherwise obtained by such applicant with respect to such drug, or with respect to animal feeds bearing or containing such drug, as the Secretary may by general regulation, or by order with respect to such application, prescribe on the basis of a finding that such records and reports are necessary in order to enable the Secretary to determine, or facilitate a determination, whether there is or may be ground for invoking subsection (e) or subsection (m)(4) of this section. Such regulation or order shall provide, where the Secretary deems it to be appropriate, for the examination, upon request, by the persons to whom such regulation or order is applicable, of similar in-formation received or otherwise obtained by the Secretary. (2) Every person required under this subsection to maintain records, and every person in charge or custody thereof, shall, upon request of an officer or employee designated by the Secretary, permit such officer or employee at all reasonable times to have access to and copy and verify such records.

[2]Applicable sections of Parts F and G of Title III Public Health Service Act [42 U.S.C. 262-264] are quoted below:

Part F – Licensing – Biological Products and Clinical Laboratories and ******

Sec. 351(c) "Any officer, agent, or employee of the Department of Health & Human Services, authorized by the Secretary for the purpose, may during all reasonable hours enter and inspect any establishment for the propagation or manufacture and preparation of any virus, serum, toxin, antitoxin, vaccine, blood, blood component or derivative, allergenic product or other, product aforesaid for sale, barter, or exchange in the District of Columbia, or to be sent, carried, or brought from any State or possession into any other State or possession or into any foreign country, or from any foreign country into any State or possession."

Part F - ****** Control of Radiation.

Sec. 360 A (a) "If the Secretary finds for good cause that the methods, tests, or programs related to electronic product radiation safety in a particular factory, warehouse, or establishment in which electronic products are manufactured or held, may not be adequate or reliable, officers or employees duly designated by the Secretary, upon presenting appropriate credentials and a written notice to the owner, operator, or agent in charge, are thereafter authorized (1) to enter, at reasonable times any area in such factory, warehouse, or establishment in which the manufacturer's tests (or testing programs) required by section 358(h) are carried out, and (2) to inspect, at reasonable times and within reasonable limits and in a reasonable manner, the facilities and procedures within such area which are related to electronic product radiation safety. Each such inspection shall be commenced and completed with reasonable promptness. In addition to other grounds upon which good cause may be found for purposes of this subsection, good cause will be considered to exist in any case where the manufacturer has introduced into commerce any electronic product which does not comply with an applicable standard prescribed under this subpart and with respect to which no exemption from the notification requirements has been granted by the Secretary under section 359(a)(2) or 359(e)."

(b) "Every manufacturer of electronic products shall establish and maintain such records (including testing records), make such reports, and provide such information, as the Secretary may reasonably require to enable him to determine whether such manufacturer has acted or is acting in compliance with this subpart and standards prescribed pursuant to this subpart and shall, upon request of an officer or employee duly designated by the Secretary, permit such officer or employee to inspect appropriate books, papers, records, and documents relevant to deter-mining whether such manufacturer has acted or is acting in compliance with standards prescribed pursuant to section 359(a)."

******

(f) "The Secretary may by regulation (1) require dealers and distributors of electronic products, to which there are applicable standards prescribed under this subpart and the retail prices of which is not less than $50, to furnish manufacturers of such products such information as may be necessary to identify and locate, for purposes of section 359, the first purchasers of such products for purposes other than resale, and (2) require manufacturers to preserve such information."

FORM FDA 482 (5/85)   PREVIOUS EDITION IS OBSOLETE   NOTICE OF INSPECTION

Figure 2.1. Form FDA 482 (Front)

Any regulation establishing a requirement pursuant to clause (1) of the preceding sentence shall (A) authorize such dealers and distributors to elect, in lieu of immediately furnishing such information to the manufacturer to hold and preserve such information until advised by the manufacturer or Secretary that such information is needed by the manufacturer for purposes of section 359, and (B) provide that the dealer or distributor shall, upon making such election, give prompt notice of such election (together with information identifying the notifier and the product) to the manufacturer and shall, when advised by the manufacturer or Secretary, of the need therefor for the purposes of Section 359, immediately furnish the manufacturer with the required information. If a dealer or distributor discontinues the dealing in or distribution of electronic products, he shall turn the information over to the manufacturer. Any manufacturer receiving information pursuant to this subsection concerning first purchasers of products for purposes other than resale shall treat it as confidential and may use it only if necessary for the purpose of notifying persons pursuant to section 359(a)."

Sec. 360 B.(a) It shall be unlawful –
    (1) ***
    (2) ***
    (3) "for any person to fail or to refuse to establish or maintain records

required by this subpart or to permit access by the Secretary or any of his duly authorized representatives to, or the copying of, such records, or to permit entry or inspection, as required or pursuant to section 360A."
    ***

Part G – Quarantine and Inspection

Sec. 361(a) "The Surgeon General, with the approval of the Secretary is authorized to make and enforce such regulations as in his judgement are necessary to prevent the introduction, transmission, or spread of communicable diseases from foreign countries into the States or possessions, or from one State or possession into any other State or possession. For purposes of carrying out and enforcing such regulations, the Surgeon General may provide for such inspection, fumigation, disinfection, sanitation, pest extermination, destruction of animals or articles found to be so infected or contaminated as to be sources of dangerous infection to human beings, and other measures, as in his judgement may be necessary."

Resources for FDA Regulated Businesses

The U.S. Food and Drug Administration strives to protect, promote and enhance the health of the American people, while minimizing the regulatory burden on the industries it regulates. You have a right to disagree with any agency decision, action, or operation without fear of retaliation. You also have a right to be treated with appropriate courtesy and respect. If you are dissatisfied with any agency decision or action, you may appeal to the supervisor of the employee who made the decision or took the action. If the issue is not resolved at the first supervisor's level, you may request that the matter be reviewed at the next higher supervisory level. This process may continue through the agency's chain of command.

To resolve a problem with your company's interaction with FDA, or if you have questions or concerns about FDA rules or procedures, we suggest that you first write or call your district office to explain your concerns. If you are not satisfied with the help provided by the district office, you may take your complaint or concern to the regional office. If that effort is not satisfactory, contact FDA's Office of the Chief Mediator and Ombudsman for further assistance and guidance.

Contact the **District Office** if you have a concern or question about an inspection, an import or export issue, or any other action taken by a FDA field representative. The District Office will provide you with the name and phone number of someone who will review the matter and provide assistance.

District	Telephone	District	Telephone
Atlanta	(404) 347-4344	Minneapolis	(612) 334-4100
Baltimore	(410) 962-3396	Nashville	(615) 781-5385
Buffalo	(716) 551-4461	New England	(781) 279-1675
Chicago	(312) 353-5863	New Jersey	(973) 526-6000
Cincinnati	(513) 679-2700	New Orleans	(504) 589-6344
Dallas	(214) 655-5310	New York	(718) 340-7000
Denver	(303) 236-3000	Philadelphia	(215) 597-4390
Detroit	(313) 226-6260	San Francisco	(510) 337-6700
Florida	(407) 475-4700	San Juan	(787) 729-6844
Kansas City	(913) 752-2100	Seattle	(425) 486-8788
Los Angeles	(949) 798-7600		

Contact the **Regional Office** for further help if you were not able to effectively resolve the issue with the assistance of the district office. Telephone numbers for the regional offices and a list of the states covered by each region are on the Internet at http://www.fda.gov/ora/hier/ora_field_names.txt.

Contact the **Office of the Chief Mediator and Ombudsman** at (301) 827-3390 if you have been unsuccessful in resolving a problem at the district and regional levels. The office's home page is on the Internet at http://www.fda.gov/oc/ombudsman/homepage.htm.

The Small Business Administration also has an ombudsman. The **Small Business and Agriculture Regulatory Enforcement Ombudsman** and ten Regional Fairness Boards receive comments from all kinds of small businesses about federal agency enforcement actions and annually evaluate the enforcement activities, rating each agency's responsiveness to small business. If you wish to comment on the enforcement actions of FDA, call 1-888-734-3247. The ombudsman's home page is on the Internet at http://www.sba.gov/regfair.

Small Business Guide to FDA
Internet at http://www.fda.gov/opacom/morechoices/smallbusiness/toc.html

Office of Regulatory Affairs (ORA)
Internet at http://www.fda.gov/ora/ora_home_page.html

Food and Drug Administration (FDA)
Internet at http://www.fda.gov

Figure 2.1. Form FDA 482 (Back)

DEPARTMENT OF HEALTH AND HUMAN SERVICES PUBLIC HEALTH SERVICE FOOD AND DRUG ADMINISTRATION	DISTRICT ADDRESS AND PHONE NUMBER VOID	
NAME OF INDIVIDUAL TO WHOM REPORT ISSUED TO: VOID	PERIOD OF INSPECTION VOID	C.F. NUMBER VOID
TITLE OF INDIVIDUAL VOID	TYPE ESTABLISHMENT INSPECTED VOID	
FIRM NAME VOID	NAME OF FIRM, BRANCH OR UNIT INSPECTED VOID	
STREET ADDRESS VOID	STREET ADDRESS OF PREMISES INSPECTED VOID	
CITY AND STATE (Zip Code) VOID	CITY AND STATE (Zip Code) VOID	

VOID

SEE REVERSE OF THIS PAGE	EMPLOYEE(S) SIGNATURE	EMPLOYEE(S) NAME AND TITLE (Print or Type)	DATE ISSUED

FORM FDA 483 (5/85)   PREVIOUS EDITION MAY BE USED   **INSPECTIONAL OBSERVATIONS**   PAGE 1 OF 1 PAGES

Figure 2.2. Form FDA 483 (Front)

The observations of objectionable conditions and practices listed on the front of this form are reported:

1. Pursuant to Section 704(b) of the Federal Food, Drug and Cosmetic Act, or
2. To assist firms inspected in complying with the Acts and regulations enforced by the Food and Drug Administration.

Section 704(b) of the Federal Food, Drug, and Cosmetic Act (21 USC374(b)) provides:

"Upon completion of any such inspection of a factory, warehouse, consulting laboratory, or other establishment, and prior to leaving the premises, the officer or employee making the inspection shall give to the owner, operator, or agent in charge a report in writing setting forth any conditions or practices observed by him which, in his judgement, indicate that any food, drug, device, or cosmetic in such establishment (1) consists in whole or in part of any filthy, putrid, or decomposed substance, or (2) has been prepared, packed, or held under insanitary conditions whereby it may have become contaminated with filth, or whereby it may have been rendered injurious to the health. A copy of such report shall be sent promptly to the Secretary."

Figure 2.2. Form FDA 483 (Back)

The Food and Drug Administration Modernization Act of 1997 (FDAMA of 1997) required FDA to assess the agency's past inspectional strategy and devise a more effective and efficient approach.

Bolstered with the new design control requirements and broadened oversight of device manufacturers' management provided by the new GMPs, FDA could now implement an investigational strategy that more closely mirrored standard auditing practices—a "top-down" inspection. A top-down audit focuses the auditor's initial attention on a firm's high-level policies and procedures. After this initial assessment, a skilled auditor selects appropriate products and/or processes and assesses their conformance to the firm's written documents, appropriate standards, or regulations. The FDA is now starting to implement a sophisticated top-down inspectional practice for routine GMP inspections.

The Quality System Inspection Technique (QSIT), as outlined in the FDA's Office of Regulatory Affairs draft *QSIT Inspection Handbook* of October 1998 is the agency's training tool for this new strategy.

Remember!

The *QSIT Handbook* teaches Investigators to concentrate their investigations on four subsystems of each manufacturer's quality system: the manufacturer's (1) management controls, (2) design controls, (3) corrective and preventive actions, and (4) production and process controls. Each of these subsystem's inspectional strategies is discussed in its own chapter.

These subsystems are the areas FDA wants Investigators to focus on as key quality indicators of a firm's quality system. These reviews start by Investigators determining whether a firm has:

- Addressed the basic requirements of each subsystem by defining and documenting appropriate procedures
- Implemented those requirements in its daily operations

Investigators are provided with 6–15 inspectional objectives for their review of each of these subsystems. The *QSIT Handbook* provides Investigators with "sampling tables" to assist them in determining how many records should be reviewed and "flow diagrams" that provide them with an overview of how the subsystem inspections should transpire. These inspectional objectives, sampling tables, and flow diagrams are discussed in their appropriate chapters.

FDA instructs Investigators that inspections following the *QSIT Handbook* strategy should last approximately five days, allowing a little more than a day for each subsystem. The agency feels that, with combinations of different devices, processes, and subsystems, an appropriately broad assessment of a firm's quality system will be achieved during their brief, periodic inspections. Investigators should inform management at the close of each day as to whether the inspection is finished and when they will return. It is not unusual for Investigators to have a gap of a day or two during an inspection.

Don't forget!

The *QSIT Handbook* also identifies another new inspectional strategy: preannounced inspections, the criteria for which were initially announced in the *Federal Register* (volume 61, number 65, April 3, 1996). Firms whose previous inspection history qualifies them for preannouncement are telephoned a week or more before an inspection and are informed of the agency's intent to conduct an inspection on specific dates.

Investigators are taught to request a copy of the firm's quality policy and high-level quality system procedures, including management review procedures, and their quality manual and quality plan or equivalent documents. Investigators then perform a table-top inspection or assessment of those documents. Compliance with this request is not required, but the Investigators indicate that their preview of these documents will facilitate the inspection.

Those copies are typically returned, but if the Investigator finds nonconformances, copies of originals will be requested and officially catalogued during the inspection.

Required document(s), procedure(s), and record(s)

The author recommends that firms create an "FDA Inspection Procedure," which details inspection responsibilities and actions. The procedure should make clear how and what documents are available for FDA inspection as well as what actions are expected by employees.

The FD&C Act authorizes inspections "for purposes of enforcement" and permits the FDA to inspect all documents specified in the Quality System Regulation. See Chapter 5 Document Controls.

Remember!

Although the agency may not enter any firm forcibly without a warrant, FDA does not need a warrant to inspect any device manufacturer. Refusal to permit an inspection is a violation of the act. The FDA Investigator will examine a firm's quality system procedures, review records, and, when appropriate, collect samples and copies of records.

Don't forget!

FDA Investigators are not required to provide firm personnel with a Miranda warning. Anything told to inspectors may be used against a firm. Any documents, once provided, may not be recovered. If inappropriate documents, such as audit results or financial records, are provided, they may not be reclaimed.

Historically, FDA has based inspections on its Track I and Track II inspection strategies. More recently, FDA has focused inspections on device-related risks and the severity of past noncompliance with regulations as the primary means of establishing inspection priorities. The goal of each inspection is to document to the FDA's satisfaction that a firm is operating in a "state-of-control" and complying with both the intent and letter of applicable FDA regulations.

Manufacturers of Class III devices are typically inspected while their PMA is pending. Class II device manufacturers are subject to inspections based on their device's risk and past inspections as assessed by the agency.

The following situations enter into the agency's inspection assessment:

- Manufacturers whose last inspection was violative and who provide little or no compelling evidence of appropriate corrective and preventive action
- Manufacturers who have received 510(k) clearance for a high-risk device within the past 12 months and who have not been inspected within the previous two years
- Manufacturers of Class II and III devices who have never been inspected
- Manufacturers who have newly registered
- Manufacturers with a recently cleared 510(k)

Class I device manufacturers typically are now inspected less frequently but may be inspected if a Medical Device Report documenting a device failure and patient injury or death occurs.

Something to note!

Inspections with Situation I findings are typically followed up with a **Warning Letter.** Typical Situation I findings are as follows:

- Failure to establish and document a formal quality program
- Failure to validate significant manufacturing processes or quality tests
- Failure to establish and implement adequate record-keeping procedures
- Failure to establish and implement adequate failure investigations
- Failure to ensure that finished devices meet all specifications before acceptance

Routine inspections generally include a review of the following firm activities:

- Submissions and changes to cleared 510(k)s
- Complaint-handling processes
- Medical Device Reporting
- Device tracking (when appropriate)
- Failure investigations
- In-process and finished device testing
- Change control procedures

- Process validation
- Component control
- Planned and periodic audits
- Recalls
- Corrective and preventive actions
- Written procedures

Remember!

During the presentation of the firm's 483 observations, the Investigator usually provides the firm with a timetable for implementing corrective and preventive actions for individual and all 483 observations. This timetable becomes part of the 483 record. Any corrective actions or procedural changes made during the inspection should be identified to the Investigator and a request made each time that that action be noted in the establishment inspection report, or EIR.

FDA considers such prompt action as "positive indications of (a firm's) concern and desire to voluntarily correct discrepancies."

Don't forget!

Disagreements about 483 observations or any other facts related to one or more objectionable conditions can and will occur. Sometimes the Investigator is in error. Occasionally an employee makes an inaccurate remark, or a statement is taken out of context. At times the Investigator may misunderstand a statement, document, or record.

Remember!

During the delivery of the 483, whenever the Investigator makes a 483 observation that you believe may not be correct, you should politely but firmly state your position and request that this position be noted in the EIR. Within 10 days of each inspection, firms should make a written request to the appropriate FDA district office for a copy of their EIR.

Unless the agency is considering further action, redacted and completed Form FDA 483 and EIRs are available to the public under the Freedom of Information Act (FOIA).

Required document(s), procedure(s), and record(s)

Your response letter should also request that a copy of your response be included with any request for your firm's 483. This will help provide a balanced presentation to the news media or any other requester. Responses should not attempt to blame or identify individuals for conditions cited as objectionable.

Responses that discuss 483 observations that the firm believes are incorrect should be stated politely and concisely but as strongly as necessary to attempt to correct the misunderstanding. In these cases, do not hesitate to provide procedures, records, checklists, or other documents that make your case. However, do not belittle or ridicule the Investigators for what you perceive as their misunderstanding or error.

Something to note!

Form FDA 483 observations are considered by the agency as a guide for corrective action and should be responded to promptly and thoroughly, generally within 10 working days. Responses should itemize voluntary corrective and preventive actions. See Chapter 11 Corrective and Preventive Action.

FDA expects firms with Situation I conditions to fully examine their entire manufacturing process to expose enterprisewide problems. Responses should also indicate that the firm is performing a comprehensive assessment of its quality system as part of preventive action to identify other problematic areas. FDA will respond to your firm's 483 responses with the agency's assessment of that response.

Don't forget!

Firms found not to have made significant compliance improvement are at great risk for a subsequent enforcement action. Firms that fail to adequately respond to Situation I conditions and Warning Letters can expect the agency to pursue enforcement actions that include administrative actions or legal remedies. Administrative actions include injunctions, administrative detention, seizures, administrative or civil penalties, or recalls.

Remember!

Firms receiving Warning Letters are required to respond within 15 working days. Warning Letters are normally received within 30 days of the firm's receipt of Form FDA 483 observations. Warning Letters are also available to the public under the Freedom of Information Act.

Required document(s), procedure(s), and record(s)

Warning Letter responses should identify and restate the 483 observation response and specify the corrective and preventive actions taken since the 483 response letter was sent. Examples of new or revised procedures and forms should be attached. Specific corrective and preventive actions should be summarized and timelined. Firms should consider offering to meet with the FDA at its district office to discuss the agency's concerns for the 483 observations and the Warning Letter.

To facilitate a review by any FDA Investigator upon reinspection, firms should create a specific file for each FDA inspection. These files should contain all appropriate FDA documents, firm responses, copies of all of the firm's corrective and preventive actions, copies of any appropriate records, and a copy of a report of management's review and approval of the inspection file.

3

Quality System Requirements, Management Responsibilities, and Personnel

INTRODUCTION

This chapter of **Mastering and Managing the FDA Maze: Medical Device Overview Training and Management Desk Reference** discusses the quality system, quality system requirements, management responsibilities, and personnel for FDA's Quality System Regulations.

SCOPE

The goal of this chapter is to provide an overview of quality system requirements, management responsibilities, and personnel as identified by the Quality System Regulation. Significant detail has been omitted, and readers should undertake further training to ensure proficiency and understanding to the level required for FDA compliance. The Quality System Regulation is printed in its entirety in Attachment A, page 230.

The book assumes that readers recognize their requirement to register with the FDA and list their products. For convenience, those regulations are provided as Attachment D, page 253.

This chapter discusses the elements of a quality system, management responsibilities, and personnel. Subsequent chapters provide additional overview material on specific elements of the Quality System Regulation (QS Regulation) and other applicable regulations.

This discussion is specific to *medical device* manufacturing establishments; it does not deal with establishments that manufacture foods, drugs, or biologics. Each of these regulatory environments has different specific FDA laws, regulations, and inspections and is beyond the scope of this training.

Readers should familiarize themselves with the definitions given in this chapter. All of these, unless followed with an asterisk, are quoted from FDA's Quality System Regulations, 21 CFR § 820.

QUALITY SYSTEM

Definitions

Manufacturer means any person who designs, manufactures, fabricates, assembles, or processes a finished device. Manufacturer includes but is not limited to those who perform the functions of contract sterilization, installation, relabeling, remanufacturing, repacking, or specification development, and initial distributors of foreign entities performing these functions.

Quality system means the organizational structure, responsibilities, procedures, processes, and resources for implementing quality management. (Note: *Quality system* includes all activities previously referred to by FDA as "quality assurance.")

Quality System Inspection Technique (QSIT) is FDA's latest inspection strategy and involves what FDA calls "top-down" inspections of the four major subsystems of each device manufacturer's quality system, that is, their management controls, design controls, corrective and preventive actions, and production and process controls.*

§ 820.5 QUALITY SYSTEM

What the regulation states

Each manufacturer shall establish and maintain a quality system that is appropriate for the specific medical devices designed or manufactured, and that meets the requirements of this part.

§ 820.5 Discussion

FDA deliberately made the Quality System Regulations generic and broad, requiring manufacturers to develop a quality system appropriate to the devices they design and/or manufacture, while meeting all the requirements of these regulations.

The remainder of these regulations, discussed in subsequent chapters, provides more than 200 "shalls" that require manufacturers to establish and maintain a state of control for every aspect of their medical device manufacturing operations.

One key to quality system compliance is written procedural control of all operations. Another is the written identification of appropriate, responsible individuals for documented reviews of those operations. A third is aggressive efforts to identify problems and create environments that not only solve those problems but ensure appropriate implementation of the solutions and also use that knowledge to search for other related and nonrelated problems.

As the adage goes, "the devil is in the details." The "devil" for each manufacturer is to provide an appropriate level of procedural and record-keeping control for each of their devices. FDA provides manufacturers with a great deal of latitude in making those decisions and in creating the necessary detail.

Manufacturers can be certain that, if the quality system they establish and maintain consistently produces medical devices that do not meet specifications, fail in users' hands, result in numerous complaints, or are subject to constant recalls or repairs, the FDA will cite that manufacturer as having failed to establish and maintain an appropriate quality system.

On the other hand, if the manufacturer consistently produces devices that meet their specifications, rarely fail in users' hands, result in few or random complaints, are rarely, if ever, subject to recalls, and require minimal or appropriate repair, service, and support, the FDA will find few, if any, significant failures of the quality system. Such a system is largely in a state of control.

FDA assesses each device manufacturer's quality system under the guidelines detailed in the Center for Devices and Radiological Health's (CDRH) *Quality System Inspection Technique Handbook (QS Inspection Handbook)*. This top-down inspection strategy focuses on the written procedures and records of the firm's four major quality subsystems: (1) management controls, (2) design controls, (3) corrective and preventive actions, and (4) production and process controls.

SUBPART B—QUALITY SYSTEM REQUIREMENTS

Definitions *Design history file (DHF)* means a compilation of records which describe the complete design history of a finished device.

Device master record (DMR) means a compilation of records containing the procedures and specifications for a finished device.

Establish means define, document (in writing or electronically), and implement.

Management with executive responsibility means those senior employees of a manufacturer who have the authority to establish or make changes to the manufacturer's quality policy and quality system.

Manufacturer means any person who designs, manufactures, fabricates, assembles, or processes a finished device. Manufacturer includes but is not limited to those who perform the functions of contract sterilization, installation, relabeling, remanufacturing, repacking, or specification development, and initial distributors of foreign entities performing these functions.

Quality means the totality of features and characteristics that bear on the ability of a device to satisfy fitness-for-use, including safety and performance.

Quality audit means an established systematic, independent examination of a manufacturer's quality system that is performed at defined intervals and at sufficient frequency to determine whether both quality system activities and the results of such activities comply with quality system procedures, that these procedures are implemented effectively, and that these procedures are suitable to achieve quality system objectives.

Quality policy means the overall quality intentions and direction of an organization with respect to quality, as established by management with executive responsibility.

Quality system means the organizational structure, responsibilities, procedures, processes, and resources for implementing quality management. (Note: Quality system includes all activities previously referred to by FDA as "quality assurance.")

Quality System Inspection Technique (QSIT) is FDA's latest inspection strategy and involves what FDA calls "top-down" inspections of the four major subsystems of each device manufacturer's quality system: their management controls, design controls, corrective and preventive actions, and production and process controls.*

§ 820.20 MANAGEMENT RESPONSIBILITY

§ 820.20 Management responsibility

What the regulation states

§ 820.20 (a)

(a) *Quality policy.* Management with executive responsibility shall establish its policy and objectives for, and commitment to, quality. Management with executive responsibility shall ensure that the quality policy is understood, implemented, and maintained at all levels of the organization.

§ 820.20 (a) Discussion

Required document(s), procedure(s), and record(s)

FDA expects each device manufacturer to establish a written quality policy that includes its objectives for and commitment to quality. FDA also expects each device manufacturer to document the identification of a management representative with executive responsibility to ensure that "the quality policy is understood, implemented, and maintained at all levels of the organization."

Management with executive responsibility may reasonably delegate specific Quality System Regulation tasks, the translation of objectives into procedures, and the implementation of the quality system but cannot delegate the legal and regulatory responsibility for ensuring that all levels of the firm understand, establish, and maintain the quality policy.

Don't forget!

FDA will hold management, particularly executive management, responsible for their firm's quality system and all failures of that system.

Please review Figure 3.1, "Management Review of Quality System," page 31, as an example of minimal management review documentation. This type of form may be attached to copies of the documentation and records reviewed by executive management or to a list referencing those documents and records.

Food and Drug Administration's (FDA) Quality System Regulation (QSR) require management to establish a quality policy which defines management's commitment to quality and management's assurance that the quality policy is understood, implemented and maintained at all levels of the firm involved with the manufacture of the firm's FDA regulated medical devices.

Further, management is required to establish and maintain adequate organizational structure to ensure that FDA regulated device(s) are designed and produced in accordance with FDA's QSR and device specifications. This form is the mechanism used by the firm to document that the firm's management conforms to these, among other, requirements. This executed and dated form documents that the firm's management has, among other actions:

❐ Established and maintained procedures and records that defines, among other responsibilities, management's commitment to quality.

❐ Established and maintained a **quality policy** that has been understood, implemented and maintained at all levels of this organization involved with the manufacture of the firm's FDA regulated medical devices through the distribution of and training in this **quality policy** procedure.

❐ Established and maintained an adequate organizational structure which ensures that the firm's FDA regulated medical devices are designed and produced in accordance with FDA's QSR by maintaining adequate and appropriate management and employees as detailed by the firm's **organizational chart,** an **EXHIBIT** to the **quality policy.**

❐ Established and maintained appropriate responsibility, authority and interrelation of all personnel who manage, perform, and assess work affecting quality and provide independence and authority necessary to perform their tasks through the firm's SOPs and work instructions.

❐ Established and maintained a written procedure for periodic audits and management review of audit results, including corrective and preventive actions.

❐ Established and maintained adequate resources, trained personnel and training, for management, performance of work and assessment of the quality system.

❐ Established and maintained a management representative, <Officer Title>, who is responsible for ensuring that the firm's quality system is established and maintained, whom, through this form and attached documents and records, reports on the performance of the quality system to the Executive Officer, who reviews these activities.

❐ Identified <Officer Title> who has periodically, at least annually, reviewed the suitability and effectiveness of the firm's quality system, and documented that review by executing this form.

❐ Established and maintained appropriate and adequate SOPs and work instructions that ensure the firm's conformance to FDA's QSR.

The undersigned has made a review of this firm's SOP, work instructions and quality records and have marked the actions listed above which this review acknowledges and, further, have found the documentation and records adequate to fulfill their intended purposes.

_____   _____   _____
Signed   Printed Name, Title   Date

_____   _____   _____
Signed   Printed Name, Title   Date

Figure 3.1.   Management Review of Quality System

§ 820.20 (b)

(b) *Organization.* Each manufacturer shall establish and maintain an adequate organizational structure to ensure that devices are designed and produced in accordance with the requirements of this part.

(1) *Responsibility and authority.* Each manufacturer shall establish the appropriate responsibility, authority, and interrelation of all personnel who manage, perform, and assess work affecting quality, and provide the independence and authority necessary to perform these tasks.

(2) *Resources.* Each manufacturer shall provide adequate resources, including the assignment of trained personnel, for management, performance of work, and assessment activities, including internal quality audits, to meet the requirements of this part.

(3) *Management representative.* Management with executive responsibility shall appoint, and document such appointment of, a member of management who, irrespective of other responsibilities, shall have established authority over and responsibility for:

   (a) Ensuring that quality system requirements are effectively established and effectively maintained in accordance with this part; and

   (b) Reporting on the performance of the quality system to management with executive responsibility for review.

§ 820.20 (b) Discussion

The goal of the strong organizational structure required by the Quality System Regulation is to ensure that the "technical, administrative and human factors functions affecting the quality of the device will be controlled, whether those functions involve hardware, software, processed materials, or services. All such control should be oriented toward the reduction, elimination, or ideally, prevention of quality nonconformities."

Remember!

FDA views executive management as the source of both authority and responsibility. Attempts to delegate responsibility to employees without appropriate authority will not deflect FDA's focus on executive management with authority.

Interrelations of "all personnel who manage, perform, and assess work affecting quality and provide the independence and authority necessary to perform these tasks" can be accomplished within the quality policy procedure and an attached organizational charts. Obviously, as firms grow, the quality policy procedure and organizational charts must be appropriately revised and approved to reflect those changes.

Don't forget!

FDA understands that manufacturers of differing sizes and products with different risks will establish different quality policies and have different quality systems. FDA expects firms with higher risk devices to establish appropriately more sophisticated quality policies and quality systems. FDA expects larger firms to establish appropriately more procedural and instructional form and checklist control than do smaller, less complex firms.

§ 820.20 (c)

(c) *Management review.* Management with executive responsibility shall review the suitability and effectiveness of the quality system at defined intervals and with sufficient frequency according to established procedures to ensure that the quality system satisfies the requirements of this part and the manufacturer's established quality policy and objectives. The dates and results of quality system reviews shall be documented.

§ 820.20 (c) Discussion

***Required
procedure(s),
document(s),
and record(s)***

Management review should be identified in the quality policy proce-dure and should establish the review's suitability and effectiveness. The defined interval and frequency of review should also be identified to ensure that the quality system satisfies the regulation and the quality policy. The review must be by the "management representative" and should include a report concerning that review.

- Problems or issues identified in the review and corrected should be identi-fied in this report. In smaller companies (that is, those in which the management representa-tive is senior management), the report would be a report to appropriate files and not to senior management. In larger companies, the report would be distributed to appropriate senior man-agement and other appropriate parties. See below for other activities to be identified in any "management review report."
- The review should identify any changes to the quality policy procedure, the management rep-resentative, or other global changes to the quality system since the last report.
- Each review might carry an appropriate numbering system, such as "Management Review Report," <year> <n>, and <date>, where "year" is the reporting year, "n" is the sequential report number (for example, 1, 2, 3, and so on), and "date" is the date the report is issued.
- The report might be in sections (for example, quality system, quality procedure, quality plan, quality system procedures and instructions). Each of these sections should discuss their appro-priate review activities, problems or issues identified, corrective and preventive actions taken, and any changes made since the last report.
- Problems or issues identified should include only those that have any significant impact on the quality system (for example, a new or revised product design process, new manufacturing equipment, a new or revised manufacturing process, a new or revised software application controlling design, manufacturing, testing, distribution, or support). Minor changes in proce-dures or instructions need not be discussed in the report because the status of each procedure, its latest version date, and appropriate changes made since the last report would be included or attached to the report.

***What the
regulation states***

§ 820.20 (d)

(d) *Quality planning.* Each manufacturer shall establish a quality plan which defines the quality practices, resources, and activities relevant to devices that are designed and manufactured. The manufacturer shall establish how the requirements for qual-ity will be met.

§ 820.20 (d) Discussion

Required document(s), procedure(s), and record(s)

The quality policy procedure and the quality assurance procedure can individually or collectively establish a "quality plan," defining quality practices, resources, and activities relevant to devices designed and manufactured.

- Establishing how requirements are met is typically achieved in individual appropriate procedures (for example, procedures on design control, manufacturing processes, device transfer, verification, validation, and finished device acceptance).

- During management review and its subsequent report, quality planning should be briefly discussed, any problems or issues and their corrective actions should be identified, and any appropriate changes made since the last report should be noted.

A quality plan should reference existing quality system documentation and requires the development of comprehensive procedures or work instructions over those that already exist.

What the regulation states

§ 820.20 (e)

(e) *Quality system procedures.* Each manufacturer shall establish quality system procedures and instructions. An outline of the structure of the documentation used in the quality system shall be established where appropriate.

§ 820.20 (e) Discussion

Required document(s), procedure(s), and record(s)

Documentation on procedures, the quality policy procedure, or the quality assurance procedure should spell out all the procedures established and maintained by the firm. The quality policy procedure and the quality assurance procedure can attest that they maintain the structure of the documentation used in the quality system.

During management review and its subsequent report, quality system procedures, instructions, forms, and checklists should be discussed, and any problems or issues and their corrective actions should be identified. A table of the status of each procedure, instruction, form, and checklist, its latest version, date, and appropriate changes made since the last report may be attached to the report.

What the FDA Investigator will want to see during an inspection

Under the FDA's new Quality System Inspection Technique (QSIT) Handbook instructions, Investigators will focus on management controls as one of the four major quality subsystems of each firm.

The QSIT Handbook's *Inspectional Objectives for Management Controls* include verification that:

- A quality policy, management review and quality audit procedures, quality plan, and quality system procedures and instructions are defined and documented
- A quality policy has been implemented
- The firm's organizational structure provides for management responsibilities, authorities, and necessary resources
- A management representative with appropriate purview has been identified
- Management review includes documented reviews of the suitability and effectiveness of the quality system
- Quality audits and, where appropriate, reaudits of identified nonconformances are conducted (see Chapter 20 Quality Audits)

For qualifying firms, FDA's preannouncement call will request a copy of the firm's quality policy, high-level quality system procedures (including management review procedures), quality manual, and quality plan. As noted in chapter 2, these documents do not have to be supplied prior to the inspection, but FDA contends that, if supplied, the documents can facilitate the inspection. Firms that do not supply them prior to the inspection will be requested by the Investigators to supply them at the start of their inspection.

The Investigators will review the written quality policy and will assess it to ensure that it defines the firm's overall intentions and directions with respect to quality. The Investigators will also determine whether the firm's "management with executive responsibility" ensures that the quality policy is understood and implemented at all levels of the organization. This means that personnel must be familiar with the policy and know where to obtain a copy. Investigators will determine whether management reviews and quality audits are being conducted according to written procedures and at defined intervals. They will also evaluate the firm's quality plan to determine whether the plan defines the firm's quality practices, resources, and activities relevant and specific to the regulated medical devices being designed and manufactured. They will determine whether the firm has written procedures that describe how the firm intends to meet their quality requirements.

FDA understands that such written documentation may be found in the firm's quality manual, design history file (DHF), device master records, production procedures, and other documents. FDA also understands that quality plans may be specific for specific devices, be generic to all devices manufactured, and be specific to individual processes or overall systems. For this reason, it is important for the quality plan to be what FDA refers to as a "roadmap" to the firm's quality system.

Readers should understand FDA's perspective, as described in the QSIT Handbook, of each device manufacturer's compliance obligations:

Each manufacturer must prepare and implement all activities, including but not necessarily limited to the applicable requirements of the Quality System Regulation, that are necessary to assure the finished device, the design process, the manufacturing process, and all related activities conform to approved specifications.

The handbook teaches FDA Investigators to ensure that "manufacturing processes are controlled and adequate for their intended use, documentation is controlled and maintained, equipment is calibrated, inspected, tested," and so on.

Investigators will review the quality system to ensure that it identifies quality problems and recommends or provides for their solutions. They expect to see statistical techniques, process and product acceptance, rejection data, and a complaint system among the activities applied to the problem identification process.

Investigators will assess the firm's organizational structure to ensure their devices are designed and manufactured in compliance with the Quality System Regulation. The Investigators should be expected to review a firm's organizational chart and ask a number of early questions for documentation of which individuals are provided authority and responsibility for the quality system. FDA expects firms to have identified and documented a management representative who is responsible for ensuring the quality system is effectively established and maintained and who reports on the system's performance to executive management. Investigators will assess this management representative's authority and responsibility by assessing the firm's:

- Organizational chart and quality manual to determine whether the management representative has review and approval responsibility for appropriate milestones in the quality system, including changes to documents and processes
- Appropriate design control activities
- Complaint procedures, Medical Device Reporting procedures, in-process and finished device product failure reports
- Quality audit procedure and schedule to ensure audits are conducted at least every 12 months or more frequently if quality failures and problems warrant
- Quality reaudits, audit reports, and corrective and preventive actions as appropriate and being reviewed and approved

The identified management representative's "fingerprints" are expected to be on all those activities and any others related to the firm's quality system. Furthermore, the management representative should be able to document an appropriate reporting activity to the firm's executive management.

Executive management is expected to periodically document a written review of the quality system for suitability and effectiveness. Those reviews must be dated and frequent enough to ensure executive management is informed of on-going quality issues and problems. Executive management's review report must measure the firm's quality system against the Quality System Regulations and the firm's written quality objectives as defined in their quality policy. FDA should consider these reviews and reports a part of the firm's auditing procedure beyond their detailed review. Firms might provide a dated, signed cover document attached to those reports as evidence of appropriate review. See Figure 3.1, "Management Review of Quality System," page 31.

FDA's goal is to determine whether the firm's organizational structure and executive management work together to reduce, eliminate, and, where possible, prevent finished product nonconformities. Firms can expect failures in these areas to be recorded on the firm's Form FDA 483.

The QSIT Handbook illustrates a "Management Controls Decision Flow Chart" that is provided in the Figure 3.2, page 37.

SUBPART B–QUALITY SYSTEM REQUIREMENTS

§ 820.25 Personnel

What the regulation states

§ 820.25 (a)

(a) *General.* Each manufacturer shall have sufficient personnel with the necessary education, background, training, and experience to assure that all activities required by this part are correctly performed.

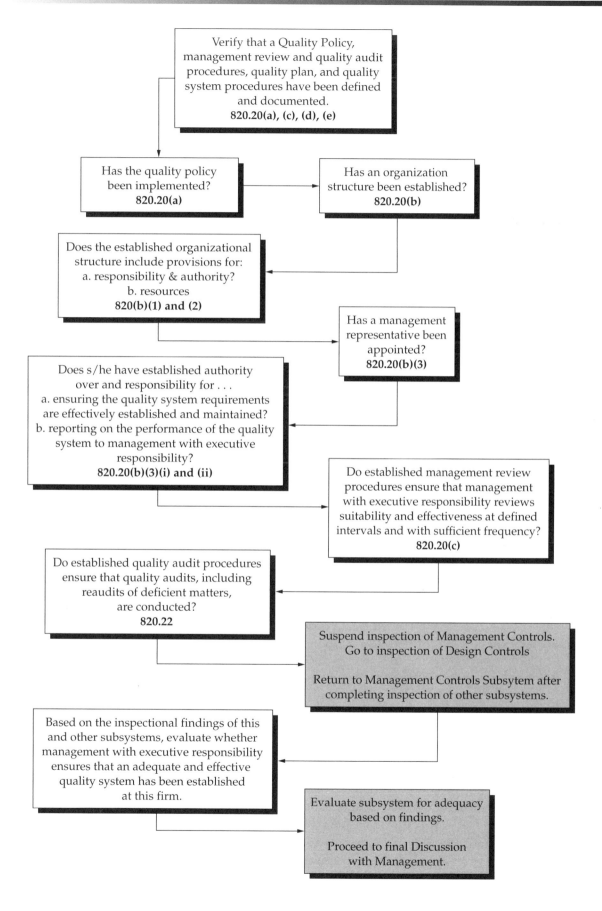

Verify that a Quality Policy, management review and quality audit procedures, quality plan, and quality system procedures have been defined and documented.
820.20(a), (c), (d), (e)

Has the quality policy been implemented?
820.20(a)

Has an organization structure been established?
820.20(b)

Does the established organizational structure include provisions for:
a. responsibility & authority?
b. resources
820(b)(1) and (2)

Has a management representative been appointed?
820.20(b)(3)

Does s/he have established authority over and responsibility for . . .
a. ensuring the quality system requirements are effectively established and maintained?
b. reporting on the performance of the quality system to management with executive responsibility?
820.20(b)(3)(i) and (ii)

Do established management review procedures ensure that management with executive responsibility reviews suitability and effectiveness at defined intervals and with sufficient frequency?
820.20(c)

Do established quality audit procedures ensure that quality audits, including reaudits of deficient matters, are conducted?
820.22

Suspend inspection of Management Controls. Go to inspection of Design Controls

Return to Management Controls Subsytem after completing inspection of other subsystems.

Based on the inspectional findings of this and other subsystems, evaluate whether management with executive responsibility ensures that an adequate and effective quality system has been established at this firm.

Evaluate subsystem for adequacy based on findings.

Proceed to final Discussion with Management.

Figure 3.2. Management Controls Decision Flow Chart

§ 820.25 (a) Discussion

The objective of this regulation is to require manufacturers to provide sufficient personnel with the necessary education, background, training, and experience to ensure compliance with the Quality System Regulations.

What the regulation states

§ 820.25 (b)

(b) *Training.* Each manufacturer shall establish procedures for identifying training needs and ensure that all personnel are trained to adequately perform their assigned responsibilities. Training shall be documented.

(1) As part of their training, personnel shall be made aware of device defects which may occur from the improper performance of their specific jobs.

(2) Personnel who perform verification and validation activities shall be made aware of defects and errors that may be encountered as part of their job functions.

§ 820.25 (b) Discussion

Required document(s), procedure(s), and record(s)

This part of the Quality System Regulation requires manufacturers to establish procedures for:

- Identifying training needs
- Ensuring that all personnel are adequately trained to perform their assigned responsibilities
- Documenting the required training

The requirement means that manufacturers must focus documented training efforts on:

- Making employees aware of the Quality System Regulations
- Relating the employee's job functions to the manufacturer's quality system
- Ensuring that employees are aware of any device defects that may occur from the improper performance of their specific jobs
- Ensuring that employees with verification or validation functions are aware of defects and errors that may be encountered during the performance of their specific jobs.

What the FDA Investigator will want to see during an inspection

Manufacturers should expect FDA Investigators to ask the firm's personnel about their firm's quality policy. Personnel are not expected to have the policy memorized, but they should know it exists and be able to procure a copy.

FDA Investigators can also be expected to review employee training records, particularly of those employees involved in key operations, and to document that they have been trained in the firm's quality policy and quality objectives.

FDA Investigators will review a manufacturer's training procedures and records to document that they establish that personnel are adequately trained to perform their jobs. Investigators also review the manufacturing records (for example, in-process nonconformance reports) for indications of training failures or inadequacies.

Investigators will do the following:

- Verify procedures identifying training needs
- Review training records to ensure training is documented and being conducted
- Verify all personnel are made aware of defects and errors that may occur if they fail to properly perform their jobs
- Verify that personnel involved with verification and validation activities have been made aware of defects and errors they may encounter during the performance of their jobs

Investigators will expect to find procedures or documents that describe the personnel responsible for performing specific tasks or responsible for functional areas required in the firm's Quality Policy. Investigators will determine whether personnel involved in managing, performing, or assessing work affecting quality have the necessary independence and authority to perform those tasks. They will also determine whether the firm has dedicated adequate resources, including staff, funds, and supplies, to ensure conformance with their quality system. Investigators may ask the management representative how these resources are allocated and obtained.

Executive management should understand that if adequate resources, authority, or responsibility are not provided, FDA's Investigators may identify this deficiency and cite a firm for quality system nonconformance.

4

Design Controls

INTRODUCTION

This chapter of **Mastering and Managing the FDA Maze: Medical Device Overview Training and Management Desk Reference** discusses FDA's regulatory oversight of device design controls.

SCOPE

The goal of chapter 4 is to provide an overview of FDA's regulations regarding medical device design controls. Significant detail has been omitted, and readers should undertake further training to ensure proficiency and understanding to the level required for FDA compliance.

This chapter discusses the most recent of FDA's good manufacturing practice (GMP) regulations, Subpart C Design Controls. These new GMPs, or Quality System Regulations, finalized on October 7, 1996, became effective June 1, 1997. These regulations implemented, for the first time, FDA oversight of all regulated Class II and Class III medical devices' design controls. Some, but not all, Class I devices are subject to design control oversight. FDA's oversight of design controls became effective June 1, 1998.

This chapter discusses the heart of FDA's oversight of medical devices, that is, each device's design and development. Assuming that a firm can provide all other appropriate controls to a device without appropriate design controls, an unreasonable risk will exist that the device will fail to be safe and effective and may be unsuitable for release as a finished device. To ensure that finished devices are safe and effective for their intended use, each step in the design must fulfill its quality system role.

This discussion is *basic*. Readers will require significant additional study and implementation before they can be assured that the design controls they establish and maintain meet FDA expectations. The definitions, unless followed by an asterisk, are quoted from FDA's Quality System Regulations.

DESIGN CONTROLS

Definitions

Absurd conditions are those testing activities that are performed even though there is little likelihood the conditions will occur during normal medical device use.*

Beta testing is testing of a finished medical device performed at a user's facility.*

Controlled document means a document subject to procedural control as well as review and approval by an appropriate individual or group.*

Design history file means a compilation of records which describe the complete design history of a finished device.

Design input means the physical and performance requirements of a device that are used as a basis for device design.

Design output means the results of a design effort at each design phase and at the end of the total design effort. The total finished design output consists of the device, its packaging and labeling, the associated specifications and drawings, and the production and quality assurance specifications and procedures. The finished design output will be the basis for the device master record.

Design review means a documented, comprehensive, systematic examination of a design to evaluate the adequacy of the design requirements, to evaluate the capability of the design to meet these requirements, and to identify problems.

Design risk analysis is the ongoing investigation of available information to identify hazards, potential failures, their causes or mechanisms, and the degree of risk to ensure these risks are addressed during the design process or any subsequent design review and change.

Design teams are teams of appropriate individuals, departments, and activities representing (among others) management, sales and marketing, design and development, manufacturing, quality assurance, and service and support who are charged with managing and controlling a device's design and development.*

Design validation means establishing by objective evidence that device specifications conform with user needs and intended use(s).

Device master record (DMR) means a compilation of records containing the procedures and specifications for a finished device.

Failure mode and effects analysis (FMEA) is an inductive technique that assesses the frequency and consequence of individual fault modes related to product functions and components.*

Failure mode, effects and criticality analysis (FMECA) is a FMEA process that includes an assessment of the criticality of identified fault modes.*

Fault tree analysis (FTA) is a systematic inductive technique that diagrams information on a system and can be used to assess a system's known, probable, or potential failures.*

Human factors are those design activities that address the human interface, for example, the device and user performance, and the user's training in the operation, maintenance, and installation of a medical device.*

Master verification or validation plan is a document that identifies all responsibilities, expectations, systems, and subsystems involved with a specific verification or validation activity and the qualification approaches that ensure verification or total system validation.*

MDR means medical device report or medical device reporting.* See chapter 19.

Quality System Inspection Technique (QSIT) is FDA's latest inspection strategy. QSIT involves what FDA calls "top-down" inspections of the four major subsystems of each device manufacturer's quality system, that is, their (1) management controls, (2) design controls, (3) corrective and preventive actions, and (4) production and process controls.*

Requirements are documented functions, conditions, or capabilities that a medical device must meet or possess to satisfy a user's needs, standards, or regulatory expectations.*

Risk analysis is the ongoing investigation of available information to identify hazards and estimate their risk.*

Risk management is the systematic application of management policies, procedures, and practices regarding identification, analyses, control, and monitoring of risks.*

Specification means any requirement with which a product, process, service, or other activity must conform.

Test plan is a step-by-step plan to be followed during the verification or validation of a product or process.*

Verification means confirmation by examination and provision of objective evidence that specified requirements have been fulfilled.*

Design Controls Regulation § 820.30 Design Controls

What the regulation states

§ 820.30 (a)

(a) *General.*

(1) Each manufacturer of any class III or class II device, and the class I devices listed in paragraph (a)(2) of this section, shall establish and maintain procedures to control the design of the device in order to ensure that specified design requirements are met.

(2) The following class I devices are subject to design controls:

(a) Devices automated with computer software; and

(b) The devices listed in the following chart.

Section	Device
868.6810	Catheter, Tracheobronchial Suction.
878.4460	Glove, Surgeon's.
880.6760	Restraint, Protective.
892.5650	System, Applicator, Radionuclide Manual.
892.5740	Source, Radionuclide Teletherapy.

§ 820.30 (a) Discussion

The diagram "Overview of Medical Device Design and Its Control" depicts an example of a simple "waterfall" method of medical device development with appropriate design control measures. This is an example only, intended for instructional purposes, and is not intended to illustrate any required device development process used by any specific firm.

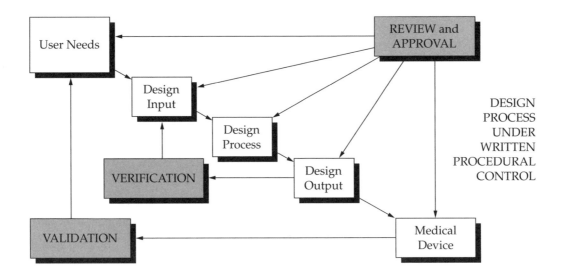

Overview of Medical Device Design and Its Control

Adapted from "Design Control Guidance for Medical Device Manufacturers," Figure 1, CDRH, March 11, 1997

As the FDA views the design and development process, design inputs or requirements result in finished, reviewed, and approved requirements that become the blueprint for the development of design outputs or specifications. Design outputs or specifications, reviewed and approved, become the blueprint for design transfer to device production or manufacturing specifications. At appropriate steps or phases, either design verification or validation ensures that the right product is made and made according to reviewed and approved requirements and specifications. In practice, most sophisticated medical devices involve concurrent engineering or other more complex engineering models, involving multidepartmental representatives working on teams throughout the design and development process. However, the underlying requirements (diagrammed on page 44) for procedural control, review, and approval, verification, and validation still apply to any design and development process implemented by any firm regulated by FDA.

Two resolute practices about design control can be identified—total procedural control and appropriate review and approval. The FDA fully expects manufacturers to control each step in any design process that produces regulated medical devices. The agency also fully expects manufacturers to identify the individuals responsible for review and approval and the design history file (DHF) to document that procedurally controlled review and approval.

Devices in distribution prior to the enactment of the Quality System Regulations are not *required* to have retrospective design control applied; however, firms should identify those devices and have management review and approval of that record. Design control will be required for the regulated devices identified **in section** 820.30 (a) General and for the following:

- Any new design activity, since October 7, 1997
- Any changes to new or existing devices

Design Control Strategy

The following discussion and the figures of this chapter describe a scheme of design and development control. That control starts with the identification of management responsibilities as described in Chapter 3 Quality System, Management Responsibilities, and Personnel and Figure 3.1, Management Review of Quality Systems.

Specific design control is initiated with a description of interfaces, followed up with the identification and description of design teams and a design development stage identification matrix.

Specific design control is expanded with a design input document control matrix, design input requirements control matrix, and individual intended use requirements documents.

Design output is controlled with a design output document control matrix, design output specifications control matrix, and individual intended use specifications documents.

Notes/minutes documents, design review and approval documents, and a design review checklist control the required design review activity.

Test plans and checklists are two mechanisms to control verification and validation activities. Transfer and change requests and checklists may be used to control design transfer and design change activities.

The following Figure, 4.1, page 46, illustrates this design control strategy:

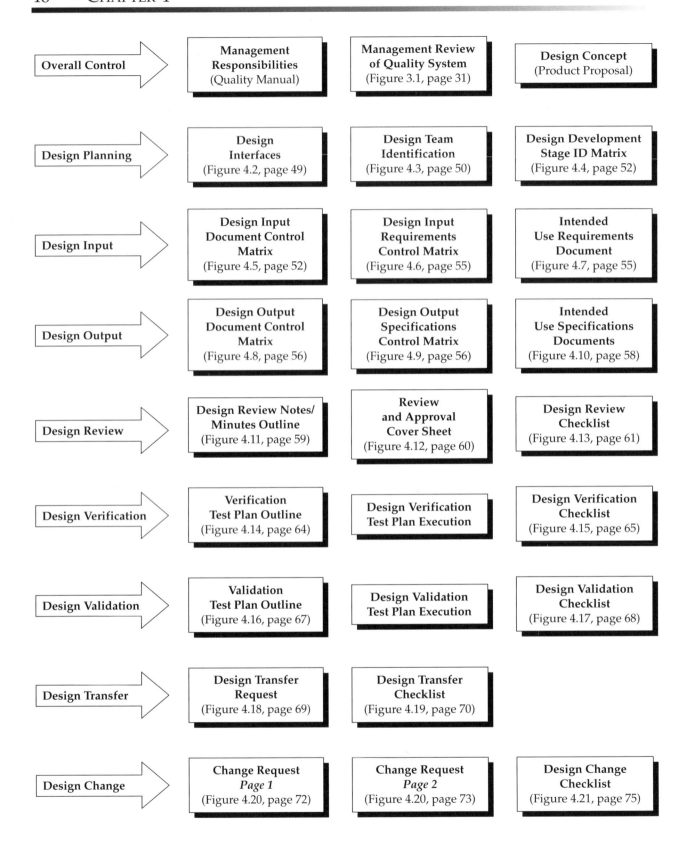

Figure 4.1 Sample Design Control Strategy

The preceding sample design control strategy is only an example of one approach to design control; others can and should be implemented. Individual medical devices may require more or less control, depending upon their complexity and risks to patient health. In some cases, individual devices may require appropriate specific design control strategies.

What the regulation states

§ 820.30 (b)

(b) *Design and development planning.* Each manufacturer shall establish and maintain plans that describe or reference the design and development activities and define responsibility for implementation. The plans shall identify and describe the interfaces with different groups or activities that provide, or result in, input to the design and development process. The plans shall be reviewed, updated, and approved as design and development evolves.

§ 820.30 (b) Discussion

FDA has stated that design controls *do not* apply to what typically is described as the concept phase of any regulated medical device. Even concept phases can involve a number of departments and/or activities and may include user input. However, it is the *output* of the concept phase that will usually start design control activities.

This output, which is sometimes called a product proposal, may consist of the following:

- A comprehensive description of the functional characteristics and physical features of the device's design
- Initial identification of user needs, an initial safety assessment, regulatory requirements, and business requirements
- Review and approval of the product proposal by appropriate management

Remember!

Management should document the identification of medical devices subject to design controls, indicating by dates when design efforts were initiated, whether they are original devices that predate design control regulations, new devices since regulations, or modified devices since regulations (which modifications therefore are subject to design controls). For each identified device, the elements of design planning should be described.

Required procedure(s), document(s), and record(s)

Management should procedurally identify appropriate design control departments and/or activities, including design and development planning and the review responsibility for each department or activity. This may be a simple one-page document or a complex, multipage document, depending on the complexity of the device.

Management should also identify appropriate activities, stages, departments, and participants. Often this is done with design teams. A name or numbering system, along with a name or numbering system for each product design and development being controlled, often identifies these teams.

Don't forget!   Design and development interfaces or interactions are those groups or activities that provide or result in input to the design and development process. These interfaces can be described in detail and illustrated by creating a dated diagram of the interfaces. Both of these documents must reviewed and approved for each device or group of devices. Obviously, the more complex the design project, the more complex the interface description and any interface diagram.

A sample document and diagram are provided in Figures 4.2 and 4.3, pages 49 and 50. Figure 4.4, page 52 illustrates the additional control provided by a design development stage identification matrix detailing reviews, participants, and managers.

Because their input may be reflected in original design activities and will be reflected in design changes, the interface identification process should be as broad as appropriate, for example, extending to the service and support activities of the finished device.

What the regulation states

§ 820.30 (c)

(c) *Design input.* Each manufacturer shall establish and maintain procedures to ensure that the design requirements relating to a device are appropriate and address the intended use of the device, including the needs of the user and patient. The procedures shall include a mechanism for addressing incomplete, ambiguous, or conflicting requirements. The design input requirements shall be documented and shall be reviewed and approved by a designated individual(s). The approval, including the date and signature of the individual(s) approving the requirements, shall be documented.

§ 820.30 (c) Discussion

Departments or activities typically involved in a design input team include marketing, research and development, quality assurance, regulatory affairs, quality control, implementation, and service and support. Design inputs are often referred to as requirements.

Required procedure(s), document(s), and record(s)

Design input procedural control must ensure that each device's initial through final design input is documented, reviewed, and approved by appropriate management. This can be—and often is—a long, complex, and arduous process that seems to defy simple management. The FDA understands that the process is ordinarily not simple; however, they fully expect that the more complex the process, the more procedurally controlled it becomes and the more documentation is associated with that control.

A firm's design control procedure can assist in this control by implementing appropriate forms and checklists. Among the activities that must be documented are the following:

- Intended use
- User needs
- Patient needs
- A mechanism for addressing incomplete, ambiguous, or conflicting requirements
- Design and development interfaces

DESIGN IDENTIFICATION: _____

DESIGN INTERFACE DESCRIPTION Doc No.: _____

DATE: _____

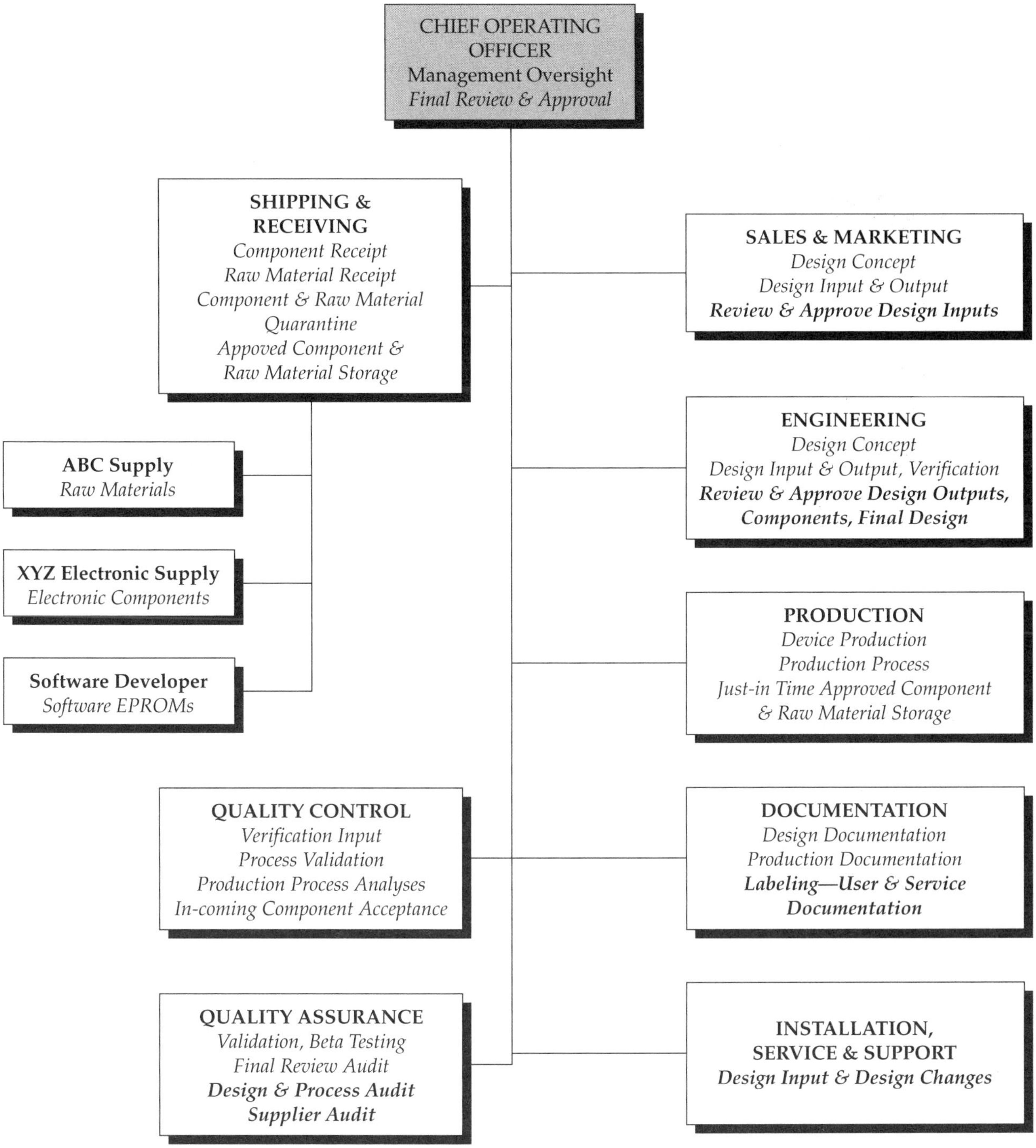

CHIEF OPERATING OFFICER
Management Oversight
Final Review & Approval

SHIPPING & RECEIVING
Component Receipt
Raw Material Receipt
Component & Raw Material Quarantine
Appoved Component & Raw Material Storage

SALES & MARKETING
Design Concept
Design Input & Output
Review & Approve Design Inputs

ABC Supply
Raw Materials

XYZ Electronic Supply
Electronic Components

Software Developer
Software EPROMs

ENGINEERING
Design Concept
Design Input & Output, Verification
Review & Approve Design Outputs, Components, Final Design

PRODUCTION
Device Production
Production Process
Just-in Time Approved Component & Raw Material Storage

QUALITY CONTROL
Verification Input
Process Validation
Production Process Analyses
In-coming Component Acceptance

DOCUMENTATION
Design Documentation
Production Documentation
Labeling—User & Service Documentation

QUALITY ASSURANCE
Validation, Beta Testing
Final Review Audit
Design & Process Audit
Supplier Audit

INSTALLATION, SERVICE & SUPPORT
Design Input & Design Changes

Reviewed and Approved By: _____
                                                             (Signature)

Printed Name and Title: _____

Date: _____

Figure 4.2. Design Interfaces

Design Team ID: _____

Date: _____

The following individuals, departments or activities are identified as members of the above listed Design Team and, during any design review activity, shall include an individual who does not have direct responsibility for the design stage being reviewed:

Responsibility	Individual, Department or Activity
Management Oversight	Chief Operating Officer
Design Concept	Sales and Marketing Engineering Installation & Support
Design Input	Sales and Marketing Engineering Installation & Support
Design Output	Sales and Marketing Engineering Installation & Support
Design Review	Sales and Marketing Engineering
Design Verification	Engineering Quality Control
Design Validation	Quality Assurance Beta Testing Site
Design Change (Preproduction)	Design Team
Documenation & Labeling	Documentation
Raw Materials & Components	Engineering Shipping & Receiving
Production—Process Control	Production
Auditing	Quality Assurance
Installation, Service & Support	Installation, Service & Support

I have reviewed and approve the identified individuals, departments and activities for this design team.

_____

    <Printed Name>   <Approver Title>   <Signature>   <Date>

Figure 4.3. Design Team Identification

One effective mechanism to control design input documentation is to create a design input document control matrix. A sample is provided in Figure 4.5, page 52.

- By establishing a document that provides overall control to the design input process, firms provide design teams, reviewers, approvers, and FDA with a mechanism to identify overall control of this design phase.
- Included in any firm's mechanism for addressing incomplete, ambiguous, or conflicting requirements may be a checklist that is required at appropriate stages and that identifies completed activities. See the design review discussion below.
- Elements that should be documented, providing even "does not apply" documentation, include the following:
  — The purpose of the device and its intended use
  — A description or theory of operation
  — Compopents of the device
  — Operational modes
  — Preliminary risk analysis following approved risk management procedures
  — Controls and alarms
  — Interfaces or connectors
  — Standards or applicable regulations
  — Performance and/or reliability specifications
  — Environmental specifications
  — Physical specifications
  — Safety specifications
  — Master verification plan and master validation plan requirements
  — Preliminary labels and labeling

Possible mechanisms to control input requirements include the following:

- A design input requirements control matrix
- Detailed input documents

A design input requirements control matrix is a controlled document that identifies, in tabular format, each device's input requirements. The matrix may be divided into individual sections for major elements of the input requirements (for example, intended use, user needs, patient needs, operational requirements, standard requirements, regulatory requirements, safety requirements, performance requirements, environmental requirements, labeling requirements, packaging requirements, and documentation requirements, among others. This document will have numerous iterations or versions and can be controlled by version number. The matrix may require an 11" × 17" or larger report format. A sample of a design input requirements control matrix is provided in Figure 4.6, page 55.

Detailed input documents identified in the design input requirements control matrix may include, for example, intended use, user needs, patient needs, operational requirements, standard requirements, regulatory requirements, safety requirements, performance requirements, environmental requirements, labeling requirements, packaging requirements, and documentation requirements, among others.

Design Development Stage Identification Matrix for: _____

Design Team ID: _____

Date: _____

Development Stages	Periodic Review	Scheduled Review	Final Review	Participants, Individuals, Independent Specialists	Review Manager
Concept	Yes, if Mgr Identifies	Yes, if Mgr makes specific schedule	Yes, Manager determines date	<names>	<name>
Requirements, individual parts & all	Yes, if Mgr Identifies	Yes, if Mgr makes specific schedule	Yes, Manager determines date	<names>	<name>
Specifications, individual parts & all	Yes, if Mgr Identifies	Yes, if Mgr makes specific schedule	Yes, Manager determines date	<names>	<name>
Review, individual parts & all	Yes, if Mgr Identifies	Yes, if Mgr makes specific schedule	Yes, Manager determines date	<names>	<name>
Master Verification Plan	Yes, if Mgr Identifies	Yes, if Mgr makes specific schedule	Yes, Manager determines date	<names>	<name>

[Note: These Matrix tables often are created in the "landscape" view of 'document setup' to provide an 11 inch by 8.5 inch format, or created in landscape view for 11 inch by 17 inch paper.]

I attest that I am the approved Manager identified to review this matrix and that the individuals identified on the matrix are appropriate for their assigned activity.

_____

    <Printed Name>   <Title Review Manager>   <Signature>   <Date>

Figure 4.4. Design Development Stage Identification Matrix

Design Input Document Control Matrix for: _____

Design Team ID: _____

Date: _____

Document Name/ID	Creation Date	Responsibility of	Reviewed by	Approved by

I attest that I am the approved Manager identified to review this matrix and that the individuals identified on the matrix are appropriate for their assigned activity.

_____

    <Printed Name>   <Title Review Manager>   <Signature>   <Date>

Figure 4.5. Design Input Document Control Matrix

Each of these detailed input documents should be version number controlled, carry the requirements document number identified in the design input requirements control matrix and provide details of each requirement identified by the matrix. Each final design input document should be marked "Final" and have a document cover with appropriately dated review and approval signatures, including those of the responsible executive management.

Detailed requirements documents may have elements similar to those provided in the example in Figure 4.7, page 55. This example is only one of the mechanisms that may be used to control design inputs or requirements. Individual firms must define and document all their design input control mechanisms.

What the regulation states

§ 820.30 (d)

(d) *Design output.* Each manufacturer shall establish and maintain procedures for defining and documenting design output in terms that allow an adequate evaluation of conformance to design input requirements. Design output procedures shall contain or make reference to acceptance criteria and shall ensure that those design outputs that are essential for the proper functioning of the device are identified. Design output shall be documented, reviewed, and approved before release. The approval, including the date and signature of the individual(s) approving the output, shall be documented.

§ 820.30 (d) Discussion

Required procedure(s), document(s), and record(s)

Design output procedural control must ensure that each device's initial through final design output is documented, reviewed, and approved by appropriate management. As with design input, this can also be a long, complex, and arduous process that seems to defy simple management. Again, the FDA understands that the process is typically not simple; however, the agency fully expects that the more complex the process, the more procedurally controlled it becomes and the more documentation is associated with that control.

Again, procedural control can assist by implementing appropriate forms and checklists. Among the items that must be documented are the following:

- Output documents for all new design or development activities and any modifications or changes to a new or existing regulated product
- The intended use of each device, including the needs of both the user and the patient

Design output team members should again identify the activities or departments that are appropriate to output specification development, oversight, review, and approval for each device. The output team is usually tasked to do the following:

- Create a functional model of the device
- Partition the design appropriately to facilitate design feasibility
- Identify critical design outputs
- Continue development and complete the risk analysis following approved risk management procedures
- Finalize and approve the functional design specification created by the project team
- Finish detailed design documents used to create the medical device. They include the following:
  — Schematics
  — Device components
  — Subassemblies
- Define physical design specifications, including the architectural requirements of the device, its subassemblies, and components
- Define packaging specifications
- Implement change control procedures for all activities in the design output specification stage
- Create a master verification plan and test plans used to verify that the design conforms to its functional safety specifications and reliability requirements
- Review and approve all documents used to implement the preceding activities
- Prepare for a formal design review and approval at the completion of the design process

Mechanisms to document control over output specifications might include the following:

- A design input requirements control matrix
- Detailed input documents

A design output document control matrix is a tabular listing of the documents created to control design output specifications. This matrix might follow the format of the sample provided in Figure 4.8, page 56, or a format created by the design team, but its format should parallel that of the design input document control matrix.

A design output specifications control matrix is a controlled document that identifies, in tabular format, each device's output specifications. The matrix may be divided into individual sections for major elements of the output specifications (for example, intended use, user needs, patient needs, operational specifications, standard specifications, regulatory specifications, safety specifications, performance specifications, environmental specifications, labeling specifications, packaging specifications, and documentation specifications, among others). Like the design output requirements control matrix, this document will have numerous iterations or versions and can be controlled by version number and date. The matrix may require an 11" × 17" or larger report format. A sample of a design output specifications control matrix is provided in Figure 4.9, page 56.

Detailed output documents identified in the design output specifications control matrix may include, for example, intended use, user needs, patient needs, operational specifications, standard specifications, regulatory specifications, safety specifications, performance specifications, environmental specifications, labeling specifications, packaging specifications, and documentation specifications, among others.

Design Input Requirements Control Matrix for: _____

Design Team ID: _____

Date: _____ Version: _____

Input Req. No.	Input Requirements	Req. Doc. No.	Responsibility of	Reviewed by	Approved by
1.0	Intended Use	IU 001	<name>	<name(s)>	<name(s)>
1.1	Intended Use 1	IU 001	<name>	<name(s)>	<name(s)>
1.2	Intended Use 2	IU 001	<name>	<name(s)>	<name(s)>
2.0	User Needs	UN 001	<name>	<name(s)>	<name(s)>
2.1	User Needs 1	UN 001	<name>	<name(s)>	<name(s)>
2.2	User Needs 2	UN 001	<name>	<name(s)>	<name(s)>
2.3	User Needs 3	UN 001	<name>	<name(s)>	<name(s)>
3.0	Patient Needs	PN 001	<name>	<name(s)>	<name(s)>
3.1	Patient Needs 1	PN 001	<name>	<name(s)>	<name(s)>
3.2	Patient Needs 2	PN 001	<name>	<name(s)>	<name(s)>

I attest that I am the approved Manager identified to review this matrix and that the individuals identified on the matrix are appropriate for their assigned activity.

_____
   <Printed Name>   <Title Review Manager>   <Signature>   <Date>

Figure 4.6. Design Input Requirements Control Matrix

DOCUMENT NUMBER IU 001

Version 1.0 Date: <date>

Design Team ID: _____

<Name> is responsible for this document
<Names> are responsible for review of this document
<Names> are responsible for approval of this document

Requirement(s)   **Description/Discussion/Comment**

      1.1   Intended Use description number 1

      1.2   Intended Use description number 2

I have reviewed this Intended Use Requirements Document:

_____
   <Printed Name>   <Title Review Manager>   <Signature>   <Date>

I have reviewed and approved this Intended Use Requirements Document:

_____
   <Printed Name>   <Title Review Manager>   <Signature>   <Date>

Figure 4.7. Intended Use Requirements Document

Design Output Document Control Matrix for: _____

Design Team ID: _____

Date: _____

Document Name/ID	Creation Date	Responsibility of	Reviewed by	Approved by

I attest that I am the approved Manager identified to review this matrix and that the individuals identified on the matrix are appropriate for their assigned document activity.

_____

        <Printed Name>   <Title Review Manager>   <Signature>   <Date>

Figure 4.8. Design Output Document Control Matrix

Design Output Requirements Control Matrix for: _____

Design Team ID: _____

Date: _____   Version: _____

Output Spec No.	Output Specifications	Req. Doc. No.	Responsibility of	Reviewed by	Approved by
1.0	**Intended Use**	OIU 001	<name>	<name(s)>	<name(s)>
1.1	Intended Use 1	OIU 001	<name>	<name(s)>	<name(s)>
1.2	Intended Use 2	OIU 001	<name>	<name(s)>	<name(s)>
2.0	**User Needs**	OUN 001	<name>	<name(s)>	<name(s)>
2.1	User Needs 1	OUN 001	<name>	<name(s)>	<name(s)>
2.2	User Needs 2	OUN 001	<name>	<name(s)>	<name(s)>
3.0	**Patient Needs**	OPN 001	<name>	<name(s)>	<name(s)>
3.1	Patient Needs 1	OPN 001	<name>	<name(s)>	<name(s)>

I attest that I am the approved Manager identified to review this matrix and that the individuals identified on the matrix are appropriate for their assigned activity.

_____

        <Printed Name>   <Title Review Manager>   <Signature>   <Date>

Figure 4.9. Design Output Specifications Control Matrix

Each of these detailed input documents should be version number and date controlled, carry the specifications document number identified in the design output specifications control matrix and provide details of each specification identified by the matrix. Each final design output document should be marked "Final" and have a document cover that has appropriately dated review and approval signatures. Detailed specifications documents may have a style and format similar to that in the sample provided in Figure 4.10, page 58.

What the regulation states

§ 820.30 (e)

(e) *Design review.* Each manufacturer shall establish and maintain procedures to ensure that formal documented reviews of the design results are planned and conducted at appropriate stages of the device's design development. The procedures shall ensure that participants at each design review include representatives of all functions concerned with the design stage being reviewed and an individual(s) who does not have direct responsibility for the design stage being reviewed, as well as any specialists needed. The results of a design review, including identification of the design, the date, and the individual(s) performing the review, shall be documented in the design history file (the DHF).

§ 820.30 (e) Discussion

FDA fully expects device manufacturers to identify appropriate design reviewers to ensure that each device's design is formally reviewed at appropriate stages of each device's design process. That review should:

- Be performed by appropriate design teams or individuals with identified review responsibility
- Occur at appropriate stages of each device's design process
- Include design team participants that include representatives of all functions concerned with that design stage *and an individual who does not have direct responsibility for the design stage being reviewed* as well as any other needed specialists.

Required procedure(s), document(s), and record(s)

Review should include all final design documentation, including the following:

- Schematics
- Device components
- Subassemblies
- Final risk analysis documents
- Final master verification plan and test plans and complete performance testing to prove the device meets functional safety specifications and reliability requirements
- Device manufacturing specifications and documentation
- Process validation protocol, if required
- Draft user, maintenance, and service documentation
- Initiation of clinical trials if required
- Design and completion of any required integrity testing of the device packaging
- All documentation and verification activities

Review meeting notes and/or minutes are the responsibility of each review manager to create or cause to be created. These notes and/or minutes should contain information specific to the device being designed or changed. An example of review meeting notes or minutes is provided in Figure 4.11, page 59. (Note: If any heading is not reviewed, it should be identified as "not reviewed," or if a heading is not applicable, it should be marked as "not applicable.")

As previously noted, forms and checklists are also useful mechanisms to control design review activities. They may include the following:

- Design development stage identification matrix would identify appropriate design development stages and the type of reviews appropriate for those stages. Those identifications may take the form of a controlled document, design development stage identification matrix, or similar controlled document. A sample matrix is provided in Figure 4.4, page 52.
- A review and approval cover sheet for each stage, part, or version reviewed, and the final version of each controlled document, a review and approval cover sheet may be attached. A sample review and approval cover sheet is provided in Figure 4.12, page 60.
- Review checklists may identify appropriate items for the review stages. Those checklists should take the form of a controlled document and should be specific to the stages being reviewed. A sample checklist is provided in Figure 4.13, page 61.

DOCUMENT NUMBER OIU 001

Version 1.0 Date: <date>

Design Team ID: _____

<Names> are responsible for this document
<Names> are responsible for review of this document
<Names> are responsible for approval of this document

Specifications	Description/Discussion/Comment
1.1	Intended Use description number 1 Minim veniam, quis nostrud citation ullam corper suscipit lobortis nisil ut aliquip ex ea commodo consequat. Duis dolore te feugait nulla fa cilisi. Nam liber tempor cum soluta nobis eleifend option congue nihil. Ut wisi enim ad minim veniam, quis nostrud exercitation ullam corper suscipit. Ut wisi benim.
1.3	Intended Use description number 2 Minim veniam, quis nostrud citation ullam corper suscipit lobortis nisil ut aliquip ex ea commodo consequat. Duis dolore te feugait nulla fa cilisi. Nam liber tempor cum soluta nobis eleifend option congue nihil. Ut wisi enim ad minim veniam, quis nostrud exercitation ullam corper suscipit. Ut wisi benim.

I have reviewed this Intended Use Specification Document:

_____

| <Printed Name> | <Title Review Manager> | <Signature> | <Date> |

I have reviewed and approved this Intended Use Specification Document:

_____

| <Printed Name> | <Title Review Manager> | <Signature> | <Date> |

Figure 4.10. Intended Use Specifications Document

Date: _____   Design Team ID: _____

Design Identification: _____

Design Stage: _____

Design Document Name: _____

Review is a:
❏ Periodic   ❏ Scheduled   ❏ Final Team   ❏ Final Management

Review Manager: _____

Participants: _____

Independent Individuals: _____

Specialists: _____

Outline Format

A. Notes from previous meeting reviewed:

B. Purpose of review meeting:

C. Items or activities reviewed:

D. Output specifications reviewed to ensure input requirements met:

E. Identified problems:

F. Identified problems corrected by change control or corrective activity:

G. Assignments to design team members:

H. Notes for next meeting:

I. Review & documents reviewed filed as part of Design History File (DHF) or Device Master Record (DMR) for device production specifications.

I attest that the above-identified review was performed on the date listed.

_____

<Printed Name>   <Title Review Manager>   <Signature>   <Date>

Figure 4.11.   Design Review Notes/Minutes Outline

What the regulation states

§ 820.30 (f)

(f) *Design verification.* Each manufacturer shall establish and maintain procedures for verifying the device design. Design verification shall confirm that the design output meets the design input requirements. The results of the design verification, including identification of the design, method(s), the date, and the individual(s) performing the verification, shall be documented in the DHF (see design history file, see page 75).

§ 820.30 (f) Discussion

Design verification and validation are terms often used by some individuals interchangeably but are in fact two different activities. Design verification's intent is to ensure that the design output or specifications meet the design input or requirements. Design verification can be described as those activities involved with determining whether the device was "made right."

Design validation, as described below, refers to activities that determine whether the device was made correctly and whether the device meets its intended uses.

Intended Use Specifications
Document Number IU 001

Review and Approval Cover Sheet

Version x.x   Date: <date>

Design Team ID: _____

Review is a: ❐ Periodic   ❐ Scheduled   ❐ Final Team   ❐ Final Management

The appropriate Design Team Reviewers for the above listed device signatures indicate they have review this version of this document:

<Printed Name>	<Title>	<Signature>	<date>
<Printed Name>	<Title>	<Signature>	<date>
<Printed Name>	<Title>	<Signature>	<date>
<Printed Name>	<Title>	<Signature>	<date>

The appropriate Design Team Approval Individuals for the above listed device signatures indicate they have review this version of this document:

<Printed Name>	<Title>	<Signature>	<date>
<Printed Name>	<Title>	<Signature>	<date>

❐ If the review is a Final Management Review:

I/We attest that I/We have reviewd the attached documents and records and confirm that the design identified by these documents and records are approved and the design has received its Final Management Review and are approved for Design Transfer:

<Printed Name>	<Title Review Manager>	<Signature>	<date>
<Printed Name>	<Title Review Manager>	<Signature>	<date>

Figure 4.12.   Review and Approval Cover Sheet

Date: _____   Design Team ID: _____

Design Identification: _____

Design Stage: _____

Design Document Name: _____

Note: Check off all appropriate items as part of each review:

Review is a: ❒ Periodic   ❒ Scheduled   ❒ Final Team   ❒ Final Management

❒ Identication of design control departments and/or activities completed.

❒ Identication of design and development activities completed.

❒ Design and development interfaced completed.

    ❒ Review participants identified   ❒ Independent review individuals identified

    ❒ Specialists identified ❒ Specialists not needed.

Review documents are:

    ❒ Design input document control matrix ❒ Design input requirements control matrix ❒ General device requirements ❒ Detailed input documents

    ❒ Design output document control matrix ❒ Design output specifications control matrix ❒ General device specifications ❒ Detailed output

❒ Documents confirm that output specifications meet the approprite input requirements

❒ Documents that output specifications have not met the appropriate input requirements

Reviewed documents are: ❒ Master verification plan ❒ Design verification

❒ Design validation ❒ Design transfer ❒ Design change ❒ Design process

❒ Design process verification ❒ Design process validation

❒ More complex devices are reviewed more frequently

❒ Requirements are appropriate and address intended use of device

❒ Review has identified problems.   ❒ Review has not identified problems(s).

❒ Identified problems have been integrated into design process change control.

❒ Identified problems have been addressed.   ❒ Identified problems have not been addressed.

    Addressed requirements: ❒ Incomplete ❒ Ambiguous ❒ Conflicting

Review includes any: ❒ Risk analysis ❒ Performance issues ❒ Safety issues

    ❒ Compatibility with other devices issues ❒ Human factors issues

    ❒ Environmental issues ❒ Drawings, manufacturing instructions, test specifications, and so on

❒ Review meeting ❒ notes   ❒ minutes are attached to checklist.

❒ Review & document reviewed identified and filed as part of design history file (DHF) or device master record (DMR)

I attest that I am the approved Manager identified to complete this checklist and that the individuals identified on the attached review coversheet have performed the review identified in this checklist.

_____

    \<Printed Name\>   \<Title Review Manager\>   \<Signature\>   \<date\>

Figure 4.13.   Design Review Checklist

The following table identifies verification and validation characteristics and activities:

Characteristic or Activity	Verification	Validation
Written plan	Yes	Yes
Written activity description	Yes	Yes
Written testing requirements and acceptance criteria	Yes	Yes
Review and approval of written documents prior to use	Yes	Yes
Training personnel whenever required	Yes	Yes
Requires review of requirements (inputs)	Yes	No
Requires review of specifications (outputs)	Yes	No
Confirms the design output specifications meets the input requirements	Yes	No
Confirms actual outputs against expected outputs	Partially*	Yes
Inputs include normal, abnormal, and absurd conditions	Yes	Yes
Includes software testing (when applicable)	Yes	Yes
Includes labeling	Yes	User documents only
Document testing deviations, failures, & their analysis	Yes	Yes
Corrective actions performed when appropriate	Yes	Yes
Change in specification performed when appropriate	Yes	Yes
Retesting required when appropriate	Yes	Yes
Integrated with risk analysis	Yes	Yes
Considers premarket notification requirements	Yes	Yes
Performed by design & development staff	Yes	No
Performed on parts or components of a device	Yes	No
Performed on a final prototype device	Yes	No
Performed on an initial production finished device	No	Yes
Performed as beta testing by a user	No	Yes
Performed as a clinical evaluation	No	Yes
Performed under actual or simulated use conditions	Not required	Yes
Requires user-defined test plan	No	Yes
Confirms the device meets user's requirements	May*	Yes
Confirms the device meets its intended use	May*	Yes
Performed independently of design and development oversight	No	Yes
Review and approval at all steps	Yes	Yes

*Not required; depends upon the master verification plan or individual test plan.

Something to note!

Design verification activities include the following:

- Verification training by the design team to ensure that individuals responsible for verification testing are adequately trained in verification processes; may require third-party assistance or training
- Pretesting review that consists of a complete and thorough review of the following:
  — Design input or requirements
  — Design output or specifications

- Assessments to ensure that the design output or specifications meet the design input or requirements
- Risk analysis and control of identified individual hazards
- All labeling against requirements, specifications, and risk analysis, including documentation risks or hazards
- Master verification plan, including the following:
  - Verification criteria
  - Verification assumptions and expectations
  - Verification personnel, their qualifications and responsibilities
  - Design personnel, their qualifications and responsibilities
- Appropriate testing of the following:
  - Individual parts, elements, components, modules, software components
  - All inputs under normal, abnormal, and absurd conditions
  - Testing deviations or failures
  - Deviations or failures after appropriate corrective action or changes (retesting)
- Equipment calibrated with test equipment and controlled with appropriate requirements
- Master verification plan and test plans should do the following:
  - Consider any premarket notification documentation requirements
  - Perform according to written and approved master verification plan and test plans
  - Ensure identified risks or hazards are fully tested via written plans
- Documentation that verifies design review and appropriate testing:
  - Identification of the device
  - Methods used in the verification
  - Dates
  - Individuals performing the verification
  - All verification documentation should be considered controlled documentation
- Verification review in which appropriate individuals review and approve all verification activities, including master verification plan, test plans, test results, and any retesting after corrective actions or changes

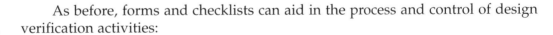

Required procedure(s), document(s), and record(s)

As before, forms and checklists can aid in the process and control of design verification activities:

- Verification test plans are created following the master verification plan to ensure that each new or modified device is appropriate for its intended use and is reviewed and approved prior to implementation. Test results of any retesting after corrective actions or changes require review and approval. Verification test plans should clearly identify the design's individual parts, elements, components, modules, or software components being verified. A sample verification test plan outline is provided in Figure 4.14, page 64.
- The design verification checklist can ensure that each device's design output or specifications or part thereof meet design input or requirements. Design teams should identify appropriate design verification checklists to control this process. Those checklists should take the form of a controlled document and should be specific for the device being verified. A sample design verification checklist is provided in Figure 4.15, page 65.

Date: _____   Design Team ID: _____

Design Identification: _____

A. Design verification description

B. Premarket notification documentation requirements

C. Verification method(s)

D. Verification equipment

E. Master verification plan
  1. Establish verification criteria
  2. Establish verification assumptions and expectations
  3. Identify verification personnel, their qualifications and responsibilities
  4. Identify design personnel, their qualifications and responsibilities

F. Verification testing requirements—Follow sound verification testing techniques identified by the design team, including:
  1. Objectives and constraints of testing
  2. Test procedures
  3. Test cases
  4. Test inputs against expected outputs—inputs under normal, abnormal and absurd conditions
  5. Traceability to design inputs and outputs
  6. Ensure all hazards identified in risk analysis are appropriately correctly mitigated or eliminated
  7. Acceptance criteria.

G. Verification unit and integration testing of software—Follow sound software verification techniques identified by the design team's Master Verification Plan, including:
  1. Objectives and constraints of testing
  2. Test procedures
  3. Unit testing checks for typographic, syntactic and logical errors
  4. Integration testing checks intermodule communication links and aggregate functions of groups of modules
  5. Test inputs against expected outputs (inputs under normal, abnormal and absurd conditions)
  6. Traceability to design inputs and outputs
  7. Ensure all software hazards identified in risk analysis are appropriately and correctly mitigated or eliminated
  8. Acceptance criteria.

H. Error report(s) and analysis.

I. Corrective Action/Change of Specifications—Perform appropriate re-testing to confirm corrective action/change appropriate.

J. Verification Testing Review and Approval of Results.

Figure 4.14. Verification Test Plan Outline

Date: _____   Design Team ID: _____

Design Identification: _____

Design Verification Description: _____

❏ Prior to any vertification testing, the design team has established a Master Validation Plan with verification criteria, assumptions, and expectations.

❏ Prior to any verification testing, the individuals responsible for verification have been properly trained in verification processes.

❏ Prior to any verification testing, the individuals responsible for the verification have reviewed the verification project's individual parts, elements, components, modules, or software components inputs and outputs, Risk analysis, labeling, and other documentation to develop the best understanding of the verification task at hand.

❏ After the preverification review, the individuals responsible for the verification have created Verification Test Plans appropriate for the element, module, component, or device being verified.

❏ The individuals responsible for the Verification Test Plans should ensure they are written in a format that tests all functionality, including user functionality, service functionality, and support functionality for the verification project's individual parts, elements, components, modules, or software components.

❏ The individuals responsible for the Verification Test Plans should use the approved Verification Test Plans or a design team-approved test plan guidance.

❏ The individuals responsible for the Verification Test Plans should ensure that any equipment used is appropriately calibrated, if required, and controlled by appropriate testing requirements.

❏ The individual responsible for the Verification Test Plans should ensure that the methods used are clearly defined.

❏ Appropriate individuals will review and approve any Verification Test Plans created prior to their use.

❏ Appropriate individual will review and approve all test results and any retesting after corrective actions or changes.

I attest that I am the approved Manager identified to complete this checklist and certify that the above checked activities or actions are accurately reflected by documentation attached or listed and attached to this checklist.

_____

       <Printed Name>   <Title Review Manager>   <Signature>   <date>

Figure 4.15.   Design Verification Checklist

What the regulation states

§ 820.30 (g)

(g) *Design validation.* Each manufacturer shall establish and maintain procedures for validating the device design. Design validation shall be performed under defined operating conditions on initial production units, lots, or batches, or their equivalents. Design validation shall ensure that devices conform to defined user needs and intended uses and shall include testing of production units under actual or simulated use conditions. Design validation shall include software validation and risk analysis, where appropriate. The results of the design validation, including identification of the design, method(s), the date, and the individual(s) performing the validation, shall be documented in the DHF.

§ 820.30 (g) Discussion

Design validation refers to activities that determine whether the "right device was made" and whether the device meets its intended use.

Remember!   The intent of design validation is to ensure that the design input or requirements and design output or specifications, by examination and objective evidence, can be consistently fulfilled and conform to user needs and intended uses. Validation ensures that the design team "makes the right product." Design validation must be of initial production units, lots, batches, or their equivalents.

Design teams should ensure that design validation includes the following:

- Validation training: The design team should ensure that individuals responsible for validation testing are adequately trained in validation processes. This may require third-party assistance or training.
- Validation activities, which are typically performed
  — Under defined operating conditions
  — On initial production units, lots, batches, or their equivalents
  — Under actual or simulated conditions
  — With any software
  — With a review of all risk analyses
- Master validation plan, which will
  — Establish validation criteria
  — Establish validation assumptions and expectations
  — Identify validation personnel, their qualifications and responsibilities
  — Identify design personnel, their qualifications and responsibilities
- Testing, which requires
  — Appropriate testing of the finished device, under written defined operating conditions
  — Appropriate testing of all user inputs under normal, abnormal, and absurd conditions
  — Appropriate testing of all device outputs against expected outputs
  — Explanations, corrections, and retesting of all deviations and unexpected results
  — "Beta testing" or clinical evaluation when appropriate. Beta testing is user testing in a user's environment.
  — Appropriate testing of equipment. Any equipment used should be calibrated with test equipment and controlled with appropriate requirements.
- Master validation plan and test plans should:
  — Consider any premarket notification documentation requirements
  — Be performed according to written and approved test plans or protocols
  — Ensure identified risks or hazards are fully tested
- Documentation (considered controlled documentation) which includes—the following written documents and records that verify design review and appropriate testing:
  — Identification of the device
  — Methods used in the validation
  — Dates
  — Names of persons who performed the validation
- Validation review: Appropriate individuals will review and approve all validation activities, including master validation plan, test plans, test results, and any retesting after corrective actions or changes.

A sample design validation checklist is provided in Figure 4.17, page 68. A sample validation test plan outline is provided in Figure 4.16, page 67.

Date: _____   Design Team ID: _____

Design Identification: _____

A. Design verification description

B. Premarket notification documentation requirements

C. Verification methods

D. Verification equipment

E. Master verification plan
 1. Establish verification criteria
 2. Establish verification assumptions and expectations
 3. Identify verification personnel, their qualifications and responsibilities
 4. Identify design personnel, their qualifications and responsibilities

F. Validation requirements—Follow sound validation techniques identified by the design team, including:
 1. Objectives and constraints of testing
 2. Test procedures
 3. Test cases
 4. Test inputs against expected outputs (inputs under normal, abnormal and absurd conditions)
 5. Traceability to design inputs and outputs
 6. Ensure all hazards identified in risk analysis are correctly mitigated or eliminated
 7. Acceptance criteria of the device's final production unit.

G. Validation system testing of software—Follow sound software validation techniques identified by the design team, including:
 1. Objectives and constraints of testing
 2. Test procedures
 3. System tests against expected outputs (inputs under normal, abnormal and absurd conditions)
 4. Traceability to design inputs and outputs
 5. Ensure all software hazards identified in risk analysis are appropriately mitigated or eliminated
 6. Acceptance criteria of the device's final production sofware version.

H. Error report(s) and analysis.

I. Corrective action/change of specifications—Perform appropriate re-testing to confirm CA/change appropriate.

J. Validation testing review and approval of results—Approval of final device's production unt

K. Beta testing or clinical evaluation—After approval of final device's production unit, delivery of one or more units for beta testing or clinical evaluation.
 1. Identification of device being beta tested or undergoing clinical evaluation
 2. User defined test plans and protocols to ensure independence of testing
 3. Objectives and Constraints of Testing
 4. Test procedures
 5. Test cases
 6. Test inputs against expected outputs—Inputs under normal, abnormal and absurd conditions
 7. Traceability to user documentation
 8. Ensure all system warnings, alerts, and documentation related to hazards are appropriate and sufficient
 9. Acceptance criteria of beta tested or clinical evaluation unit

Figure 4.16. Validation Test Plan Outline

Date: _____   Design Team ID: _____

Design Identification: _____

Design Verification Description: _____

❏ Prior to any validation testing, the design team has established a Master Validation Plan criteria, assumptions, and expectations.

❏ Prior to any validation testing, the individuals responsible for validation have been properly trained in validation processes.

❏ Prior to any validation testing, the individuals responsible for the validation have reviewed the verification results, risk analysis, labeling, and other documentation to develop the best understanding of the validation task at hand.

❏ After the prevalidation review, the individuals responsible for the validation have created Verification Test Plans appropriate for the element, module, component, or device being validated.

❏ The individuals responsible for the Validation Test Plans should ensure they are written in a format that tests all final and approved device functionality, including user functionality, service functionality, and support functionality for the validation project.

❏ The individuals responsible for the Validation Test Plans should ensure that any equipment used is appropriately calibrated, if required, and controlled by appropriate testing requirements.

❏ Appropriate individuals will review and approve any Validation Test Plans created prior to their use.

❏ Appropriate individuals will review and approve all test results and any retesting after corrective actions or changes.

❏ If required, appropriate beta testing or clinical evaluation has been completed prior to the final approval and release of the device.

I attest that I am the approved Manager identified to complete this checklist and certify that the above checked activities or actions are accurately reflected by documentation attached or listed and attached to this checklist.

| <Printed Name> | <Title Review Manager> | <Signature> | <date> |

Figure 4.17.   Design Validation Checklist

What the regulation states

§ 820.30 (h)

(h) *Design transfer.* Each manufacturer shall establish and maintain procedures to ensure that the device design is correctly translated into production specifications.

§ 820.30 (h) Discussion

Design transfer is the device design's translation into production specifications. The design team should ensure that each completed element, component, or the complete device's design is correctly translated into production specifications.

A sample design transfer request is provided in Figure 4.18, page 69.

Don't forget!

Design transfer control should ensure that each device's design, or part thereof, meets input requirements, and, where needed, contains acceptance criteria and design parameters that have been appropriately verified, are complete and approved for use, and are under change control. Design teams should identify appropriate design transfer checklists to control this process.

Those checklists should take the form of a controlled document and should be specific for the device being translated to production specifications. A sample design transfer checklist is provided in Figure 4.19, page 70.

Date: _____   Design Team ID: _____

Design Identification: _____

Design transfer activity:

❑ Complete design transfer   ❑ Partial design transfer
❑ Component design transfer   ❑ Software design tranfer
❑ Documentation   ❑ Other: _____

_____

_____

_____

Detailed transfer description:

_____

_____

_____

_____

_____

Attachments:

❑ Written documents   ❑ Assembly drawings
❑ Specifications   ❑ Documentation
❑ Manufacturing instructions
❑ Other: _____

Attachment description:

_____

_____

_____

_____

_____

I attest that I have reviewed the above identified device design and found the activities required by our design control procedures and FDA regulations to have been fulfilled and approve this device design for transfer to ❑ Production ❑ Documentation for ❑ Production or ❑ Label and labeling production.

_____
    \<Printed Name>   \<Title Review Manager>   \<Signature>   \<date>

Figure 4.18.   Design Transfer Request

Date: _____   **Design Team ID:** _____

Design Identification: _____

Design Transfer of Completed: ❐ Design Element   ❐ Component   ❐ Device

Transfer description: _____

❐ Final Device Review documents and records are complete, including, all design review notes/minutes, design review checklists, and an executed review and approval cover sheet.

❐ Results have been presented to management for final management review (design review checklist) and approval based on that final design review checklist.

❐ A limited number, at least three, of approved, finalized medical devices have been manufactured, inspected and tested and validate the manufacturing process.

❐ Manufacturing documentation and quality assurance procedures are verified as complete, appropriate and accurate.

❐ Any personnel training requirement has been assessed and, if required, has been implemented.

❐ All manufacturing equipment and their testing requirements have been assessed, tested and approved.

❐ Verification testing of the finished device has been performed and demonstrates that the device meets functional, safety specifications and reliability requirements.

❐ If required, reliability and environmental testing has been initiated.

❐ All records related to items identified in this design transfer checklist are either attached to this checklist or identified in a listing attached to this checklist.

I attest that I am the approved Manger identified to complete this Checklist and that the ❐ completed design element ❐ Completed component ❐ Completed device identified is approved for production or manufacturing:

_____
    \<Printed Name\>   \<Title Review Manager\>   \<Signature\>   \<date\>

I/We attest that I/We have reviewed the attached documents and records, and confirm that the design has been approved, received its final management review, has been approved for design transfer, and is approved for production or manufacturing:

_____
    \<Printed Name\>   \<Title Review Manager\>   \<Signature\>   \<date\>

_____
    \<Printed Name\>   \<Title Review Manager\>   \<Signature\>   \<date\>

Figure 4.19. Design Transfer Checklist

§ 820.30 (i)

(i) *Design changes.* Each manufacturer shall establish and maintain procedures for the identification, documentation, validation or where appropriate verification, review, and approval of design changes before their implementation.

§ 820.30 (i) Discussion

Design changes are a part of overall medical device change control. Because of the implementation of the new Quality System Regulations, FDA has emphasized its concern for design changes with the specific regulation stated above. Other elements of the Quality System Regulations also emphasize change control, including, but not limited to, device components, labeling and packaging, device manufacturing processes, production equipment, manufacturing materials, and all associated documentation. Many of these elements of change control will be discussed in later chapters. The remainder of this discussion is specific to design change control.

Remember!

Design change control must be implemented during both the original design activities and any subsequent change to a formally approved final design of each device, that is, a design that has achieved formal design transfer. Changes after design transfer must be controlled to ensure that the original problem is resolved and no new problems are introduced. If new problems are created, they must be tracked to resolution.

Required procedure(s), document(s), and record(s)

A design controls procedure, its forms and checklists can be used by the design teams to provide the process control necessary for change control of any device during its original design or any changes made after formal design transfer. This will ensure that appropriate design documentation is updated to accurately reflect the revised design.

Change control documentation for changes implemented as a result of any corrective action are an important part of tracking those actions to completion. A change request form can provide change control to devices in development or devices changed after formal design transfer. A sample is provided in Figure 4.20, pages 72 and 73.

Approved change requests are reviewed by the design team to determine whether the change is simple, for example, an addition or correction to a manual does not require full change control processing. Such a determination would be made in the design review notes/minutes. Approved change requests that are reviewed and determined to require full design control are subject to design team oversight, review, and approval of the documents and records that result, often initiated by a new product proposal describing the change.

The design team must document any rejected or deferred change requests with the reasons for the rejection or deferral.

Change Request

Any proposed changes to a device's approved design input requirements or design output specifications must be controlled by first completing this change request form. This form must be used for any new device's changes to approved input requirements or approved output specifications, even prior to the completion of the design transfer. However, changes to input requirements or output specifications *prior* to their review and approval are considered part of the normal design and development activity. any change, including labeling change, to an existing finished device must be initiated with this form. All proposed changes to design input requirements will require a review for appropriate change or creation of new design output specifications. This firm believes that changes to output specifications may not require changes to input requirements, therefore, the design team will determine if any proposed changes to design output specifications require a review to determine the applicability of a change or creation of a new design input requirements.

Note: All reviewed and approved device changes must be assessed according to design control procedures or to a design change guideline approved by the appropriate design team. Record these assessments in the design review notes/minutes for the identified device.

Design Team Identification: _____

❐ Change to an approved new design or development activity   ❐ Change to an approved finished device

❐ Proposed change to design input requirements (*will require review for change or creation of new design output specifications* ❐ Proposed change to design output specifications (*may require review for change or creation of new design input requirements*

❐ Change is a result of a corrective action. ❐ Change corrects or changes device's intended use.

❐ Change corrects or changes an element that affects the safety or effectiveness of the device.

    ❐ Labeling change   ❐ User notification required   ❐ Only on future labeling

Description of the proposed changes: (*Complex or lengthy descriptions can be attached.*)

_____

I request the above described or ❐ attached change be reviewed and acted upon by the Design Team:

_____

| <Printed Name>   <Title >   <Signature>   <date>

Figure 4.20.   Change Request (page 1)

Review of the proposed change by the Design Team:

❏ Proposed change review has been documented in Design Team's design review notes/minutes of _____

❏ Proposed change **not** approved for further action

❏ Proposed change approved for further action

❏ Proposed change ❏ will   ❏ will not require full design control
    ❏ Labeling change   ❏ User notification required   ❏ Only on future labeling

❏ Product proposal required: ❏ Yes   ❏ No

❏ Proposed change to design input requirements and
    ❏ will   ❏ will not require change or creation of new design output specifications

❏ Proposed change to design output specifications ❏ will   ❏ will not require change or creation of new design input requirements

❏ Risk analysis required: ❏ Yes   ❏ No

❏ Change   ❏ is   ❏ is not a result of a corrective action.

❏ Change   ❏ does   ❏ does not correct or change device's intended use.

❏ Change   ❏ does   ❏ does not correct or change an element that affects the safety or effectiveness of the device.

❏ Proposed change will require: ❏ Design Verification   ❏ Design Validation   ❏ Design Transfer control

I attest that I am the approved Manager identified to complete this Change Request and my signature certifies that the Design Team identified above has performed the review and action identified in this form.

       <Printed Name>   <Title Review Manager>   <Signature>   <date>

Figure 4.20.   Change Request (page 2)

Required procedure(s), document(s), and record(s)

Device change control is accomplished through the design controls procedures and may contain the following output documents, forms, or checklists to achieve that goal:

- Product proposal: A device concept document that can be required and prepared by appropriate departments, activities, or individuals to manage change control for any changes to a device during its original design or any changes made after formal design transfer.
  — The product proposal is the output of any change to a device during its original design or any change after formal design transfer.
  — Appropriately executed forms can control review and approval of the product proposal.
- Design Input Requirements: Design teams can manage change control for any changes to a device's requirements by these forms and checklists.
  — For those documents affected by these changes, new document names and dates; new version numbers of existing documents with dates; new or revised design input document control matrix; new or revised general device requirements; new or revised design input requirements control matrix; and new or revised detailed input documents will provide documentation of any of these changes.

- — Design review forms and checklists will provide design team and design management oversight. Those documents include a design development stage identification matrix, review and approval cover sheet, design review checklist, and design review notes/minutes.
- Design output specifications can manage change control from any changes to a device's specifications by these forms and checklists.
  - — For those documents affected by these changes, new document names and dates, new version numbers of existing documents with new dates, new or revised design output document control matrix, new or revised general device specifications, and new or revised design output specifications control matrix, and new or revised detailed output documents will provide documentation of any of these changes.
- Design review forms and checklists will provide design team and design management oversight, those documents include a design development stage identification matrix, review and approval cover sheet, design review checklist, and design review notes/minutes.
  - — Design review can manage design review of the changed device's product proposal, input requirements, and output specifications using the same review and approval process as used during the device's initial design.
- Design verification can manage change control to any device that has had design verification activities with appropriate new or revised master verification plan, as directed by the design team. This may mean new or revised design verification of only the changes, or, in some cases depending on the significance of the changes a completely new design verification as determined by the design team.
  - — For those documents affected by these changes, new or revised design verification checklist and verification test plans will provide documentation of any of these changes.
  - — Design team and design management oversight can be controlled by documents that include a design development stage identification matrix, review and approval cover sheet, design review checklist, and design review notes/minutes.
- Design validation can manage change control to any device that has had design validation activities with appropriate new or revised master validation plan, as determined by the design team. This may mean new or revised design validation of only the changes, or, in most cases based on the significance of the changes, significant new design validation, and in some cases, completely new design validation as determined by the design team.
  - — For those documents affected by these changes, new or revised design validation checklist, and validation test plans will provide documentation of any of these changes.
  - — Design review oversight will provide design team and design management oversight. Those documents include a design development stage identification matrix, review and approval cover sheet, design review checklist, and design review notes/minutes.
- Design transfer can manage change control to any device that has completed all design input, output, verification and validation activities with appropriate new or revised design transfer, as determined by the design team.
  - — The design team can create a new design transfer checklist that identifies the changed element, component, or complete device and attached documents and records.
  - — The design team can create a new review and approval cover sheet, new design review checklist, and design review notes/minutes that will document both design team and design management oversight and control.
  - — Upon completion of the design review process, the design transfer of any change to any device is complete.

A design change checklist can provide change control to help manage the entire design change process. A sample is provided in the Figure 4.21, page 75.

Date: _____   Design Team ID: _____

Design identification: _____

Design stage _____

Design document name: _____

Note: Check off all appropriate items as part of each change control activity.

❐ A change request has been completed, reviewed by the design team and approved for change control processing.

❐ The change request and subsequent documentation is the result of a corrective action.

❐ The change request and subsequent documentation corrects or changes an element of the device's intended use.

❐ The change request and subsequent documentation corrects or changes an element that affects the safety or effectiveness of the device.

❐ The change request and subsequent documentation has been reviewed and assessed for its impact on the design inputs and intended uses.

❐ The change request is an addition or correction to labeling and only requires review and approval by the design team for implementation.

❐ The design team has determined that the change request is significant and will require typical design controls procedure processing, documentation, review and approval.

I attest that I am the approved Manger identified to complete this Checklist and that the ❐ Completed design element ❐ Completed component ❐ Completed device identified is approved for production or manufacturing.

_____

<Printed Name>   <Title Review Manager>   <Signature>   <date>

Figure 4.21. Design Change Checklist

What the regulation states   **§ 820.30 (j)**

(j) *Design history file.* Each manufacturer shall establish and maintain a DHF for each type of device. The DHF shall contain or reference the records necessary to demonstrate that the design was developed in accordance with the approved design plan and the requirements of this part.

§ 820.30 (j) Discussion

Each manufacturer's design history file (DHF) should include one or more documents that are specific to each device. The device specific documents should be sufficiently robust to identify all the appropriate records associated with that device. The DHF for individual devices can differ depending upon each device's sophistication and risk to patient health. To reduce duplicate efforts, most manufacturers find it practical to create uniform procedures and processes that apply to as many devices as practical.

Manufacturers also find that by embedding "DHF" into a controlled document's identification, they provide a simple mechanism to ensure that document is identified as part of a specific device's DHF.

Required procedure(s), document(s), and record(s)

Each firm's design controls procedures will identify a variety of forms, documents, checklists, and records that become the design history file (DHF). Those DHF documents include, but are not limited to the following:

- The design controls procedure, forms, and guidelines
- Executed forms that identify design control departments or activities
- Executed forms that identify design and development teams
- Executed forms that identify design and development interfaces
- Executed forms that identify design and development change requests
- All product proposals
- All design input document control matrixes
- All general device requirements
- All design input requirements control matrixes
- All detailed input documents
- All design output document control matrixes
- All general device specifications
- All design output specifications control matrixes
- All detailed output documents
- All design development stage identification
- All review and approval cover sheets
- All design review checklists
- All design review notes/minutes
- All maser verification plans and design verification checklists
- All verification test plans
- All master validation plans and design validation checklists
- All validation test plans
- A copy of the design transfer checklist to document approved, final design transfer
- All change requests and design change checklists

Note: Final, approved documents associated with the design transfer deal with final device manufacturing specifications and initiate the device's device master record (DMR), which is discussed in chapter 13.

Don't forget!

Design controls are high on FDA Investigators' priority list. Design controls were finalized in the new Quality System Regulations of 1997, and implementation was finalized for affected manufacturers in mid-1998, after a full year of training and understanding by both FDA employees and the device industry.

Although FDA will probably move cautiously during the first full year following implementation of design controls, larger firms can expect FDA Investigators to anticipate full compliance with design controls regulations. All firms should be able to document substantial effort toward design controls compliance and full compliance as quickly as possible. Failure to comply or nonconformances should be expected to result in 483 observations and possibly Warning Letters.

DESIGN CONTROLS

What the FDA Investigator will want to see during an inspection

Under the FDA's new Quality System Inspection Technique (QSIT) Handbook instructions, Investigators will also focus on design controls as one of the four major quality subsystems of each firm. The QSIT Handbook's inspectional objectives for design controls include verification that:

- Design control procedures that address Section 820.30 have been defined and documented.
- A design plan for any selected design project identifies the layout of the design and development activities, including assigned responsibilities, interfaces, and risk analysis.
- Design inputs were established.
- Design outputs essential for proper functioning of the device are identified.
- Acceptance criteria are established prior to performance of verification and validation activities.
- Design verification confirms that design outputs met the design input requirements.
- Design validation data were reviewed and approved and met predetermined user needs and intended uses.
- Completed design validation left no unresolved discrepancies.
- Devices containing software document software validation.
- Validation was performed using initial production units or their equivalents
- Any changes included, where appropriate, verification and validation.
- Design reviews were conducted.
- Approved design was correctly transferred.

A reconstruction of the QSIT Handbook's Design Controls Decision Flow Chart is provided in the Figure 4.22, page 83.

The following is a detailed description of what FDA Investigators will expect to review during their assessment of any firm's design controls activities. If a firm has no ongoing, planned, or completed design projects, Investigators are instructed to assess the firm's design control procedures. If the firm has not made any design change, Investigators will expect to see only the required design change procedures. However, if the firm has any ongoing, planned, or completed design projects, Investigators will expect to see appropriate design control procedures.

FDA Investigators will expect written procedural control of each firm's device design activities. They expect to see procedural control that follows or corresponds to the eight elements the regulation imposes on control of device design:

- Planning
- Inputs
- Outputs
- Review
- Verification
- Validation
- Transfer
- Changes

Manufacturers should understand that FDA should not make any assessment of a firm's device conceptual or feasibility studies. These documents should be clearly marked to distinguish them from any documents that are produced as a result of a device's actual design and development, once a concept or feasibility study has been approved.

PLANNING

Typically, Investigators select a single design project, especially one containing software, for their assessment of a firm's design control system. Their goal is to select a project that provides the "best challenge to the firm's design control system."

Investigators are trained to understand that the type of design control system and its implementation details are the prerogative of each firm. However, the Investigators expect that the complexity and risks of each device be fully appraised during the firm's documentation of each device's control system.

Investigators will review the firm's assessment of devices subject to design control regulations, their identification of applicable devices, and their dates of design activities. For each applicable device, the Investigator wishes to be shown what design planning, assigned responsibilities, interfaces, and risk analysis have been identified for each device or device group as well as how the input requirements were identified and reviewed for adequacy.

Although the requirement to conduct risk analysis appears in the Quality System Regulation in section 820.30(g) Design validation, FDA expects Investigators to initiate risk analysis in the design planning stage and carry it through the complete design control process. Risk analysis should be completed in design validation.

FDA Investigators expect to see a robust risk analysis with the identification of individual hazards in both normal and fault conditions. Manufacturers should assess the risks associated with each hazard in normal and fault conditions. Unacceptable risks should be reduced to acceptable levels or eliminated. Investigators will check design planning to ensure that design changes are reassessed for new hazards introduced by the change. Investigators are instructed to look for procedures that use fault tree analysis (FTA), failure modes and effects analysis (FMEA), or other risk analysis tools.

Manufacturers should understand that a determination of the appropriateness, safety, or effectiveness of any device is not the purpose of an inspection and is in fact precluded by the Food, Drug, and Cosmetic Act, as amended. However, Investigators may provide an establishment inspection report (EIR) with findings related to each of those issues for possible additional investigations.

DESIGN INPUT

An Investigator may review the following design inputs, depending upon the device:

- Intended use
- User/patient/clinical issues (interviews, usability studies [for example, user evaluation, task analysis, risk analysis, or workload analysis])
- Performance characteristics
- Safety
- Limits and tolerances

- Risk analysis (methods and inputs)
- Toxicity and biocompatibility
- Electromagnetic compatibility (EMC) (use environment, interference from and to other medical devices or from consumer electronic products, and conformity to relevant EMC standards [for example, IEC 601-1-2] identified as device design specifications)
- Compatibility with accessory/auxiliary devices
- Compatibility with environment of intended use
- Human factors (with emphasis on hardware and/or software interfaces)
- Physical/chemical characteristics
- Labeling/packaging
- Reliability
- Statutory and regulatory requirements
- Voluntary standards
- Manufacturing processes
- Sterility
- MDRs/complaints/failures
- Device history files (DHFs)

Investigators will review the firm's process for resolving incomplete, ambiguous, or conflicting requirements and attempt to identify any incomplete, ambiguous, or conflicting requirements that were not resolved per procedures. Additionally, the Investigators will want to understand how general input information and requirements are translated to specific requirements.

DESIGN OUTPUT

Investigators will want to see the manufacturer's procedures that define and control design output and be able to document how:

- The design system identifies and defines design outputs.
- Outputs are expressed and compared to inputs.
- The characteristics for proper functioning are identified.
- The acceptance criteria are determined for design output.
- The design output has been reviewed and approved prior to release. Who is responsible for these actions?

Manufacturers' risk analyses can be assessed by Investigators to ensure that essential outputs have been identified. Investigators understand that design projects can produce a large volume of records. They also understand that a manufacturer's design control procedures can indicate that only approved design output records need to be retained. Manufacturers are assessed to ensure that their output documentation is comprehensive enough to characterize the device and ensure appropriate verification and validation.

DESIGN REVIEW

Investigators will want to see the manufacturer's procedures that define and control formal design review (including design change review) and be able to document that:

- The manufacturer identified appropriate stages of development for formal design reviews.
- Documentation exists to demonstrate that the manufacturer has conducted formal design reviews at the identified appropriate stages.
- Mechanisms exist to ensure that design reviews are comprehensive and systematic.
- Appropriate organizational functions are represented at formal design reviews. They should include at least one individual who does not have direct responsibility for the design state being reviewed.
- The design review system ensures that identified design inputs are addressed by design outputs.

Investigators understand that design review does not always mean convened meetings with agendas and minutes. Sometimes distributed, documented, and signed "desk reviews" may be appropriate if provided for by the firm's procedures. Design reviews will always be checked to ensure they include at least one individual without direct responsibility for the design stage being reviewed.

Investigators will assess the design review to ensure that it provides feedback to designers, provides assessments of the designs progress, confirms that the design is ready to move to the next phase of development, and focuses on the design's outputs meeting the input requirements. They can also be expected to ensure that action items identified in design reviews are being or have been resolved.

Investigators will also focus their attention on the design review's assessment of the device's risk analysis and its robustness. They will also assess appropriate change control review and any appropriate risk analysis reassessment and review.

DESIGN CHANGES

Investigators will want to see (1) the manufacturer's procedures that define and control design changes, (2) an individual who is authorized to review and approve design changes before they are implemented, and (3) indication of how the approval is documented.

Investigators may select both a preproduction and postproduction design change and as well as documentation and records that identify:

- The stage of the design process the firm identifies when changes to the approved design inputs begin to be controlled
- The criteria in the design change system that are used to accept changes to approved design inputs
- The manner in which the design change system implements a change to the design inputs
- The procedures that are followed to evaluate when verification and/or validation of design changes are necessary

Investigators are taught that all design changes must be verified, and, unless only verification can be justified and documented, design changes must be validated. They would expect, for example, that change to the intended use of a device would require verification and validation. However, a design change in the material used in a device might require only verification.

Investigators understand that some firms may use their postproduction change control procedures to control preproduction design changes, whereas other firms may establish separate preproduction design control change procedures.

DESIGN VERIFICATION

Investigators will want to (1) see the manufacturer's procedures that define and control design verification; (2) review the design history file to identify the design methods of verification, dates, and individuals performing verification activities; and (3) see what the agency refers to as high (general) and low level (details) documents used.

They will also want to (1) see examples of significant points during the verification of the design project and (2) be able to confirm the number of times that a specific input requirement has been fulfilled by the design output and (3) identify whether these activities are quantitative and/or qualitative. To assess the documentation of verification activities, Investigators may use the sampling plans instructions and tables provided in the QSIT Handbook, which reference the second edition of the CRC Handbook of Probability and Statistics.

Investigators will want to understand, in terms of the user interface, (1) the verification methods that have been employed to confirm that input requirements are met (for example, usability testing such as prototyping, simulations, clinical trials, and so on) and (2) the verification data that show that output meets input, or if output does not meet input, how the company resolved the discrepancies.

DESIGN VALIDATION

Investigators will want to see the manufacturer's procedures that define and control design validation and to document that the validation activities performed are on devices that were produced using the same methods and procedures as those to be used in routine production.

If validation activities were performed on nonproduction devices, the Investigator will want to know how the tested devices were shown to be equivalent to production devices. They will assess to ensure that validation activities addressed the needs of all relevant parties, including the device user, patient, and other human factors.

The Investigators may ask the following questions:

- What evaluations (clinical and other activities) were performed to assist in validating that the device design meets defined user needs and intended uses?
- What labels and labeling, packaging, and so on are to be used?
- What clinical data were generated from studies with approved FDA compliant protocols for nonsignificant risk devices?
- Was a 510(k) historical database search performed?
- Did clinical evaluations include home use?
- Were there literature searches?
- Was there any historical product knowledge?
- Under what actual or simulated use conditions was the finished device tested? (The investigator will ask to see these.)
- How did the firm resolve discrepancies encountered during validation activities?
- Did discrepancy resolutions necessitate a new risk analysis? If not, why not?

- Does the product contain software? (The investigator will want to be informed of the method by which the software has been validated.)
- How have risks been identified and analyzed (fault tree analysis [FTA], failure mode and effects analysis [FMEA], failure mode, effects, and criticality analysis [FMECA] or other methods)?
- Does the DHF documentation identify the design, methods of validation, dates, and individuals performing validation activities?

Investigators will want to assess that design validation provides objective evidence that device outputs conform to user needs and the device's intended use.

DESIGN TRANSFER

Investigators will want to see the manufacturer's procedures that define and control design transfer, in other words, the procedures for transferring the design output of the device from the design team to the manufacturing group. Note: FDA understands that sometimes design transfer occurs in stages, prior to the overall final design output's review, approval, and transfer.

Typically the Investigator will select one or more design features and review the transfer process to confirm that procedures for design transfer were followed. Again, the Investigator may use the QSIT Handbook's sampling tables to select the number of records to assess design transfer.

DESIGN HISTORY FILE

Investigators will want to see how the manufacturer maintains and retains the contents of the design history file (DHF).

They may make a list of the key elements of the DHF to ensure that during the inspection they assess how these elements verify that the design was developed in accordance with the design plan and procedures. When more than one device shares a common design history file, the Investigators will want to understand how the firm identifies each device within the family or group having common design characteristics.

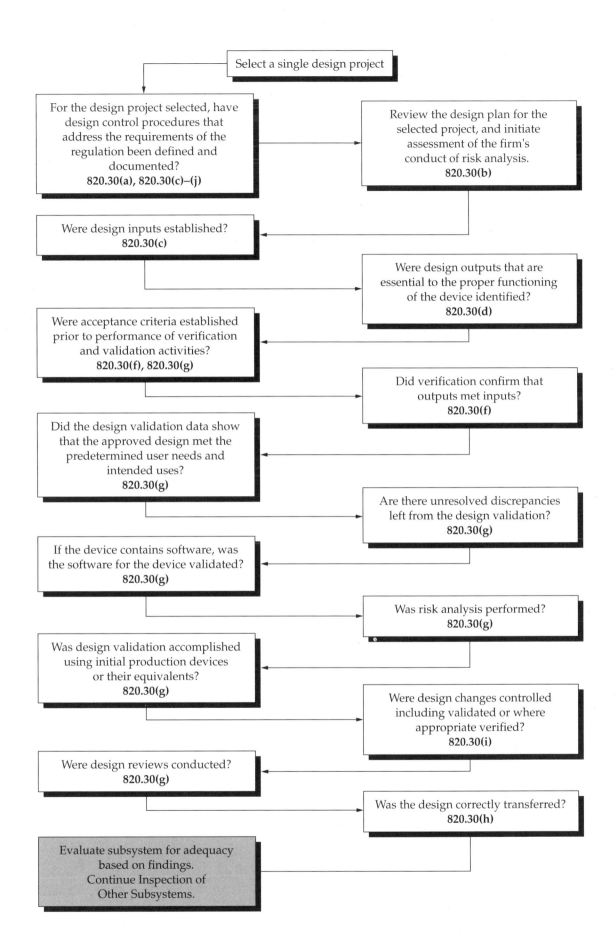

Figure 4.22. Design Controls Decision Flow Chart

Redrawn by author from original FDA Flow Chart, **QSIT Handbook,** *page 29*

5

Document Controls

INTRODUCTION

This chapter of **Mastering and Managing the FDA Maze: Medical Device Overview Training and Management Desk Reference** discusses FDA's regulatory oversight of device document controls.

SCOPE

The goal of this chapter is to provide an overview of FDA's regulations regarding medical device document controls. Significant detail has been omitted, and readers should undertake further training to ensure proficiency and understanding to the level required for FDA compliance.

This chapter discusses the FDA's most recent good manufacturing practice (GMP) regulations, the Quality System (QS) Regulations, which were finalized on October 7, 1996, (specifically Subpart D Document Controls) and became effective June 1, 1997.

The chapter discusses the "eyes" of FDA's oversight of medical devices, that is, the devices' document control activities. Documents and records, or their lack, are the evidence FDA requires of medical device manufacturers to prove their compliance or to confirm noncompliance with FDA regulations. Assuming that a firm can provide appropriate manufacturing controls for a device, unless appropriate document controls are implemented, there will be an unreasonable risk that the manufacture of the device will result in devices that fail to meet FDA's and the marketplace's expectations for safety and effectiveness and may be unsuitable for release as finished devices.

To ensure that finished devices are safe and effective for their intended use, each step in the documentation activities must fulfill its quality system role.

It should be emphasized that this discussion is *basic*. Individuals will require significant additional study and before they can be assured that the document controls they establish and maintain meet FDA expectations. The definitions, unless followed by an asterisk, are quoted from FDA's Quality System Regulations.

DOCUMENT CONTROLS

Definitions   *Design history file* (DHF) means a compilation of records which describes the design history of a finished device. See Design Controls discussions.

Device master record (DMR) means a compilation of records containing the procedures and specifications for a finished device.

Device history record (DHR) means a compilation of records containing the production history of a finished device.

Documentation means any records—written, electronic or automated—that provide information describing, defining, specifying, reporting, certifying, or auditing a manufacturer's FDA regulatory activities, requirements, verifications, or validations.*

Quality System Inspection Technique (QSIT) is FDA's latest inspection strategy. QSIT involves what FDA calls "top-down" inspections of the four major subsystems of each device manufacturer's quality system: (1) their management controls, (2) design controls, (3) corrective and preventive actions, and (4) production and process controls.*

Record means any written, electronic, or automated document, including books, manuals, papers, photographs, and machine-readable materials, which contain specifications, procedures, work instructions, protocols, standards, methods, plans, files, notes, reviews, analyses, corrections or changes, checklists, reports, training materials, or instructions, regardless of their physical form or characteristics, made during the design, development, change, testing, manufacture, review, approval, labeling, packaging, promotion, shipment, distribution, service, or support of any regulated medical device.*

Document Controls Regulation § 820.40 Document Controls

What the regulation states

§ 820.40 (a)

Each manufacturer shall establish and maintain procedures to control all documents that are required by this part. The procedures shall provide for the following:

(a) Document approval and distribution. Each manufacturer shall designate an individual(s) to review for adequacy and approve prior to issuance all documents established to meet the requirements of this part. The approval, including the date and signature of the individual(s) approving the document, shall be documented. Documents established to meet the requirements of this part shall be available at all locations for which they are designated, used, or otherwise necessary, and all obsolete documents shall be promptly removed from all points of use or otherwise prevented from unintended use.

§ 820.40 (a) Discussion

Don't forget!

Each document created and maintained for any medical device should have an individual who is designated for adequacy review and who approves the document prior to issuance. That review and approval should include the date and signature of the individual approving the document. See Figure 5.1, page 88.

Documents created and maintained for any medical device should be available at all locations for which they are designated, used, or necessary. Distribution of those documents should be controlled to identify what was sent or delivered, to whom it was delivered, and when it was delivered. See Figure 5.2, page 89.

Remember!

Obsolete documents should be promptly removed from all points of use to ensure prevention of any unintended use. The same mechanism that identifies distribution of a document can also document the removal and/or destruction of obsolete documents. See Figure 5.3, page 90, for an example of a form to control distribution and removal of documents.

What the regulation states

§ 820.40 (b)

(b) Document changes. Changes to documents shall be reviewed and approved by an individual(s) in the same function or organization that performed the original review and approval, unless specifically designated otherwise. Approved changes shall be communicated to the appropriate personnel in a timely manner. Each manufacturer shall maintain records of changes to documents. Change records shall include a description of the change, identification of the affected documents, the signature of the approving individual(s), the approval date, and when the change becomes effective.

Procedure #:   <name>   Reviewed by:
Form #:   <name>   ❑ <name>
Work instruction #:   <name>   ❑ <name>
Checklist #:   <name>   ❑ <name>
                                           ❑ <name>
Title: ❑ <name>
                                           ❑ <name>
New or changed:

Originated by: <name>

Date:

Return to   <name & department>
by: <date>

Statement of need for   ❑ Procedure   ❑ Form   ❑ Checklist   ❑ Summary changes:

Comments: (Reviewers may provide written comments below, on the back of this form, and on the procedure or document draft. Initial and date all comments.)

Signatures/Dates:

_____   _____   _____
(Signature)   (Signature)   (Signature)

_____   _____   _____
<Printed/Typed name>/Date   <Printed/Typed name>/Date   <Printed/Typed name>/Date

Figure 5.1.   Standard Operating Procedure Review Form

§ 820.40 (b) Discussion

Documentation change control is typically established by one or more procedures that control the creation, review, approval, and distribution of procedures, forms, checklists, and similar controlled documents. Documentation changes to instruction manuals and packaging must also be controlled.

Remember!   FDA expects manufacturers to maintain records of changes to these documents, which should include the following:

- Description of the change
- Identification of the affected documents
- Signature of the approving individuals
- Approval date
- Effective date of the change

Procedure Title: <title>   Procedure #: <number>
Originated by: <name>, <title>

My approval signature certifies that I believe that this documentation is adequate to fulfill its
intended purpose or requirement.

Title: <title>   Date:

Approval Signature:

<Printed/typed Department Manager/Head name>

My approval signature certifies that I believe that this documentation is adequate to fulfill its
intended purpose or requirement.

Title: <title>   Date:

Approval Signature: _____

<Printed/typed Department Manager/Head name>

My approval signature certifies that I believe that this documentation is adequate to fulfill its
intended purpose or requirement.

Title: <title>   Date:

Approval Signature: _____

<Printed/typed Individual Responsible for Quality Assurance>

If applicable:

My approval signature certifies that I believe that this documentation is adequate to fulfill its
intended purpose or requirement.

Title: Chief operating officer   Date:

Approval Signature:

<Printed/typed COO name>

Effective Date: <date>

Figure 5.2.   Standard Operating Procedure Approval Form

Date:

To: \<name\>   Department/activity: \<department name/activity\>

From: \<name\>   Department/activity: \<department name/activity\>

Acknowledge receipt of the attached documents as listed below. Ensure that your copy procedure manuals are updated and that all obsolete revisions are destroyed.

Title   No.   Effective Date
_____

_____

_____

_____

_____

Receipt acknowledged by: _____

This will certify that this activity had ❑ No or ❑ _____ copies of the previous version.

I further certify that all of the _____ copies of the previous version of this/these document(s) have been destroyed and, that to my knowledge, there remain *NO* copies of the previous version at this activity.

_____
\<Signature\>

_____
\<Printed/typed name\>   Title/Department   Date

Figure 5.3.   Standard Operating Procedure Distribution Record

---

Required procedure(s), document(s), and record(s)

The FDA's Quality System Regulations require document control over the following comprehensive groups of documents:

- Approval of design plans § 820.30(b)
- Approval of design input § 820.30(c)
- Approval of design output § 820.30(d)
- Results of design review § 820.30(e)
- Results of design verification § 820.30(f)
- Results of design validation § 820.30(g)
- Approval of the device master record (DMR) or changes to the DMR § 820.40
- Equipment maintenance and inspection activities § 820.70(g)
- Calibration performance § 820.72(b)

- Approval of process validation § 820.75(a)
- Performance of validated processes § 820.75(b)(1),(2)
- Release of finished devices § 820.80(d)
- Device acceptance activities performed § 820.80(e)
- Authorization to use nonconforming product § 820.90(b)
- Labeling inspection § 820.120(b)
- Audit certification § 820.180(c)
- Complaints—decisions not to investigate § 820.198(b)

Some smaller firms can create a few change control procedures to cover documents, design, manufacturing, testing, and other processes. In larger firms, change control procedures can be established in individual departments to control changes in:

- Product requirements
- Product specifications
- Engineering specifications
- Components
- Verification, validation, and testing (VV&T) activities
- Design processes
- Manufacturing processes
- Quality control processes
- Quality assurance processes
- Distribution and support processes

For samples of forms that illustrate the control of document changes, see Figure 5.1 (page 88), an example of a "Standard Operating Procedure Review Form"; Figure 5.2 (page 89), an example of a "Standard Operating Procedure Approval Form"; and Figure 5.3 (page 90), an example of a "Standard Operating Procedure Distribution Record."

Required procedure(s), document(s), and record(s)

Change control mechanisms, such as revision numbers, version numbers, component numbering system, assembly numbering system, labeling versions, and assembly drawing numbering systems should be identified in their appropriate procedures.

Changes to any device, accessory, labeling, packaging, and process should be thoroughly verified and/or validated by an appropriate activity. A designated individuals or group should review this verification and validation testing activity.

Care must be taken when implementing changes to documents, product designs, requirements, specification, components, VV&T, and processes to ensure that in-process devices are reprocessed or discarded.

Something to note!

Changes that affect a variety of individuals, activities, or entities should be identified in the change control process prior to review and approval. Care must be taken to ensure that those changes are communicated to all affected parties, including production, purchasing, contractors, and suppliers.

Changes may also affect device installation or servicing or require remedial field servicing or rework of warehouse stock. These changes require control to ensure appropriate action and follow-up if appropriate.

Remember!

Note: Depending upon the nature of the change, some remedial field servicing may be classified as a recall by FDA. Individuals responsible for these activities should constantly advise their counterparts responsible for regulatory affairs of remedial field servicing actions or anticipated actions.

Additional Discussion: Document Change Control and Premarket Submissions

Don't forget!

Changes to any device's intended use will most likely require a premarket submission. Changes to a finished device's functionality—and sometimes labeling—may also require a premarket submission. These types of changes to devices should be evaluated and documented individually—and periodically as a group—to assess the changes for premarket submission or resubmission.

Quality Assurance (QA) personnel who may be involved with identifying the need for change, making, evaluating, and reviewing the change to any product or process typically determine change control assessment. QA personnel are also typically involved with the revising, distribution, and assessment of change implementation and success.

Required procedure(s), document(s), and record(s)

In some cases, in addition to a change control procedure and forms, checklists for individual kinds of change activity are appropriate. These checklists are themselves documents subject to change control. Firms should also have procedures to control premarket submissions and assess for new submissions or resubmissions.

DOCUMENT CONTROLS

What the FDA Investigator will want to see during an inspection

Under the new Quality System Inspection Technique (QSIT) inspection program of FDA, Investigators will place significant importance on document control procedures and activities. Executive management, the management representative, and appropriate quality assurance staff must ensure that document control activities are established and maintained.

FDA Investigators will want to review written procedures that establish:

- Management review and approval of the firm's quality system
- Identification and responsibilities of the management representative
- Approval and distribution of documents
- Change control of documents

These procedures must ensure that the documents meet the requirements of the Quality System Regulations and that they are adequate for their intended use.

Investigators will also look for obsolete documents in the workplace. They will want to see that obsolete documents' removal or prevention-of-use activities are documented, signed, and dated and that their removal has been verified.

- Investigators will want to establish that written procedures covering all device operations are reviewed, approved, signed, and dated. Additionally, Investigators will want to verify that all documents related to the device master record (DMR) and device history record (DHR) have been reviewed, approved, signed, and dated and are available at the point they are needed or intended to be used.
- Investigators will want to establish that all changes to approved documents are reviewed, approved, signed, dated, and communicated to appropriate personnel in a timely manner. The approving individual should be the same person or from the same activity as the original approver; if not, records should document an approval designee.
- Documented change records should identify the description of the changes, identify affected documents, establish an effective date, and establish that document changes are not implemented prior to approval.

6

Purchasing Controls

INTRODUCTION

This chapter of **Mastering and Managing the FDA Maze: Medical Device Overview Training and Management Desk Reference** discusses FDA's regulatory oversight of device purchasing controls.

SCOPE

The goal of this chapter is to provide an overview of FDA's regulations regarding medical device purchasing controls. Significant detail has been omitted, and readers should undertake further training to ensure proficiency and understanding to the level required for FDA compliance.

This chapter discusses Subpart E Purchasing Controls of the new GMPs, or Quality System Regulations, which became effective June 1, 1997.

Assuming that a firm can provide appropriate manufacturing controls to a device, unless appropriate purchasing controls are implemented, there will be an unreasonable risk that the manufacture of the device will result in devices that fail to meet FDA's and the marketplace's expectations for safety and effectiveness and may be unsuitable for release as finished devices.

To ensure that finished devices are safe and effective for their intended use, each step in purchasing must fulfill its quality system role.

It should be emphasized that this discussion is *basic*. Significant additional study and implementation will be required by individuals before they can be assured that purchasing controls they establish and maintain meet FDA expectations. The definitions, unless followed by an asterisk, are quoted from FDA's Quality System Regulations.

PURCHASING CONTROLS

Definitions

Accessory is any finished unit distributed separately but intended to be attached to or used in conjunction with another finished device.*

Component means any raw material, substance, piece, part, software, firmware, labeling, or assembly which is intended to be included as part of the finished, packaged, and labeled device.

ISO stands for the International Organization for Standardization, which is based in Geneva, Switzerland, and is a created acronym taken from the Greek word *isos,* meaning "equal."*

ISO 9000 represents a group of generic international standards for quality management, quality assurance, and implementation of a quality system.*

ISO 9001 represents a specific generic international conformance standard to which a firm, involved with design, development, production, installation, and servicing may comply with and be found compliant.*

Manufacturing material means any material or substance used in or used to facilitate the manufacturing process, a concomitant constituent, or a byproduct constituent produced during the manufacturing process, which is present in or on the finished device as a residue or impurity not by design or intent of the manufacturer.

Quality System Inspection Technique (QSIT) is FDA's latest inspection strategy. QSIT involves what FDA calls "top-down" inspections of the four major subsystems of each device manufacturer's quality system: (1) their management controls, (2) design controls, (3) corrective and preventive actions, and (4) production and process controls.*

Purchasing Controls Regulation § 820.50 Purchasing Controls

What the regulation states

§ 820.50

Each manufacturer shall establish and maintain procedures to ensure that all purchased or otherwise received product and services conform to specified requirements.

§ 820.50 Discussion

Don't forget!

The Quality System Regulation requires each manufacturer to exercise control over the quality of products during all phases of the manufacturing process. This includes purchasing control over all elements that make up the finished device. The goal of purchasing control is to ensure that unfit, inappropriate, or out-of-specification components, materials, accessories, other products, and any services do not cause any nonconforming finished devices that do not meet their intended use.

FDA's expectation is that each element of a finished device meets its written specification, including purchased services or products such as sterilization, software development, printed circuit boards, or consulting services.

What the regulation states

§ 820.50 (a)

(a) *Evaluation of suppliers, contractors, and consultants.* Each manufacturer shall establish and maintain the requirements, including quality requirements, that must be met by suppliers, contractors, and consultants. Each manufacturer shall:

(1) Evaluate and select potential suppliers, contractors, and consultants on the basis of their ability to meet specified requirements, including quality requirements. The evaluation shall be documented.

(2) Define the type and extent of control to be exercised over the product, services, suppliers, contractors, and consultants, based on the evaluation results.

(3) Establish and maintain records of acceptable suppliers, contractors, and consultants.

§ 820.50 (a) Discussion

Required procedure(s), document(s), and record(s)

The procedures associated with purchasing controls must require written evaluation criteria for suppliers, contractors, and consultants that ensure these products and services meet a firm's requirements and specifications.

- For off-the-shelf or catalogue components, the original catalogue description can be specified and follow-up orders may specify the item by catalog number or other off-the-shelf designation. Purchases of total or partial product design obviously will require greater specification detail and control.

- For nonstandard, new, or unique items, firms must be more specific and create purchasing specifications. FDA requires that the manufacturer specify the "quality characteristics, dimensions, design, materials, performance, and any other features necessary to ensure receipt of the item desired."

Something to note!

Evaluations or assessments must be documented and could include document-ing suppliers' client lists, ISO 9000 certification, manufacturer's or third-party qual-ity audit data, financial strength, industry reports, technical reports, patents, and other appropriate criteria. Contractors and consultants may be evaluated on the basis of references, education, and documented knowledge.

FDA prefers that these evaluations and assessments be performed prior to the delivery of any product or the execution of any service; however, when prospective evaluations are not possible, retrospective evaluations should be performed. These assessments should include an evaluation of how much significance the product or service has on the finished device and, therefore, what level of control the manufacturer must place over that product or service.

What the regulation states

§ 820.50 (b)

(b) *Purchasing data.* Each manufacturer shall establish and maintain data that clearly describe or reference the specified requirements, including quality requirements, for purchased or otherwise received product and services. Purchasing documents shall include, where possible, an agreement that the suppliers, contractors, and consultants agree to notify the manufacturer of changes in the product or service so that manufac-turers may determine whether the changes may affect the quality of a finished device. Purchasing data shall be approved in accordance with § 820.40.

§ 820.50 (b) Discussion

Required procedure(s), document(s), and record(s)

Manufacturers are required to maintain "purchasing data" for all purchased or otherwise obtained products and services. This information will describe or ref-erence specified product or service requirements, including quality requirements.

- All purchase orders should routinely specify suppliers of products or services to immediately notify the firm if they are aware of any event or situation that could, would, or has affected the quality of the supplied product or service. This speci-fication should also state that the ordering firm must use this information to determine whether these changes will affect the quality of their finished devices.

- Purchasing data typically include written purchase forms, engineering specifications and drawings, or other written requirements or specifications. All purchasing data must be con-sidered controlled documents and subject to appropriate review and approval

PURCHASING CONTROLS

What the FDA Investigator wants to see during an inspection

FDA Investigators focus on how manufacturers implement purchasing con-trols because the agency has identified poor purchasing control as one of the major causes of manufacturing materials and component problems that lead to recalls. FDA Investigators expect that purchasing controls will document that only acceptable manufacturing materials and components are used to manufacture finished devices. Investigators will want to verify that:

- The manufacturer's written procedures include requirements, including "quality requirements," that suppliers, contractors, and consultants must meet.
- The manufacturer evaluates and selects potential suppliers, contractors, and consultants on the basis of their ability to meet the specified requirements.
- The type and extent of control needed over the product, suppliers, services, contractors. and consultants have been defined and are based on evaluated results.
- There are records of acceptable suppliers, contractors, and consultants.
- There are written, approved, and specified requirements, including "quality requirements," for purchased or otherwise received manufacturing materials and services.
- Wherever possible, the approved purchasing documents should include an agreement that the suppliers, contractors, and consultants will notify the manufacturer of any changes in the product or service.
- Manufacturers have evaluated any notification of changes to determine their effect on the quality of their finished devices, if any.
- Procedures for audits of suppliers are written, reviewed, and approved, and supplier audits have taken place on a scheduled, periodic basis.
- Manufacturers document the performance of all providers of products and services as an additional mechanism to determine the amount of control over the purchased products or services.

Under FDA's new QSIT inspection strategy, the review of a firm's purchasing controls will be linked to other quality system activities, specifically, device design control's essential design outputs. Investigators can be expected to assess those outputs to ensure they are implemented during the purchase of product, components, services, contractors, and consultants. This review should include the purchasing controls established for any process automated with software or any software used as a component or accessory to a device. The purchasing controls associated with any of those software activities can be reviewed to ensure that appropriate software and quality requirements were established and provided to the vendor and that purchasing data documents those requirements were met.

Investigators can also be expected to focus their attention on any quality system activity involving sterilization. Expect Investigators to document that all purchasing activities associated with any sterilization process include requirements and appropriate purchasing data.

7

Identification and Traceability

INTRODUCTION

This chapter of **Mastering and Managing the FDA Maze: Medical Device Overview Training and Management Desk Reference** discusses FDA's identification and traceability regulations.

SCOPE

The goal of this chapter is to provide an overview of FDA regulations for identification and traceability for medical device manufacturers. Significant detail has been omitted, and readers should undertake further training to ensure proficiency and understanding to the level required for FDA compliance.

This chapter discusses part of the "what and where" of FDA's oversight of medical device manufacturing activities. Assuming that a firm can provide appropriate design controls to a device, unless appropriate manufacturing controls, including identification and traceability, are implemented, there will be an unreasonable risk that the manufacture of the device will result in units that fail to meet specifications and are unsuitable for release as finished devices.

To ensure that finished devices meet specifications and are suitable for release and distribution, this early step in the manufacturing process must fulfill its quality system role.

This discussion is *basic*. Individuals will require significant additional study and before they can be assured that the manufacturing controls they establish and maintain meet FDA expectations. The definitions, unless followed by an asterisk, are quoted from FDA's Quality System Regulations.

IDENTIFICATION AND TRACEABILITY

Definitions   *Component* means any raw material, substance, piece, part, software, firmware, labeling, or assembly which is intended to be included as part of the finished, packaged, and labeled device.

Control number means any distinctive symbols, such as a distinctive combination of letters or numbers, or both, from which the history of the manufacturing, packaging, labeling, and distribution of a unit, lot, or batch of finished devices can be determined.

Finished device means any device or accessory to any device that is suitable for use or capable of functioning, whether or not it is packaged, labeled, or sterilized.

Lot or batch means one or more components or finished devices that consist of a single type, model, class, size, composition, or software version that are manufactured under essentially the same conditions and that are intended to have uniform characteristics and quality within specified limits.

Manufacturer means any person who designs, manufactures, fabricates, assembles, or processes a finished device. Manufacturer includes but is not limited to those who perform the functions of contract sterilization, installation, relabeling, remanufacturing, repacking, or specification development, and initial distributors of foreign entities performing these functions.

Manufacturing material means any material or substance used in or used to facilitate the manufacturing process, a concomitant constituent, or a byproduct constituent produced during the manufacturing process, which is present in or on the finished device as a residue or impurity not by design or intent of the manufacturer.

Product means components, manufacturing materials, in-process devices, finished devices, and returned devices.

Quality System Inspection Technique (QSIT) is FDA's latest inspection strategy. QSIT involves what FDA calls "top-down" inspections of the four major subsystems of each device manufacturer's quality system: their (1) management controls, (2) design controls, (3) corrective and preventive actions, and (4) production and process controls.*

Identification and Traceability Regulation § 820 Subpart F

§ 820.60 Identification

What the regulation states

§ 820.60

Each manufacturer shall establish and maintain procedures for identifying product during all stages of receipt, production, distribution, and installation to prevent mix-ups.

§ 820.60 Discussion

Remember!

FDA's goal in requiring manufacturers to create and maintain procedures for identification of product during all stages is to prevent mix-ups. The purpose of the requirement is also to eliminate the use of improper or unapproved product and the release of unacceptable product.

Required procedure(s), document(s), and record(s)

This means that manufacturers must, with written procedures, documents, labels, tags, and records, properly control and identify all manufacturing materials, components, products, accessories, and finished devices through all stages of manufacturing and acceptance.

§ 820.65 Traceability

What the regulation states

§ 820.65

Each manufacturer of a device that is intended for surgical implant into the body or to support or sustain life and whose failure to perform when properly used in accordance with instructions for use provided in the labeling can be reasonably expected to result in a significant injury to the user shall establish and maintain procedures for identifying with a control number each unit, lot, or batch of finished devices and where appropriate components. The procedures shall facilitate corrective action. Such identification shall be documented in the DHR.

§ 820.65 Discussion

Something to note!   This "traceability" requirement must not be confused with FDA's "tracking" regulation, 21 CFR 821, which requires certain devices to be tracked to the end user or patient. Discussion of 21 CFR 821 is beyond the scope of this desk reference.

Don't forget!   Manufacturers of any device intended for surgical implant or to support or sustain life, whose failure to perform as intended may result in significant injury, must create a system of control number identification and traceability for each unit, lot, or batch of finished devices, and, where appropriate, components. FDA requires device manufacturers to be able to trace the product categories identified in the regulation to their initial consignee, ensuring the facilitation of corrective actions when needed.

Required procedure(s), document(s), and record(s)

Manufacturers should create records to demonstrate that an assessment of each device has been made for compliance with this requirement. Devices that meet the agency's traceability criteria must be appropriately controlled. Many manufacturers combine product identification and traceability control activity with product acceptance control procedures. See Chapter 9 Acceptance Activities.

The required traceability procedures and control numbers should effectively enable manufacturers to integrate all the activities associated with any complaints, investigations, recalls, market withdrawals or corrections.

Manufacturers who determine that any finished device or component does not require a control number should document that determination, including the reason or justification. This documentation must focus on evaluating and identifying any components that are "essential to the proper functioning of the device." This may mean integrating some form of documented risk analysis into this assessment or making traceability part of each device's risk analysis during the design and design change processes. See Chapter 4 Design Controls.

What the FDA Investigator will want to see during an inspection

FDA expects that manufacturers have written procedures that identify products and manufacturing materials during all stages of receipt, production, distribution, and installation to prevent mix-ups. Manufacturers have the ability to identify their products by whatever procedures they deem appropriate, which can be an individual numbering system or identification of lots or batches.

Under the new QSIT Inspection strategy, manufacturers of medical devices should expect Investigators to pay particular attention to identification and traceability issues. An Investigator may target a device requiring identification and traceability as the model selected to assess a firm's design, corrective and preventive action, and production and process controls, and to back to management controls.

FDA Investigators will compare each firm's Device History Record (DHR) against the firm's Device Master Record (DMR). Additionally, Investigators will compare the DHR against the incoming and in-process acceptance records to document that only acceptable and approved product or manufacturing materials are used during their appropriate stages of manufacturing.

Investigators will focus on the devices identified in this regulation that are:

- Intended for surgical implant into the body
- Life supporting or sustaining
- At risk of causing significant injury to the user upon failure, when used according to directions

These devices must have written procedures that identify each unit, lot, or batch of finished devices, and, where appropriate, components, with a control number. These procedures will be assessed to ensure that they facilitate corrective actions and device identification.

FDA understands that the required "control number" need not be unique and may be the same as any individual numbering system used to initially identify products, manufacturing materials, or components. However, the traceability requirement must provide the identity of the initial consignee or the first persons obtaining control of the device after the device leaves the manufacturer's control.

Investigators should also be expected to assess each firms procedures and records associated with determining which devices require control numbers and which components require control numbers based on the manufacturer's determination of whether the components are "essential to the proper functioning" of the device.

8

Production and Process Controls

INTRODUCTION

This chapter of **Mastering and Managing the FDA Maze: Medical Device Overview Training and Management Desk Reference** discusses FDA's regulations for production and process controls.

SCOPE

The goal of this chapter is to provide an overview of FDA regulations production and process controls for medical device manufacturers. Significant detail has been omitted, and readers should undertake further training to ensure proficiency and understanding to the level required for FDA compliance.

Assuming that a firm can provide appropriate design controls for a device, unless appropriate manufacturing production and process controls are implemented, there will be an unreasonable risk that the manufacture of the device will result in devices that fail to meet specifications and are unsuitable for release as finished devices.

To ensure that finished devices meet specifications and are suitable for release and distribution, each step in the manufacturing production and process must fulfill its quality system role.

This discussion is *basic*. Individuals will require significant additional study and implementation before they can be assured that the manufacturing controls they establish and maintain meet FDA expectations. The definitions, unless followed by an asterisk, are quoted from FDA's Quality System Regulations.

PRODUCTION AND PROCESS CONTROLS

Definitions   *Component* means any raw material, substance, piece, part, software, firmware, packaging, labeling, or assembly which is intended to be included as part of the finished, packaged, and labeled device.

Finished device means any device or accessory to any device that is suitable for use or capable of functioning, whether or not it is packaged, labeled, or sterilized.

Installation qualification (IQ) means establishing by objective evidence that all key aspects of the process, process equipment, and ancillary system installation adhere to the approved design criteria and that the recommendations of the manufacturer of the equipment are suitably considered.*

Lot or batch means one or more components or finished devices that consist of a single type, model, class, size, composition, and software version that are manufactured under essentially the same conditions and that are intended to have uniform characteristics and quality within specified limits.

Manufacturer means any person who designs, manufactures, fabricates, assembles, or processes a finished device. Manufacturer includes but is not limited to those who perform the functions of contract sterilization, installation, relabeling, remanufacturing, repacking, or specification development, and initial distributors of foreign entities performing these functions.

Manufacturing material means any material or substance used in, or used to facilitate, a manufacturing process, or a naturally occurring substance, that is not intended by the manufacturer to be included in the finished device, including cleaning agents, mold-release agents, lubricating oils, and sterilant residues, or other byproducts of the manufacturing process.

Nonconformity means the nonfulfillment of a specified requirement.

Operational qualification (OQ) means establishing by objective evidence parameters that result in product that meets all predetermined requirements.*

Performance qualification (PQ) means establishing by objective evidence that the process, under anticipated conditions, including worst-case conditions, consistently produces a product that meets all predetermined requirements.*

Process validation means establishing by objective evidence that a process consistently produces a result or product meeting its predetermined specifications.

Product means components, manufacturing materials, in-process devices, finished devices, and returned devices.

Quality System Inspection Technique (QSIT) is FDA's latest inspection strategy. QSIT involves what FDA calls "top-down" inspections of the four major subsystems of each device manufacturer's quality system: their (1) management controls, (2) design controls, (3) corrective and preventive actions, and (4) production and process controls.*

Reprocessing means all or part of a manufacturing operation which is intended to correct nonconformance in a component or finished device before distribution.

Specification means any requirement with which a product, process, service, or other activity must conform.

Production and Process Controls Regulation § 820 Subpart G

§ 820.70 Production and process controls

***What the
regulation states***

§ 820.70 (a)

(a) *General.* Each manufacturer shall develop, conduct, control, and monitor production processes to ensure that a device conforms to its specifications. Where deviations from device specifications could occur as a result of the manufacturing process, the manufacturer shall establish and maintain process control procedures that describe any process controls necessary to ensure conformance to specifications. Where process controls are needed they shall include:

(1) Documented instructions, standard operating procedures (SOP's), and methods that define and control the manner of production;
(2) Monitoring and control of process parameters and component and device characteristics during production;
(3) Compliance with specified reference standards or codes;
(4) The approval of processes and process equipment; and
(5) Criteria for workmanship which shall be expressed in documented standards or by means of identified and approved representative samples.

§ 820.70 (a) Discussion

Required procedure(s), document(s), and record(s)

Production controls typically include:

- Standard operating procedures (SOPs), work instructions, equipment operating instructions, guidelines, forms, and checklists that are intended to control medical device production processes
- Documented periodic or constant oversight (depending upon the assessed need) of production processes and component and device characteristics during production
- Documented regulatory compliance
- Documented reference or international standard compliance
- Documented procedural control of new and changed processes
- Documented procedural control of all process equipment
- Documentation of established "criteria for workmanship" based on standards or identified and approved representative samples

What the regulation states

§ 820.70 (b)

(b) *Production and process changes.* Each manufacturer shall establish and maintain procedures for changes to a specification, method, process, or procedure. Such changes shall be verified or where appropriate validated according to § 820.75, before implementation and these activities shall be documented. Changes shall be approved in accordance with § 820.40.

§ 820.70 (b) Discussion

Required procedure(s), document(s), and record(s)

Inherent in each firm's quality system is the ability, through approved and reviewed change control process, to change any existing specification, work instruction, equipment operating instruction, guideline, form, or checklist as appropriately determined.

These changes often, but not always, require validation. See Process Validation Discussion, page 117. If a process or piece of equipment has been validated, documented revalidation of any change is required. Additionally, any new or revalidation activity must be reviewed and approved in accordance with the Quality System Regulations' document controls, § 820.40.

What the regulation states

§ 820.70 (c)

(c) *Environmental control.* Where environmental conditions could reasonably be expected to have an adverse effect on product quality, the manufacturer shall establish and maintain procedures to adequately control these environmental conditions. Environmental control system(s) shall be periodically inspected to verify that the system, including necessary equipment, is adequate and functioning properly. These activities shall be documented and reviewed.

§ 820.70 (c) Discussion

Manufacturers should:

- Assess their product processes to determine what environmental conditions might adversely affect product quality
- Document that assessment
- Establish and maintain written procedures to control all environmental conditions that may adversely affect product quality

Required procedure(s), document(s), and record(s)

The written assessment should be based on the type of product being manufactured and its susceptibility, which will vary from product to product, to environmental conditions. When susceptibilities are identified, they must be documented, and appropriate controls must be established and maintained. That documentation should identify the frequency of inspection that is required to verify that the controls are "adequate and functioning properly." That documentation must be appropriately reviewed and approved.

What the regulation states

§ 820.70 (d)

(d) *Personnel.* Each manufacturer shall establish and maintain requirements for the health, cleanliness, personal practices, and clothing of personnel if contact between such personnel and product or environment could reasonably be expected to have an adverse effect on product quality. The manufacturer shall ensure that maintenance and other personnel who are required to work temporarily under special environmental conditions are appropriately trained or supervised by a trained individual.

§ 820.70 (d) Discussion

Required procedure(s), document(s), and record(s)

During the same written assessment for environmental conditions, manufacturers should also produce a written assessment of the need to establish and maintain requirements for "health, cleanliness, personal practices, and clothing of personnel if contact between such personnel and product or environment could reasonably be expected to have an adverse effect on product quality."

Most manufacturing environments will require personnel who are appropriately trained and supervised to ensure that their manufacturing activities are in accordance with procedures, work instructions, equipment operating instructions, guidelines, forms, or checklists.

Remember!   Special care must be used when maintenance or other temporary personnel are involved with special environmental conditions. These individuals must be "appropriately trained or supervised by a trained individual." These activities should be documented.

What the regulation states

§ 820.70 (e)

(e) *Contamination control.* Each manufacturer shall establish and maintain procedures to prevent contamination of equipment or product by substances that could reasonably be expected to have an adverse effect on product quality.

§ 820.70 (e) Discussion

Required procedure(s), document(s), and record(s)

Again, during the same written assessment for environmental conditions, manufacturers should also produce a written assessment of the need to establish and maintain requirements to prevent contamination of equipment or product by substances that may adversely affect product quality.

Depending upon the product, potential contaminants to either the manufacturing materials or the manufacturing process might include:

- Bacteria and/or fungi
- Dust or particulate matter
- Trash
- Equipment maintenance products, for example, oils, solvents, and so on
- Manufacturing by-products
- Waste effluent

The goal of contamination control is to ensure that any manufacturer's quality claims are met. This may mean that equipment or processes have written cleaning procedures and schedules that ensure compliance with regulations and manufacturing specifications.

Don't forget!   Established contamination control might include:

- Employee sanitation practice requirements and identification of appropriately maintained bathrooms, clothing, and storage and trash receptacle areas
- Hazardous substance use requirements, identifying use, handling, storage, removal, or destruction
- Employee personal activities, including food and snacks, drinks, and tobacco use

What the regulation states

§ 820.70 (f)

(f) *Buildings.* Buildings shall be of suitable design and contain sufficient space to perform necessary operations, prevent mix-ups, and assure orderly handling.

§ 820.70 (f) Discussion

FDA's requirement for buildings of suitable design and sufficient space means that specific areas are identified for receiving, storage, manufacturing, labeling, packaging, and other device manufacturing processes.

Something to note!

The prevention of mix-ups and assurance of orderly handling typically requires that the design of building use ensures the minimization of manufacturing errors and supports contamination control. This may mean that walls, dividers, or curtains are used to provide appropriate separation between operations.

What the regulation states

§ 820.70 (g)

(g) *Equipment.* Each manufacturer shall ensure that all equipment used in the manufacturing process meets specified requirements and is appropriately designed, constructed, placed, and installed to facilitate maintenance, adjustment, cleaning, and use.

(1) *Maintenance schedule.* Each manufacturer shall establish and maintain schedules for the adjustment, cleaning, and other maintenance of equipment to ensure that manufacturing specifications are met. Maintenance activities, including the date and individual(s) performing the maintenance activities, shall be documented.

(2) *Inspection.* Each manufacturer shall conduct periodic inspections in accordance with established procedures to ensure adherence to applicable equipment maintenance schedules. The inspections, including the date and individual(s) conducting the inspections, shall be documented.

(3) *Adjustment.* Each manufacturer shall ensure that any inherent limitations or allowable tolerances are visibly posted on or near equipment requiring periodic adjustments or are readily available to personnel performing these adjustments.

§ 820.70 (g) Discussion

Required procedure(s), document(s), and record(s)

Written equipment assessments should be performed both individually and collectively to ensure that equipment is appropriate in terms of design, construction, placement, and installation. Care should be taken to ensure that equipment requiring maintenance, adjustment, or cleaning is placed to facilitate those requirements.

Equipment that requires scheduled maintenance must have that schedule "posted on or near the equipment to be maintained, or otherwise made readily available to appropriate personnel." Equipment that requires periodic adjustments must have that schedule "visibly posted on or near equipment." The agency also expects that required periodic audits assess scheduled maintenance and adjustment schedules for compliance with both scheduling and posting availability.

§ 820.70 (h)

(h) *Manufacturing material.* Where a manufacturing material could reasonably be expected to have an adverse effect on product quality, the manufacturer shall establish and maintain procedures for the use and removal of such manufacturing material to ensure that it is removed or limited to an amount that does not adversely affect the device's quality. The removal or reduction of such manufacturing material shall be documented.

§ 820.70 (h) Discussion

Required procedure(s), document(s), and record(s)

Manufacturers must, again, perform a separate written assessment of each manufacturing material to determine its effect on the manufacturing process and the manufactured device. Materials that do not adversely affect the manufacturing process, the device, or its use are not required to be removed.

Remember!

The agency's definition of "manufacturing material" is broad and includes "any material or substance used in or used to facilitate the manufacturing process, which is present in or on the finished device as a residue or impurity not by design or intent of the manufacturer." Manufacturers must understand that the agency includes in that definition, cleaning compounds, oils, solvents, and mold release agents among other materials.

Required procedure(s), document(s), and record(s)

Written procedures must be implemented that ensure "the use and removal of such manufacturing material" or ensure that the material is "limited to an amount that does not adversely affect the device's quality." Some materials cannot be removed by normal cleaning procedures and will require special cleaning procedures. If any material cannot be removed to the amount that does not adversely affect device quality, particularly for users who are or may become sensitized to those materials, manufacturers may find it necessary to label their devices specifically to warn those users of that potential danger.

§ 820.70 (i)

(i) *Automated processes.* When computers or automated data processing systems are used as part of production or the quality system, the manufacturer shall validate computer software for its intended use according to an established protocol. All software changes shall be validated before approval and issuance. These validation activities and results shall be documented.

§ 820.70 (i) Discussion

Don't forget!

The FDA considers any use of computers or automated data processing systems as part of the production or quality system to require control. Manufacturers must:

- Identify the intended use of the computer or automated data processing system
- Validate the computer, software, or automated data processing system for that use
- Revalidate those systems appropriately for each software change or change to the system
- Fully document, review, and approve all validation activities

Something to note!

FDA expects that validation of computer systems fully ensures that the system performs as expected or anticipated. If knowledgeable validation resources are not available from within the manufacturer, the agency expects the manufacturer to obtain an outside, independent resource to either provide appropriate training or perform the validation.

Required procedure(s), document(s), and record(s)

Validation of either off-the-shelf or customized computer software or systems requires:

- A written procedure to control the validation activities
- A testing process, written in advance, often referred to as "test scripts"
- Test scripts that identify expected outcomes
- Identification of any problems or software "bugs" found during validation
- Elimination or mitigation of those problems
- Preparation of a validation report
- Appropriate review and approval of the validation report

§ 820.72 Inspection, Measuring, and Test Equipment

What the regulation states

§ 820.72 (a)

(a) *Control of inspection, measuring, and test equipment.* Each manufacturer shall ensure that all inspection, measuring, and test equipment, including mechanical, automated, or electronic inspection and test equipment, is suitable for its intended purposes and is capable of producing valid results. Each manufacturer shall establish and maintain procedures to ensure that equipment is routinely calibrated, inspected, checked, and maintained. The procedures shall include provisions for handling, preservation, and storage of equipment, so that its accuracy and fitness for use are maintained. These activities shall be documented.

§ 820.72 (a) Discussion

Required procedure(s), document(s), and record(s)

Manufacturers must, again, perform a separate written assessment of each piece of manufacturing inspection, measuring, and test equipment to determine it suitability for its intended use and its ability to produce valid results, which FDA defines as "works properly."

Each piece of this equipment must have a written procedure or work instruction that ensures the equipment is appropriately calibrated, inspected, checked, and maintained. These procedures or work instructions must include provisions for handling, preservation, and storage of the equipment to ensure the equipment's "accuracy and fitness for use."

What the regulation states

§ 820.72 (b)

(b) *Calibration.* Calibration procedures shall include specific directions and limits for accuracy and precision. When accuracy and precision limits are not met, there shall be provisions for remedial action to reestablish the limits and to evaluate whether there was any adverse effect on the device's quality. These activities shall be documented.

(1) *Calibration standards.* Calibration standards used for inspection, measuring, and test equipment shall be traceable to national or international standards. If national or international standards are not practical or available, the manufacturer shall use an independent reproducible standard. If no applicable standard exists, the manufacturer shall establish and maintain an in-house standard.

(2) *Calibration records.* The equipment identification, calibration dates, the individual performing each calibration, and the next calibration date shall be documented. These records shall be displayed on or near each piece of equipment or shall be readily available to the personnel using such equipment and to the individuals responsible for calibrating the equipment.

§ 820.72 (b) Discussion

Required procedure(s), document(s), and record(s)

Manufacturers must, again, perform a separate written assessment of each manufacturing process to determine its need for calibration. If any calibration activity is required, a written procedure or work instruction must be created with "specific directions and limits for accuracy and precision." These documents must also address situations in which the accuracy and precision limits are not met and provide remedial actions "to reestablish the limits and to evaluate whether there was any adverse effect on the device's quality."

Remember!

When calibration standards are required, they must "be traceable to national or international standards." If none are practical or available, the manufacturer must implement an "independent reproducible standard," and, if none exist, the manufacturer must establish and maintain the standard in house.

Required procedure(s), document(s), and record(s)

Calibration activities, including equipment ID, calibration dates, the individual performing the activity, and the next calibration date must be documented. This documentation must be displayed on or near each piece of equipment or be "readily available" to operators and calibrators.

§ 820.75 Process validation

What the regulation states

§ 820.75 (a)–(c)

(a) Where the results of a process cannot be fully verified by subsequent inspection and test, the process shall be validated with a high degree of assurance and approved according to established procedures. The validation activities and results, including the date and signature of the individual(s) approving the validation and where appropriate the major equipment validated, shall be documented.

(b) Each manufacturer shall establish and maintain procedures for monitoring and control of process parameters for validated processes to ensure that the specified requirements continue to be met.

(1) Each manufacturer shall ensure that validated processes are performed by qualified individual(s).
(2) For validated processes, the monitoring and control methods and data, the date performed, and, where appropriate, the individual(s) performing the process or the major equipment used shall be documented.

(c) When changes or process deviations occur, the manufacturer shall review and evaluate the process and perform revalidation where appropriate. These activities shall be documented.

§ 820.75 (a)–(c) Discussion

Something to note!

Process validation is an element of production and process control to which FDA is exhibiting increased oversight. FDA's expectation is that every process used in the manufacture, inspection, and quality control of any medical device must perform according to the manufacturers' expected result. Each of these processes must be validated to demonstrate that they operate repeatedly as expected.

Process validation requires the "examination" and documentation of "objective evidence" that "requirements for a specific intended use can be consistently fulfilled." Validation is not a one-time event. Validation requires multiple examinations to document the intended use is fulfilled.

Often process validation activities are defined in terms of "installation qualification (IQ)," "operational qualification (OQ)," and "performance qualification (PQ)" phases. IQ, OQ, and PQ phases each involve:

- Determination of *what, how, how many,* and *when* to verify or measure
- Definition of acceptance and rejection criteria
- Definition of required documentation

Additionally, validation activities require trained and experienced personnel. If skilled validation personnel are not available from a manufacturer's employee pool, the manufacturer is expected to obtain this resource from third-party training or an independent validation resource. The activities involved with validation qualifications need to be a part of the validation documentation.

Remember!

Process validation can be performed:

- Prospectively (before a new device is released)
- Concurrently (while a new device is undergoing initial release)
- Retrospectively (after a device has been released)

Required procedure(s), document(s), and record(s)

Each type of validation requires the same input, documentation, and control:

- A written procedure to control the validation activities
- A testing process, written in advance, often referred to as "test scripts"
- Test scripts that identify expected outcomes
- Identification of any problems found during validation
- Elimination or mitigation of those problems
- Preparation of a validation report
- Appropriate review and approval of the validation report

Don't forget!

The preferred process validation is prospective validation. Prior to the release of any device, the validation, validation report, review, and approval are completed. Concurrent validation requires that no product be released until the validation activity is complete, reviewed, and approved. Retrospective validation must be performed in the absence of validation documentation and when previous validation activities were undocumented or poorly documented.

Required procedure(s), document(s), and record(s)

Process controlled by validation must be supported by written procedures or work instructions that monitor the process and demonstrate that the results specified are being "consistently fulfilled." FDA expects that qualified personnel will perform this monitoring activity.

Changes to any validated process must be documented and require review by qualified personnel. That review must determine whether revalidation is required and the extent of the revalidation. If the review determines that no revalidation is required, that finding must be documented, reviewed, and approved.

Something to note!

FDA's guidance for process validation is "Guideline to General Principles of Process Validation," and that guide should be read and understood by all individuals involved with any medical device production equipment or process. Additionally, the Global Harmonization Task Force Study Group #3 has produced a draft "Process Validation Guidance," dated June 1, 1998.

What the FDA Investigator expects to see during an investigation

Medical device manufacturers should expect FDA Investigators to devote at least 25% of their inspection activity to their assessment of any firm's production and process controls. Readers should review the redrawn Production and Process Controls Decision Flow Chart, see Figure 8.1, page 121. Investigators will select a process to review based on the following criteria:

- Corrective and preventive action indicators of process problems
- The manufacture of higher risk devices by the process
- The likelihood of the process to cause device failures
- The manufacturer's lack of familiarity and experience with the process
- Multiple devices manufactured by the same process
- Variety in process technologies
- Process not covered in previous inspections

Investigators can be expected to focus on quality system elements that involve any sterilization activity, software control, and the training requirement for personnel involved in medical device manufacturing processes.

FDA Investigators expect to be able to verify that specifications and documented work instructions have been established and maintained for all processes involved with each finished device from which any variation could result in a failure of a device to meet specifications.

Process examples frequently reviewed include:

- Molding
- Heat treatment
- Welding
- Sterilization
- Blending
- Package sealing
- Solvent bonding

Also reviewed are drawings used for:

- Assembly
- Fabrication

FDA Investigators should acknowledge that, in some cases, training and workmanship standards would suffice in lieu of written procedures, for example, hand soldering activities. Investigators will want to verify that (1) new specifications and any specification changes, (2) procedures and work instructions and any of their changes, and (3) drawings and other instructional documents and any of their changes are all formally reviewed and approved.

Inspectors will look closely at documents described as "Engineering Change Notice (ECN)," "Drawing Change Request," or other similar documents. They will move from activity to activity to determine whether, at each activity, the appropriate versions of documents are being used.

Investigators will look closely at "rework" activity and want to see appropriate procedures and assessments of the effect of rework on the components or finished device. They will assess, or want to see assessments of, manufacturing materials, components, or finished devices that have unexpected increases in rework. They will expect to see assessments of work increases or sudden occurrences that might indicate problems in manufacturing processes, acceptance activities, training, suppliers, testing, procedures, or quality assurance activities.

Typically, Investigators do not consider routine replacement of defective parts unless the structure of the supporting materials, such as adhesives, epoxies, solders, and so on must be changed or modified. For example, replacing a defective plug-in circuit board would not be considered reworking. However, replacing integrated circuit chips requiring removal or replacement of supporting materials would be considered reworking, as would patching, regrinding, remelting, reheating, and resterilization activities.

Investigators will consider any repair or reconditioning activities that modify the finished device so that it no longer conforms to its original specifications to be remanufacturing, and they will expect to see remanufacturing procedures and specifications where appropriate.

Investigators will expect to see facilities appropriate to the devices being manufactured. Facilities will be assessed for adequacy in terms of:

- Incoming product
- Rejected or obsolete product
- In-process product
- Finished devices
- Labeling
- Rework or repaired devices
- Equipment
- Molds, patterns, tools, records, drawings, and blueprints
- Testing and laboratory activities
- Quarantined products

Investigators will expect to see assessments of manufacturing processes' environmental conditions for adverse effect on any in-process product or finished device. Where those conditions are identified as having a potential impact, Investigators will expect to see procedures that control the conditions and prevent any contamination of devices.

Where computers, computer systems or components, including software, are at risk to environmental contamination, including temperature, humidity, electrostatic discharge, electromagnetic interference, dirt, or dust, Investigators will expect to be shown procedures that control those conditions and ensure the proper functioning of those systems as well as records indicating the validation of those elements of the quality system.

Finally, Inspectors will expect that manufacturers periodically audit production activities, process controls, and environmental controls to ensure their proper functioning

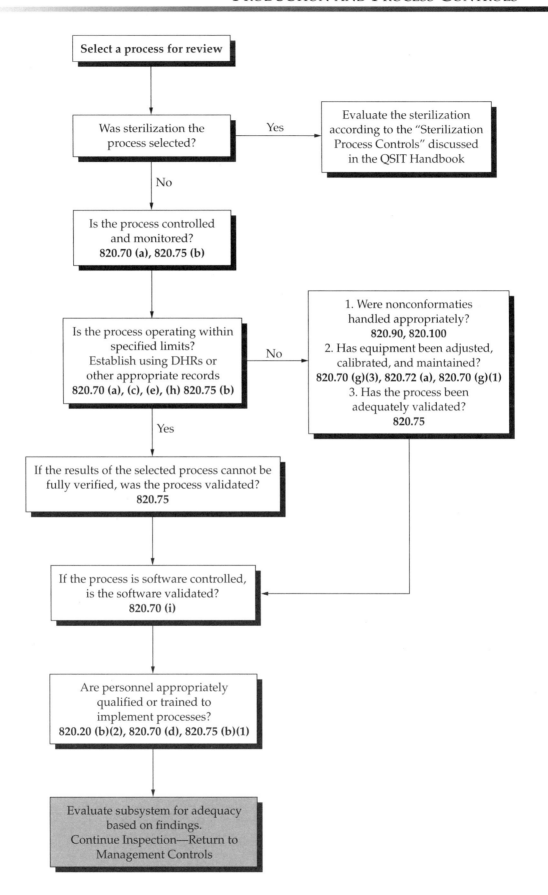

Figure 8.1. Production and Process Controls (P&PC) Decision Flow Chart

Redrawn by author from original FDA Flow Chart, **QSIT Handbook,** *page 59.*

9

Acceptance Activities

INTRODUCTION

This chapter of **Mastering and Managing the FDA Maze: Medical Device Overview Training and Management Desk Reference** discusses acceptance activities.

SCOPE

The goal of this chapter is to provide an overview of FDA regulations covering acceptance activities for medical device manufacturers. Significant detail has been omitted, and readers should undertake further training to ensure proficiency and understanding to the level required for FDA compliance.

Assuming that a firm can provide appropriatae design and manufacturing controls to a device, unless appropriate acceptance controls are implemented, there will be an unreasonable risk that the manufacturing of the device will result in devices that fail to meet specificatons and are unsuitable for release as finished devices.

To enture that finished devices meet specifications and are suitable for release and distribution, each step in the acceptance of manufacturing materials, components, in-process product, and finished devices must fulfill its quality system role.

This discussion is *basic*. Individuals will require significant additional study and implementation experience before they can be assured that the acceptance activities they establish meet FDA expectations. The definitions, unless followed by an asterisk, are quoted from FDA's Quality System Regulations.

ACCEPTANCE ACTIVITIES

Definitions

Control number means any distinctive symbols, such as a distinctive combination of letters or numbers, or both, from which the history of the manufacturing, packaging, labeling, and distribution of a unit, lot, or batch of finished devices can be determined.

Finished device means any device or accessory to any device that is suitable for use or capable of functioning, whether or not it is packaged, labeled, or sterilized.

Master verification or validation plan is a document that identifies all responsibilities, expectations, systems and subsystems involved with a specific verification or validation activity, and the qualification approaches that ensures verification or total system validation.*

Product means components, manufacturing materials, in-process devices, finished devices, and returned devices.

Quality System Inspection Technique (QSIT) is FDA's latest inspection strategy. QSIT involves what FDA calls "top-down" inspections of the four major subsystems of each device manufacturer's quality system: their (1) management controls, (2) design controls, (3) corrective and preventive actions, and (4) production and process controls.*

Specification means any requirement with which a product, process, service, or other activity must conform.

Test plan is a step-by-step plan to be followed during the verification or validation of a product or process.*

Acceptance Activities Regulation–Subpart H

§820.30 (a)–(c) General, Receiving & In-process Acceptance Activities

*What the
regulation states*

§ 820.80 (a)–(c)

(a) *General.* Each manufacturer shall establish and maintain procedures for acceptance activities. Acceptance activities include inspections, tests, or other verification activities.

(b) *Receiving acceptance activities.* Each manufacturer shall establish and maintain procedures for acceptance of incoming product. Incoming product shall be inspected, tested, or otherwise verified as conforming to specified requirements. Acceptance or rejection shall be documented.

(c) *In-process acceptance activities.* Each manufacturer shall establish and maintain acceptance procedures, where appropriate, to ensure that specified requirements for in-process product are met. Such procedures shall ensure that in-process product is controlled until the required inspection and tests or other verification activities have been completed, or necessary approvals are received, and are documented.

§820.30 (a)–(c) Discussion

Remember!

FDA requires all manufacturers to fully control acceptance activities associated with any medical device's manufacturing materials (incoming product), components and finished devices. This control includes appropriate written procedures that detail the "inspections, tests, or other verification activities."

Incoming product or manufacturing materials should be held in a shipping area until the product's or material's paperwork is complete.

---

*Required
procedure(s),
document(s),
and record(s)*

FDA requires that manufacturing materials or incoming product conform to a written specified requirement or specification. Materials that require more than visual inspection should be tagged as "quarantined" until those inspection or testing activities are finalized and the material can be documented as either accepted or rejected.

A written procedure should detail how manufacturing materials are transferred, after final acceptance, from the quarantine area to some other manufacturing storage area.

During the receiving process, manufacturers must document either the acceptance or rejection of these materials. Incoming product should be placed in a specified area designated for such receipt and storage until released to manufacturing or rejected and returned to a shipping area for removal and destruction.

A checklist as part of in-process acceptance control is a convenient mechanism to ensure appropriate acceptance activities. A sample is provided in Figure 9.1, page 126.

PURPOSE

The purpose of this checklist is to ensure that:

1. Manufacturing materials have been held in quarantine until their acceptance or rejection paperwork is complete
2. All manufacturing materials are inspected, tested, and verified as conforming to a written specified requirements or specifications.
3. The review of all documentation and records is reviewed and further manufacturing material activity is authorized by the signature of a designated individual.
4. The acceptance authorization is dated.

SCOPE

This checklist must be completed, signed, and dated before any manufacturing material is accepted for release to manufacturing or rejected for return for return to shipping for removal or destruction.

Manufacturing materials:_____

_____

❒ Purchase Order   ❒ Receiving   ❒ Lot Number:_____

Number or Quantity: _____

This manufacturing material has failed to meet ❒ specified requirements and/or ❒ specifications as determined by ❒ inspection,   ❒ testing or   ❒ other verification activities and is:
❒ Rejected for release to manufacturing
❒ Recommended for:
     ❒ Returned to source   ❒ Destruction or removal from facility

---

❒ All of the ❒ specified requirements and/or ❒ specifications of this manufacturing material have been determined to have been met by ❒ inspection, ❒ testing, or ❒ other verification activities, and the appropriate documentation and records associated with that determination are:

     ❒ Attached to this checklist   ❒ Filed:

❒ The review of the above identified documentation and records confirms that the above identified manufacturing material is approved for release from quarantine and transfer to manufacturing:

     ❒ Release from quarantine   ❒ Transfer to manufacturing

❒ The original copy of this **Final Acceptance Checklist** and any attached documents or records are to be filed in the Device Master Record (DMR) for this device.

I certify that I have reviewed the ❒ specified requirements and/or ❒ specifications for the above-identified manufacturing material and have approved the material for the action indicated above.

    \<Printed name\>   \<Title Review Manager\>   \<Signature\>   \<date\>

Figure 9.1. Manufacturing Material Acceptance Checklist

What the regulation states

§ 820.80 (d)

(d) *Final acceptance activities.* Each manufacturer shall establish and maintain procedures for finished device acceptance to ensure that each production run, lot, or batch of finished devices meets acceptance criteria. Finished devices shall be held in quarantine or otherwise adequately controlled until released. Finished devices shall not be released for distribution until:

(1) The activities required in the DMR are completed.
(2) The associated data and documentation is reviewed.
(3) The release is authorized by the signature of a designated individuals.
(4) The authorization is dated.

§ 820.80 (d) Discussion

Required procedure(s), document(s), and record(s)

FDA requires manufacturers to create written procedures that detail the acceptance activities of all finished devices, including the identification of individuals authorized to approve finished product for release to distribution. "Acceptance activities" means that the manufacturer should create specific acceptance criteria for each device.

Don't forget!

As with manufacturing materials, finished products must be "held in quarantine or otherwise adequately controlled until release." Release of any finished device for distribution requires the following:

- The completion of all activities in the device master record (DMR)
- The review of any associated data and documentation verifying the device meets acceptance criteria
- Authorization by signature of designated individuals for the acceptance and release for distribution
- Dated acceptance authorization

§ 820.80 (e) Acceptance Records

What the regulation states

§ 820.80 (e)

(e) *Acceptance records.* Each manufacturer shall document acceptance activities required by this part. These records shall include the following:

(1) The acceptance activities performed
(2) The dates on which acceptance activities are performed
(3) The results
(4) The signature of the individuals conducting the acceptance activities
(5) Where appropriate, the equipment used.

These records shall be part of the DHR.

§ 820.80 (e) Discussion

Don't forget!

Acceptance records must also clearly identify any equipment used in the inspection and testing of a finished device if that equipment's use "will be imperative for proper investigating into nonconforming product."

Acceptance records become the first records associated with the device's Device History Record (DRH). The DRH must contain records of each device's dates of manufacture, quantity manufactured, quantity released for distribution, acceptance records, labels and labeling, and device identification and control numbers used.

Control to ensure appropriate acceptance activities is often implemented as part of final acceptance. A sample is provided in Figure 9.2, page 129.

§ 820.86 Acceptance Status

What the regulation states

§ 820.86

Each manufacturer shall identify by suitable means the acceptance status of product, to indicate the conformance or nonconformance of product with acceptance criteria. The identification of acceptance status shall be maintained throughout manufacturing, packaging, labeling, installation, and servicing of the product to ensure that only product which has passed the required acceptance activities is distributed, used, or installed.

§ 820.86 Discussion

FDA requires that products passing through manufacturing processes or stages, including packaging, labeling, installation, and servicing are identified as to acceptance status (conformance or nonconformance) by "suitable means." Typically, this includes product segregation and/or some form of tagging.

Don't forget!

FDA's goal is to ensure that only documented and approved finished devices are released for distribution and installation.

What the FDA Investigator wants to see during an inspection

FDA Investigators have always placed great emphasis on acceptance activities throughout a firm's quality system. Under the new QSIT inspection strategy, this emphasis will be continued and will focus on the four subsystems QSIT identified: (1) management controls, (2) design controls, (3) corrective and preventive actions, and (4) production and process controls.

Medical device manufacturers should expect Investigators to focus on documenting that firms have established and maintained acceptance procedures for each subsystem and that appropriate records document those acceptance activities. Particular attention should be paid to those management control activities that should be or are documented to require management acceptance.

PURPOSE

The purpose of this checklist is to ensure that:

1. All activities required in the Device Medical Record (DMR) are completed.
2. Any associated data and documentation verifying the device meets acceptance criteria is reviewed.
3. The acceptance and release for distribution is authorized by the signature of a designated individual(s) and the acceptance authorization is dated.
4. The final acceptance checklist, approval and associated documents and records become part of the device's Device History Record (DHR).

SCOPE

This checklist must be completed, signed, and dated before any finished device is released for distribution.

DEVICE

❒ Serial/ ❒ Lot/ ❒ Batch Number: _____

Number or Quantity Manufactured: _____

⬚ (number) of the devices listed above have **FAILED** to meet manufacturing specifications and

⬚ (number) are **REJECTED** for release from manufacturing to distribution.

❒ (Recommend that ⬚ (number) of the devices be returned for rework.

❒ (Recommend that ⬚ (number) of the devices be destroyed or removed from the facility.

❒ All of the manufacturing specifications of this device have been met, and the appropriate documentation and records associated with those determinations are:

      ❒ Attached to this checklist   ❒ Filed:

❒ All associated data and documentation have been reviewed and that review confirms that this ❒ Serial/ ❒ Lot/ ❒ Batch Number has met written acceptance criteria, which are:

      ❒ Attached to this checklist   ❒ Filed:

❒ All final inspection, test, verification and validation activities for this ❒ Serial/ ❒ Lot/ ❒ Batch Number have been performed and found to meet acceptance criteria and are:

      ❒ Attached to this checklist   ❒ Filed:

❒ The original copy of this **Final Acceptance Checklist** and any attached documents or records are to be filed in the Device History Record (DHR) for this device.

      Number and Quantity Accepted for Distribution: _____

I certify that I have reviewed the above checked ❒ specifications, ❒ documentation and/or ❒ records and find that this ❒ Serial/ ❒ Lot/ ❒ Batch Number for the above identified device are reviewed and approved for final acceptance and release for distribution.

    <Printed name>   <Title Review Manager>   <Signature>   <date>

Figure 9.2. Final Acceptance Checklist

FDA Investigators will want to document that manufacturers have verified that all products meet their specifications. They will want to review inspection and test certificates of analysis and supplier audit actions.

In-coming products will be reviewed for receiving acceptance activities. Investigators recognize that firms do not need to inspect each lot, batch, or item: however, the firm must document the methods used to determine whether that lot, batch, or item meets their established specifications and that documented determination will be reviewed.

Investigators will also review receiving, in-process, and final acceptance of all manufacturing materials, parts, components and in-process products that become part of any finished device.

In-process product's control, by written procedures, will be reviewed to ensure that the control is at appropriate points in the process and that those specifications are met. Investigators will review written procedures that control in-process product to ensure that equipment, methods, and acceptance criteria are documented. Investigators will want to be assured that in-process product is controlled until the specified verification activities, including inspection and tests, have been completed and the necessary reviews and approvals have been received and documented.

Investigators will closely scrutinize final acceptance activities. Their review actions will include assurance that each production run, lot, or batch of finished devices is documented. That documentation should specify any equipment required, methods used in manufacturing, and the acceptance criteria prior to acceptance and release.

Investigators will review documents and records of the Device History File to ensure that each device was manufactured and accepted based on the Device Master Record requirements and specifications. These records must include a review by a designated individual and that individual's signature.

Investigators will focus on appropriate activities, dates performed, results, signatures, and equipment used.

10

Nonconforming Product

INTRODUCTION

This chapter of **Mastering and Managing the FDA Maze: Medical Device Overview Training and Management Desk Reference** discusses nonconforming products.

SCOPE

The goal of this chapter is to provide an overview of FDA regulations related to nonconforming products for medical device manufacturers. Significant detail has been omitted, and readers should undertake further training to ensure proficiency and understanding to the level required for FDA compliance.

Assuming that a firm can provide appropriate design and manufacturing controls to a device, unless appropriate nonconforming products controls are implemented, there will be an unreasonable risk that the manufacturing of the device will result in devices that fail to meet specifications and are unsuitable for release as finished devices.

To ensure that finished devices meet specifications and are suitable for release and distribution, each step in the review of nonconforming products, including manufacturing materials, components, in-process products, and finished devices, must fulfill its quality system role.

This discussion is *basic*. Individuals will require significant additional study and detailed manufacturing controls implementation before they can be assured that the manufacturing controls they establish and maintain meet FDA expectations. The definitions, unless followed by an asterisk, are quoted from FDA's Quality System Regulations.

NONCONFORMING PRODUCT

Definitions *Bottom-up Inspection* was FDA's standard inspection process for routine good manufacturing practice (GMP) inspections prior to 1998. Investigators were taught to start inspections by investigating one or more instances of quality problems, such as complaints or recalls, as a strategy to evaluate each manufacturer's GMP compliance.*

Component means any raw material, substance, piece, part, software, firmware, labeling, or assembly which is intended to be included as part of the finished, packaged, and labeled device.

Control number means any distinctive symbols, such as a distinctive combination of letters or numbers, or both, from which the history of the manufacturing, packaging, labeling, and distribution of a unit, lot, or batch of finished devices can be determined.

Finished device means any device or accessory to any device that is suitable for use or capable of functioning, whether or not it is packaged, labeled, or sterilized.

Form FDA 483, Inspectional Observations is the form FDA presents to inspected firms at the end of each inspection. Typically, the form is presented to the senior management individual available at the firm.*

Lot or batch means one or more components or finished devices that consist of a single type, model, class, size, composition, or software version that are manufactured under essentially the same conditions and that are intended to have uniform characteristics and quality within specified limits.

Manufacturer means any person who designs, manufactures, fabricates, assembles, or processes a finished device. Manufacturer includes but is not limited to those who perform the functions of contract sterilization, installation, relabeling, remanufacturing, repacking, or specification development, and initial distributors of foreign entities performing these functions.

Manufacturing material means any material or substance used in or used to facilitate the manufacturing process, a concomitant constituent, or a byproduct constituent produced during the manufacturing process, which is present in or on the finished device as a residue or impurity not by design or intent of the manufacturer.

Nonconformity means the nonfulfillment of a specified requirement.

Product means components, manufacturing materials, in-process devices, finished devices, and returned devices.

Quality System Inspection Technique (QSIT) is FDA's latest inspection strategy. QSIT involves what FDA calls "top-down" inspections of the four major subsystems of each device manufacturer's quality system: their (1) management controls, (2) design controls, (3) corrective and preventive actions, and (4) production and process controls.*

Rework means action taken on a nonconforming product so that it will fulfill the specified DMR requirements before it is released for distribution.

Specification means any requirement with which a product, process, service, or other activity must conform.

Top-down Inspection is FDA's newest inspection strategy. Inspectors are taught to evaluate device manufacturers' "quality systems," starting with the firm's quality policy, quality system procedures, and quality plan and to "touch bottom" by sampling each firm's quality system records.*

Nonconforming Product § 820 Subpart I

§ 820.90 Nonconforming Product

What the regulation states

§ 820.90 (a)

(a) *Control of nonconforming product.* Each manufacturer shall establish and maintain procedures to control product that does not conform to specified requirements. The procedures shall address the identification, documentation, evaluation, segregation, and disposition of nonconforming product. The evaluation of nonconformance shall include a determination of the need for an investigation and notification of the persons or organizations responsible for the nonconformance. The evaluation and any investigation shall be documented.

§ 820.90 (a) Nonconforming Product Control Discussion

Required procedure(s), document(s), and record(s)

FDA requires manufacturers to control "nonconforming product." Control starts with written procedures on nonconforming product. The procedures must cover the broad FDA definition of product and address nonconforming:

- Identification
- Documentation
- Evaluation
- Quarantine
- Disposition

Remember!   If any manufacturing material, product, in-process device, finished device, or accessory does not meet specifications, it is, by definition, a nonconforming product. To use nonconforming product after it has been determined to have failed specifications is against FDA regulation.

FDA understands that nonconforming product is produced by almost all manufacturing processes. However, FDA requires that nonconformances are assessed to determine whether:

- An investigation is required, or
- Individuals or activities responsible for nonconformances are required to be notified.

Required procedure(s), document(s), and record(s)   These investigation assessments and any investigations must be documented and should include "provisions for trending or monitoring the situation in the future." See Chapter 12 Statistical Techniques.

What the regulation states

§ 820.90 (b)

(b) *Nonconformity review and disposition.*

(1) Each manufacturer shall establish and maintain procedures that define the responsibility for review and the authority for the disposition of nonconforming product. The procedures shall set forth the review and disposition process. Disposition of nonconforming product shall be documented. Documentation shall include the justification for use of nonconforming product and the signature of the individual(s) authorizing the use.

(2) Each manufacturer shall establish and maintain procedures for rework, to include retesting and reevaluation of the nonconforming product after rework, to ensure that the product meets its current approved specifications. Rework and reevaluation activities, including a determination of any adverse effect from the rework upon the product, shall be documented in the DHR.

§ 820.90 (b) Nonconformity Review & Disposition Discussion

Required procedure(s), document(s), and record(s)   Each nonconforming product activity's procedure should clearly identify those responsible for review and those with authority to dispose of nonconforming product. The disposition of all nonconforming products must be documented, and that documentation should include any justification for the continued use of any nonconforming product. The individual's signature authorizing and responsible for disposition, either as "waste" or justified use, perhaps after rework, must be included in the documentation.

Don't forget!

Some nonconforming product may go through a "reworked" process, controlled by written procedures, to correct out-of-specification conditions. Any reworked product should be tested to at least the same specifications as other product before acceptance is completed. Such rework activity must be supervised to ensure the activity meets product specifications and completely documented as part of the design history file.

See Chapter 4 Design Controls and Chapter 9 Acceptance Activities.

What the FDA Investigator expects to see during an inspection

Under FDA's former "bottom-up" form of inspections, nonconforming products were one of the first elements FDA Investigators attempted to assess. With the new QSIT "top-down" inspection strategy, nonconforming product assessments are integrated into assessments of the four subsystems: (1) management controls, (2) design controls, (3) corrective and preventive actions, and (4) production and process controls.

Under management controls, Investigators will attempt to determine whether, through quality audits and their management review, the firm's quality system adequately prevents the production of unsafe or nonconforming product.

Further, under corrective and preventive action, Investigators will determine whether management is aware of both specific nonconforming product issues and processes that appear to fail to control nonconforming product. They will want to see evidence that management has reviewed these situations and failures.

FDA Investigators will attempt to determine whether any products that failed to meet any specification was released and distributed. They will review the device history record, specifically in-process control records for any lots, portions of lots, components, or manufacturing materials that had been rejected for failure to meet any specification. Any distribution of these failed or out-of-specification products will be reviewed to determine that action's justification. Investigators will review material, component, or engineering review board records and evaluate that board's justification decision.

Under the new QSIT Inspection strategy, Investigators are taught to assess nonconforming product through the use of sampling plans. Based on varying statistically significant numbers of records assessed, Investigators will make observations on their Form FDA 483 related to "objectionable conditions."

Investigators will also review any rework activity to ensure that specifications were met and the safety or performance of any device was not compromised. These reviews will be assessed to ensure that appropriate sampling, inspection, and testing activities are based on acceptable statistical rationale and technique. Investigators will assess statistical analysis (for example, trend analysis of manufacturing materials, components, in-process, and finished devices) for failures. Investigators will consider that high rework rates or high failure rates provide strong evidence that the manufacturing process is not in a state of control.

In addition to identification, documentation, segregation, and disposition, Investigators will expect to find "investigation" activity associated with nonconforming products. They expect that these investigations be documented and that any reasons for not performing investigations are documented with an explanation.

Investigators will review records to ensure that nonconforming products are afforded proper disposition and are not used in the distribution of any defective, out-of-specification, or returned devices. FDA expects that any allowance for nonconforming product to be used in device manufacturing will be based on scientific evidence, documented, reviewed, and approved by an appropriate authority, perhaps a "material review board."

Allowances for the use of nonconforming product that result in changes in specifications, for example, form, fit, or function, will also be reviewed by Investigators for documented risk analysis and possible 510(k) resubmission or submission.

11

Corrective and Preventive Action

INTRODUCTION

This chapter of **Mastering and Managing the FDA Maze: Medical Device Overview Training and Management Desk Reference** discusses corrective and preventive actions.

SCOPE

The goal of this chapter is to provide an overview of FDA regulations for corrective and preventive actions for medical device manufacturers. Significant detail has been omitted, and readers are advised to undertake further training to ensure proficiency and understanding to the level required for FDA compliance.

Assuming that a firm can provide appropriate design and manufacturing controls for a device, unless appropriate corrective and preventive actions are implemented, there will be an unreasonable risk that the manufacture of the device will result in devices that fail to meet specifications and are unsuitable for release as finished devices.

To ensure that finished devices meet specifications and are suitable for release and distribution, each step in any device's manufacturing process must be subject to corrective and preventive actions to fulfill their Quality System role.

This discussion is *basic*. Individuals will require significant additional study and implementation before they can be assured that the manufacturing controls they establish and maintain meet FDA expectations. Definitions, unless followed by an asterisk, are quoted from FDA's Quality System Regulation.

CORRECTIVE AND PREVENTIVE ACTION

Definitions

Complaint means any written, electronic, or oral communication that alleges deficiencies related to the identity, quality, durability, reliability, safety, effectiveness, or performance of a device after it is released for distribution.

Correction means the repair, modification, adjustment, relabeling, destruction, or inspection (including patient monitoring) of a device without its physical removal from its point of use to some other location.*

Manufacturer means any person who designs, manufactures, fabricates, assembles, or processes a finished device. Manufacturer includes but is not limited to those who perform the functions of contract sterilization, installation, relabeling, remanufacturing, repacking, or specification development, and initial distributors of foreign entities performing these functions.

Manufacturing material means any material or substance used in or used to facilitate the manufacturing process, a concomitant constituent, or a byproduct constituent produced during the manufacturing process, which is present in or on the finished device as a residue or impurity not by design or intent of the manufacturer.

Nonconformity means the nonfulfillment of a specified requirement.

Product means components, manufacturing materials, in-process devices, finished devices, and returned devices.

Quality audit means an established systematic, independent examination of a manufacturer's quality system that is performed at defined intervals and at sufficient frequency to ensure that both quality system activities and the results of such activities comply with specified quality system procedures, that these procedures are implemented effectively, and that these procedures are suitable to achieve quality system objectives.

Quality System Inspection Technique (QSIT) is FDA's latest inspection strategy. QSIT involves what FDA calls "top-down" inspections of the four major subsystems of each device manufacturer's quality system: their (1) management controls, (2) design controls, (3) corrective and preventive actions, and (4) production and process controls.*

Removal means the physical removal of a device from its point of use to some other location for repair, modification, adjustment, relabeling, destruction, or inspection.*

Risk to health means:
(1) A reasonable probability that use of, or exposure to, the product will cause serious adverse health consequences or death; or
(2) That use of, or exposure to, the product may cause temporary or medically reversible adverse health consequences or an outcome where the probability of adverse health consequences is remote.*

Specification means any requirement with which a product, process, service, or other activity must conform.

Validation means confirmation by examination and provision of objective evidence that the particular requirements for a specific intended use can be consistently fulfilled.

Verification means confirmation by examination and provision of objective evidence that specified requirements have been fulfilled.

Corrective and Preventive Action § 820 Subpart J

§ 820.100 (a) (b) Corrective and Preventive Action

What the regulation states

§ 820.100 (a) (b)

(a) Each manufacturer shall establish and maintain procedures for implementing corrective and preventive action. The procedures shall include requirements for:

(1) Analyzing processes, work operations, concessions, quality audit reports, quality records, service records, complaints, returned product, and other sources of quality data to identify existing and potential causes of nonconforming product, or other quality problems. Appropriate statistical methodology shall be employed where necessary to detect recurring quality problems;
(2) Investigating the cause of nonconformities relating to product, processes, and the quality system;
(3) Identifying the action(s) needed to correct and prevent recurrence of nonconforming product and other quality problems;
(4) Verifying or validating the corrective and preventive action to ensure that such action is effective and does not adversely affect the finished device;
(5) Implementing and recording changes in methods and procedures needed to correct and prevent identified quality problems;
(6) Ensuring that information related to quality problems or nonconforming product is disseminated to those directly responsible for assuring the quality of such product or the prevention of such problems; and
(7) Submitting relevant information on identified quality problems, as well as corrective and preventive actions, for management review.

(b) All activities required under this section, and their results, shall be documented.

§ 820.100 (a) (b) Corrective and Preventive Action Discussion

Remember!

FDA Quality System regulations are designed to include the concepts of continuous quality improvement. One of the foundations of continuous quality improvement is the use of corrective and preventive actions, which must involve all aspects of the quality system, including employee training, procedures, work instructions, development activities, manufacturing product, processes, acceptance activities, distribution, installation, and support.

Also see FDA regulations 21 CFR 7 on recalls and 21 CFR 806 on reports of removal and corrections. Although detailed discussions of both of these regulations are beyond the scope of this introductory text, they require manufacturers' compliance. Chapter 19 Medical Device Reporting briefly discusses 21 CFR 7. See **Additional FDA Regulations that Apply—21 CFR 806** for a brief discussion of 21 CFR 806. The regulation is provided in its entirety in the **ATTACHMENTS**.

Required procedure(s), document(s), and record(s)

FDA requires device manufacturers to integrate their quality systems with written procedures for corrective and preventive actions, which include:

- Analysis of quality data from all sources, including appropriate statistical techniques
- Investigations of the root causes of nonconforming product, processes, or other quality system problems
- Identification of the root causes of nonconforming product, processes, or other quality system problems needed to correct and prevent recurrence
- Verification and validation of corrective and preventive actions to ensure such actions are effective and do not adversely affect finished devices
- Implementation and documentation of changes in methods and procedures
- Dissemination of information related to corrective and preventive changes to those responsible for ensuring product quality or preventing quality problems
- Submission of relevant information on identified quality problems and corrective and preventive actions for management review
- Documentation of all corrective and preventive actions

Corrective and preventive action procedures must identify actions to be taken for devices that have been implicated as nonconforming prior to and after distribution. During analysis, investigation, and identification, manufacturers may assess individual nonconformities against established criteria and use that assessment to prioritize corrective and preventive actions. An appropriate philosophy for any device manufacturer to establish is that corrective and preventive actions are integrated into each activity associated with any device's design, manufacture, testing, labeling, packaging, handling, storage, distribution, installation, service, and support.

A high-level procedure might call for appropriate corrective and preventive actions in each of the following areas: (1) establish training practices (2) identify tools, statistical methods, and appropriate review and management reports. Certainly procedures or work instructions related to the required formally designated complaint unit, complaints, and Medical Device Reporting must be integrated with corrective and preventive actions and activities. See Chapter 18 Complaint Files and Chapter 19 Medical Device Reporting.

Additionally, manufacturers should take care to ensure that procedures related to installation, warranty service, repair, and service support integrate appropriate corrective and preventive actions.

Don't forget!   Manufacturers must understand that documents and records created under § 820.100 are subject to FDA review, unlike § 820.22 Quality Audit.

Additional FDA Regulations That Apply—21 CFR 806

What the   *21 CFR 806.10 Reports of Corrections and Removals*
regulation states   (a) Each device manufacturer, importer, or distributor shall submit a written report to FDA of any correction or removal of a device initiated by such manufacturer or distributor if the correction or removal was initiated:

(1) To reduce a risk to health posed by the device; or
(2) To remedy a violation of the act caused by the device which may present a risk to health unless the information has already been provided as set forth in paragraph (f) of this section or the corrective or removal action is exempt from the reporting requirements under Sec. 806.1(b).

(b) The manufacturer, importer, or distributor shall submit any report required by paragraph (a) of this section within 10-working days of initiating such correction or removal. The report shall be submitted to the appropriate FDA district office listed in Sec. 5.115 of this chapter. A foreign manufacturer or owner or operator of devices must submit reports of corrective or removal actions.

21 CFR 806.10 Discussion
Section 21 CFR 806 became effective May 17, 1998, affecting manufacturers, importers, and distributors of medical devices. Section 21 CRF 806 is provided in its entirety as Attachment B, page 239. The regulation requires them to report device corrections or removals actions made to reduce the risk to health or remedy a violation of the FD&C Act, unless such an action has been reported by FDA's Medical Device Reporting regulations or requirement to correct electronic products under 21 CFR 1004.

Subparts B of 21 CFR 806 detail a reporting requirement with a specific identifier number. This number includes the firm's seven-digit registration number, the month, day, and year of the report, a sequence number, and a report-type designation of either "C," for correction, or "R," for removal. For example, a firm with a registration number of 1234567, reporting a second correction action on August 30, 1998, would provide an identifier number of 1234567-8/30/98-002-C. Firms that do not have a seven-digit registration number may use seven zeros followed by the month, date, year, and sequence number.

Further, the required report will include the following:

- The firm's name, address, and telephone number
- Information on the responsible individual or representative for conducting the device correction or removal
- Specific information on the device
- The event giving rise to the action
- Any illness or injury that occurred with the use of the device
- The number of devices manufactured or distributed
- The date of manufacture or distribution, any expiration dates, or expected life
- Names, addresses, and telephone numbers of all domestic and foreign consignees of the device and dates and number of devices distributed to each such consignee

- A copy of all communications regarding the correction or removal and the names and addresses of all recipients of the communications not provided in accordance with paragraph (c)(11) of the regulation
- If any required information is not immediately available, a statement as to why it is not available and when it will be submitted

§ 806.20 details records of corrections and removals not required to be reported; § 806.30 details FDA access to records; and § 806.40 details public availability of reports.

Needless to say, the corrections and removal reporting regulation's compliance will be a significant burden on device manufacturers. Readers are encouraged to review this regulation in detail and develop strategies, procedures, documents, and records for compliance.

What the FDA Investigator expects to see during an inspection

Under the new QSIT Inspection strategy, the review of each firm's corrective action and preventive action (CAPA) quality subsystem can be expected to involve 25% or more of the FDA Investigator's activities. Investigators are expected to integrate CAPA assessments as part of their review of management controls, design controls, and production and process controls. The QSIT Handbook's CAPA Decision Flow Chart is redrawn as Figure 11.1 on page 144.

FDA Investigators will verify that the firm's written CAPA procedures appropriately address the Quality System Regulation's requirements. These procedures may be integrated into other procedures, including Medical Device Reporting (MDR), or exist as standalone procedures. They may also be integrated into procedures associated with screening service and repair reports. In any case, trend analysis, monitoring, appropriate investigations, and CAPAs, even MDR reports, are considered part of a firm's overall CAPA activity. Investigators will attempt to verify that appropriate statistical methods, investigations, records, and reports are implemented. Investigators are required to state in their Establishment Inspection Report (EIR) that complaints, service records, repair records, and so on were reviewed and that review included MDR reportability.

FDA Investigators will determine whether the documented management representative interacts with the firm's CAPA activities. They may assess management's involvement with corrective actions associated with objectionable findings of previous FDA inspections. They may also determine whether management broadened those corrective actions to preventive actions in appropriate elements of the firm's quality system. Additionally, Investigators will determine whether the CAPA activities were verified or validated prior to their implementation.

Investigators would expect to find that management and the management representative are involved with the firm's written quality audit procedures and its CAPA activities. They could be expected to assess management's involvement with documentation that CAPAs were implemented, found to be effective, and appropriately disseminated.

When reviewing design controls, FDA Investigators can be expected to determine whether appropriate CAPAs were routinely implemented as inputs to design outputs, changes, and transfers.

FDA Investigators understand that many, if not most, corrective actions are the result of complaints of device failures or service records that point to device failures. Investigators requesting to review device complaints are looking for a variety of problems, including appropriate corrective and preventive actions. Investigators reviewing service or repair reports are also interested in determining whether reports identified and investigated as device failures result in appropriate CAPAs. In either situation, Investigators also understand that not all investigations result in a definitive cause for each device failure but will assess these investigations for completeness, accuracy, and timeliness. They will also assess the depth of firm's CAPA investigations to determine whether they are consistent with the significance and risk of the failure.

Section 820.198(c) requires that device manufacturers investigate possible device failures to determine whether a failure can be confirmed and/or a cause can be found. Whenever a failure is confirmed, § 820.100, Corrective and Preventive Action, regulations are triggered. FDA Investigators also understand that occasionally the activities associated with statistical analysis of device failures, such as trending or constant monitoring of complaints for specific failures, are actions related to CAPAs.

Investigators will review service and warranty repair records to determine whether the manufacturer has reviewed these records for premature failures of specific components, subassemblies, or device design. Investigators are trained to consider device failures within warranty periods to be highly likely to be related to design or Quality System Regulation-related failures, causing them to focus on failures that are:

- Product design-related, such as electrical safety, EMC, consistent user error, product robustness associated with problems of assembly, packing, handling, storage, or distribution.
- Quality system related, including product specifications, product receiving and/or acceptance issues, or process validation

Investigators are also trained to focus on reliability issues that have not been documented for CAPA and are instructed to note the continued distribution of devices with known problems on the manufacturer's FDA 483 report. Such observations may lead to a subsequent Warning Letter.

FDA Investigators will closely monitor manufacturers for compliance with 21 CFR 806, Reports of Corrections or Removals. Manufacturers must be aware of this new regulation and its reporting requirements. Investigators will review any procedures, documents, and records associated with corrections and removals. In addition, during any inspection, if Investigators uncover or determine that corrections and removals have been made without compliance with § 806, that observation will be added to the firm's form 483 and a Warning Letter will most likely be issued that details that nonconformance.

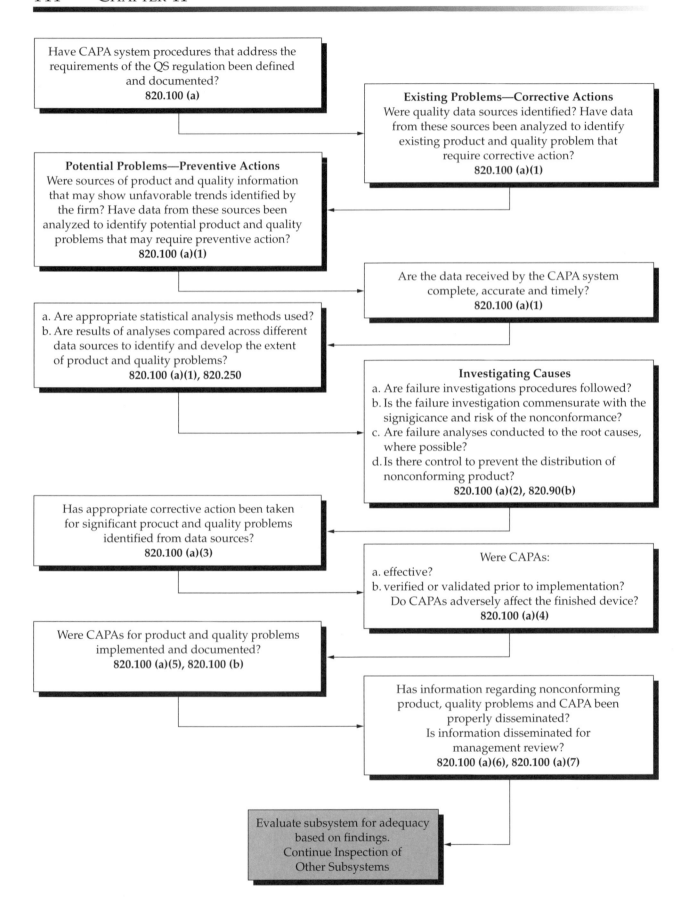

Figure 11.1. Corrective and Preventive Actions (CAPA) Decision Flow Chart
Redrawn by author from **QSIT Handbook,** *page 45.*

12

Statistical Techniques

INTRODUCTION

This chapter of **Mastering and Managing the FDA Maze: Medical Device Overview Training and Management Desk Reference** discusses FDA's statistical techniques regulation.

SCOPE

The goal of this chapter is to provide an overview of FDA regulations for statistical techniques for medical device manufacturers. Significant detail has been omitted, and further training to ensure proficiency and understanding to the level required for FDA compliance will be needed.

Assuming that a firm can provide appropriate design, manufacturing, acceptance, and corrective and preventive action controls to a device, unless appropriate statistical techniques are used with those activities, there will be an unreasonable risk that the manufacturing of the device will result in devices that fail to meet specifications and are unsuitable for release as finished devices.

To ensure that finished devices meet specifications and are suitable for release and distribution, this use of statistical techniques throughout the design, manufacturing, and remaining processes helps ensure manufacturers fulfill their quality system role.

It should be emphasized that this discussion is *basic*. Individuals will require significant additional study and implementation before they can be assured that the statistical techniques they establish and maintain meet FDA expectations. The definitions, unless followed by an asterisk, are quoted from FDA's Quality System Regulation.

STATISTICAL TECHNIQUES

Definitions

Control chart is a graphic representation of any characteristic of a process or any process output documenting individually plotted statistical values, a central line, and one or two control limits used to assess the state of control and maintain statistical control of any process or output.*

Design validation means establishing by objective evidence that device specifications conform with user needs and intended use(s).

Finished device means any device or accessory to any device that is suitable for use or capable of functioning, whether or not it is packaged, labeled, or sterilized.

Nonconformity means the nonfulfillment of a specified requirement.

Pareto analysis is the use of a Pareto bar chart with problems prioritized in descending order of importance, providing users with information on the state of control associated with these problems.*

Process is a combination of people, equipment, machines, tools, including software, raw materials, methods, and an environment that results in a specific product or service.*

Process validation means establishing by objective evidence that a process consistently produces a result or product meeting its predetermined specifications.

Quality System Inspection Technique (QSIT) is FDA's latest inspection strategy. QSIT involves what FDA calls "top-down" inspections of the four major subsystems of each device manufacturer's quality system, that is, their management controls, design controls, corrective and preventive actions, and production and process controls.*

Record means any written or electronic document, including specifications, procedures, protocols, standards, methods, instructions, plans, files, forms, notes, reviews, analyses, data, and reports.

Root cause is the most basic cause of any undesirable condition or problem, which when eliminated or mitigated, will prevent or significantly reduce the effect of the condition or problem.*

Specification means any requirement with which a product, process, service, or other activity must conform.

Statistic is any value calculated from or based upon sampling data used to assess a process or the sampled output of a process.*

Statistical Process Control (SPC) is the use of statistical techniques to analyze any process or any process's outputs to provide information on the state of control of the process or output and improve the capability of the process or improve the quality of the output.*

Trends are patterns identified on a control chart that demonstrate the continued rise or fall of a series of data points.*

Validation means confirmation by examination and provision of objective evidence that the particular requirements for a specific intended use can be consistently fulfilled.

Verification means confirmation by examination and provision of objective evidence that specified requirements have been fulfilled.

Statistical Technique § 820 Subpart O

§ 820.250 (a) (b) Statistical Techniques

What the regulation states

§ 820.250 (a) (b)

(a) Where appropriate, each manufacturer shall establish and maintain procedures for identifying valid statistical techniques required for establishing, controlling, and verifying the acceptability of process capability and product characteristics.
(b) Sampling plans, when used, shall be written and based on a valid statistical rationale. Each manufacturer shall establish and maintain procedures to ensure that sampling methods are adequate for their intended use and to ensure that when changes occur the sampling plans are reviewed. These activities shall be documented.

§ 820.250 (a) (b) Discussion

This regulation requires procedures for "identifying valid statistical techniques" to verify process capability and product characteristics "where appropriate." FDA does not "require" all manufacturers to use sampling plans but does require that, when used, they must be based on a valid statistical rationale. FDA understands that sampling plans are most frequently used during product receiving acceptance activities.

Statistical methods should be implemented in:

- Product design
- Risk analysis
- Product limits
- Process design
- Process control
- Process limits
- Nonconformity control

- Verification, including design verification
- Validation, including process validation
- Problem analysis
- Root cause determination
- Assessment of Quality System characteristics.

Firms should select statistical techniques and sampling plans carefully. These include:

- Graphical methods, including histograms, sequence charts, scatter plots, Pareto charts, cause-and-effect diagrams, and other methods of documenting any statistic.
- Statistical control charts that monitor and control production and measurement processes.
- Design of experiments that determine the candidate variable having significant influence in process and product performance and qualify the effects.
- Regression analyses that provide quantitative models of the behavior of a process or product when conditions of process operation or product design are changed.
- Analysis of variance, from which variance component estimates can be created and which are useful in designing sample structures for control charts, product characterization, and approved product release criteria.
- Methods of sampling and acceptance, including sampling at all stages of production, and statistical methods for inspections and testing.

Required document(s), procedure(s), and record(s)

It would be prudent for manufacturers to implement techniques and plans from appropriate reference materials and reference those materials in their documentation.

FDA requires manufacturers to create and maintain statistical technique procedures to establish, control, and verify acceptable processes and products.

Written statistical technique procedures should include product and process testing based on a sampling plan. Such sampling plans must be based on acceptable statistical rationale, and manufacturers must be able to document their plan's acceptability. Often statistical technique testing plans are selected from established standards, such as that of the American National Standards Institute (ANSI), ANSI Z1.4.

Sampling plans are often augmented with charts and graphs that illustrate effectiveness, probabilities, and risks. FDA understands that all sampling plans, even those with 100% testing, have a built-in risk of not prohibiting all nonconforming product from distribution. Sampling plans should be selected to maximize effectiveness and to reduce probabilities and risks of nonconformances being delivered. Among the many questions these plans should resolve or attempt to resolve are the following:

- What are the consequences of using a defective device?
- Will the defect be obvious to the user?
- What is the level of confidence (as a percentage) of the statistical technique?
- Is the testing technology chosen statistically sound?
- Is the testing destructive?
- What sampling plans do other manufactures in the industry use?
- Does the marketplace require or expect devices that have been sample tested?

As with any manufacturing activity, sampling plans must be verified and validated for their intended use, and that verification and validation must be documented. If any software application is used to facilitate statistical techniques or sampling plans, that software application must be validated for its intended use, and that validation must be documented.

Whenever a manufacturer determines that statistical techniques and/or sampling plans are not required or appropriate in a device manufacturing environment, that decision should be documented, dated, and signed by appropriate individuals.

Remember!

Many manufacturers find that aggressive design and process validation combined with appropriate product sampling and testing and monitored by aggressive audits and corrective and preventive actions will continually produce a device that meets its specifications.

What the FDA Investigator will want to see during an inspection

Under the FDA's new QSIT inspection strategy, firms can expect a significant emphasis placed on their statistical techniques and sampling plans. The agency has even adopted a statistical technique with QSIT inspections, that is, "binomial staged sampling plans" adapted from the CRC Handbook of Probability and Statistics, Second Edition.

FDA Investigators can be expected to select a number of completed and incomplete failure investigations and expect to find evidence of appropriate sampling methods employed that ensure the firm's detection of recurring quality problems. They will expect that these sampling methods are broadly implemented, wherever required, and results are promptly analyzed to identify the depth and breadth of product and quality problems. These techniques might include Pareto analysis, spreadsheets, trend analysis, and pie charts. Investigators will expect to see appropriate reference materials used by manufacturers that document the validity of their statistical techniques and sampling plans.

Investigators will also evaluate the firm's implementation of statistical techniques for activities associated with preventive actions. Wherever appropriate, Investigators will expect to see techniques such as statistical process control (SPC) implemented to monitor processes throughout their written and approved specification limits. They will also expect to see appropriate review of those techniques and their integration into process validation activities. Firms can expect that Investigators may focus on process validation activities if levels of product failures or quality problems indicate failures in process validation. Processes involving sterilization can be expected to undergo these evaluations, particularly if failures are evident.

Investigators will expect to see manufacturers routinely analyzing service records and reports with appropriate statistical methods based on their written procedures. Investigators will also expect to see statistical techniques integrated with nonstatistical techniques, such as quality review boards and quality review committees, wherever appropriate.

13

Device Master Record (DMR)

INTRODUCTION

This chapter of **Mastering and Managing the FDA Maze: Medical Device Overview Training and Management Desk Reference** discusses FDA's device master record regulations.

SCOPE

The goal of this chapter is to provide an overview of FDA regulations for a device master record (DMR) for medical device manufacturers. Significant detail has been omitted, and further training to ensure proficiency and understanding to the level required for FDA compliance will be needed.

Assuming that a firm can provide appropriate design and manufacturing controls to a device, unless appropriate controls are placed over manufacturing procedures, specifications, and records, that is, a DMR, there will be an unreasonable risk that the manufacturing of the device will result in devices that fail to meet specifications and are unsuitable for release as finished devices.

To ensure that finished devices meet specifications and are suitable for release and distribution, the control of procedures, specifications, and records of the manufacturing process must fulfill its quality system role.

It should be emphasized that this discussion is *basic*. Individuals will require significant additional study and implementation before they can be assured that the manufacturing controls they establish and maintain meet FDA expectations. The definitions, unless followed by an asterisk, are quoted from FDA's Quality System Regulations.

DEVICE MASTER RECORD (DMR)

Definitions

Device master record (DMR) means a compilation of records containing all the procedures and specifications related to a specific finished device, as required by this part.

Finished device means any device or accessory to any device that is suitable for use or capable of functioning, whether or not it is packaged, labeled, or sterilized.

Quality System Inspection Technique (QSIT) is FDA's latest inspection strategy. QSIT involves what FDA calls "top-down" inspections of the four major subsystems of each device manufacturer's quality system, that is, their management controls, design controls, corrective and preventive actions, and production and process controls.*

Record means any written or electronic document, including specifications, procedures, protocols, standards, methods, instructions, plans, files, forms, notes, reviews, analyses, data, and reports.

Specification means any requirement with which a product, process, service, or other activity must conform.

21 CFR § 820.181 DEVICE MASTER RECORD

What the regulation states

§ 820.181

Each manufacturer shall maintain device master records (DMR's). Each manufacturer shall ensure that each DMR is prepared and approved in accordance with § 820.40.

§ 820.181 Discussion

The device master record (DMR) is FDA's term for all documentation required to manufacture regulated devices and ensure that devices consistently meet requirements and specifications.

Remember!

A DMR should be created for each device, device type, or family. Because many Class I devices are not required to comply with design control regulations, the required DMR for these devices are those specified in § 820.181. See Chapter 4 Design Controls.

Don't forget!

The DMR should be written with its audience in mind: the employees who are manufacturing the device and the device's end users. Specific components of the DMR should be written to the needs of the individuals involved with that DMR activity. Because individual DMR documents are written to the needs of the individual employee, those documents and records will be located where those employees work.

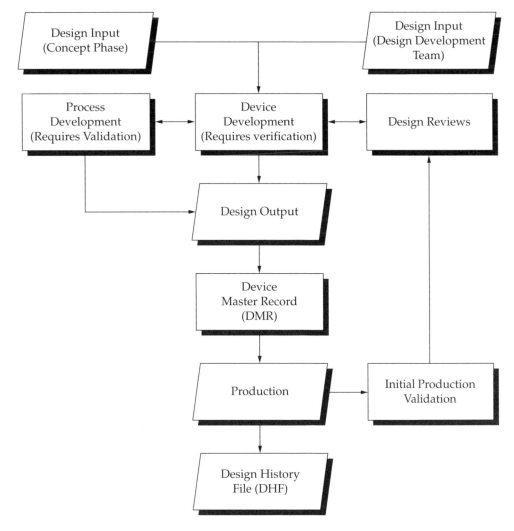

Elements of the Device Master Record

Redrawn and enhanced from an FDA drawing by the author.

Device specific tables, logs, and files are frequently used to comply with the requirement that the DMR for each type of device include or provide a listing or index of documents and records contained in those files. Additionally, those documents should refer to the location of the DMR documents and records because these documents are found wherever there is manufacturing activity.

Something to note!

A reasonable filing practice used by many manufacturers is to label or identify each piece of filing equipment with its location, contents, and responsible party. Documents or records moved off-site should also be identified and their specific location and responsible party recorded. If a third party maintains these off-site locations, that activity must be in compliance with § 820.50 Purchasing Controls. See Chapter 6 Purchasing Controls.

Care must be taken to periodically monitor the recorded location of documents and records to ensure that they have not been moved without appropriate location record changes. This can easily be integrated into required periodic quality system audits. See Chapter 20 Quality Audit.

Remember!

DMR documents are required to be created, reviewed, and approved according to § 820.40 Document Controls. FDA expects that individuals will be designated to review, date, approve, and authorize changes to all documents required by the Quality System Regulation including the DMR. See Chapter 5 Document Controls.

Typical Location of Device Master Records

DMR Document or Record	Originals	Working Copies
Reference Lists or Index	Engineering master files	—
Component drawings	Engineering or manufacturing master files	Manufacturing &/or purchasing activity
Component acceptance procedures	SOP master files	Receiving activity
Device input specifications (final versions)	Engineering master files	Marketing &/or engineering activities
Manufacturing procedures	Engineering or manufacturing master files	Manufacturing activity
Master validation plan	Engineering or manufacturing master files	Manufacturing, QA, QC, &/or final test activity
Test procedures	Engineering or manufacturing master files	Manufacturing, QA, QC, &/or final test activity
Test specifications	Engineering master files	Engineering &/or manufacturing activities
Inspection procedures	Manufacturing, QC, or SOP master files	Manufacturing &/or QC
Label control procedures	Manufacturing, QC, or SOP master files	Manufacturing
Label drawings	Engineering master files	Engineering &/or purchasing activities
General cleaning procedure	Quality system record master file	—
Specific cleaning procedure	SOP master files	Manufacturing
Quality system audit procedure	Quality system record master file	—
Employee training procedures	Quality system record master file	—

SOP = Standard Operating Procedure; QA = Quality Assurance; QC = Quality Control

The following is a list of some DMR documents requiring the identification:

DMR Activities Requiring Identification of Individuals for Review

Regulatory Reference	Activity
820.30(b)	Approval of design plans
820.30(c)	Approval of design input
820.30(d)	Approval of design output
820.30(e)	Results of design review
820.30(f)	Results of design verification
820.30(g)	Results of design validation
820.40	Approval of device master record or changes
820.75(a)	Approval of process validation
820.75(1)(2)	Performance of validated process
820.80(e)	Acceptance of activities conducted

***What the
regulation states***

§ 820.181 (a)–(e)

The DMR for each type of device shall include, or refer to the location of, the following information:

(a) Device specifications including appropriate drawings, composition, formulation, component specifications, and software specifications;

(b) Production process specifications including the appropriate equipment specifications, production methods, production procedures, and production environment specifications;

(c) Quality assurance procedures and specifications including acceptance criteria and the quality assurance equipment to be used;

(d) Packaging and labeling specifications, including methods and processes used; and

(e) Installation, maintenance, and servicing procedures and methods.

§ 820.181 (a)–(e) DMR Discussion

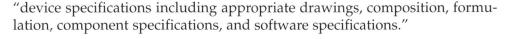

***Required
procedure(s),
document(s),
and record(s)***

Note the above detailed listing of documents and records FDA considers part of the DMR includes:

"device specifications including appropriate drawings, composition, formulation, component specifications, and software specifications."

As with design specifications, production process specifications are part of the DMR and include:

"appropriate equipment specifications, production methods, production procedures, and production environment specifications."

Production process specifications cover typical manufacturing activities such as the following:

- Procurement
- Assembly
- Labeling

- Testing and inspection
- Packaging
- Sterilization (when applicable)

Quality assurance procedures and specifications as well as manufacturing materials and finished device acceptance documents are required parts of each device's DMR. As with any design and production equipment, any quality assurance equipment documents and records are part of the DMR. Many times the majority of these procedures, work instructions, and some records are not device specific and should be referenced, with their location, in device DMR files.

All packaging and labeling procedures, specifications, and work instructions are part of each device's DMR and are typically referenced by location in device DMR files. Installation, maintenance and servicing procedures, and work instructions are part of each device's DMR. Some of these procedures and work instructions may be generic and apply to a number of manufactured devices; these documents are typically referenced by location in device DMR files.

The DMR is required to accurately reflect the device intended to be produced by the manufacturer. Most individual DMR production documents should be created knowing what information the individual reader needs (that is, documentation for the intended employee). In some cases, that may be a new employee, in others a long-term employee, a supervisor, or someone doing "rework," but all require an understanding of the following:

- What task is to be done (correct, complete, and current)?
- How should the task be done (what tools, equipment, parts, and components are necessary)?
- Who is to do the task (who is authorized, trained, or approved to perform the task)?
- How should the task be properly done (what step-by-step processes are required)?
- What are the results of the task (what is the output of the work process)?

Engineering drawings may not be appropriate unless employees are trained to read and use them. Assembly drawings and parts lists, exploded-view drawings, and step-by-step work instructions are typically appropriate and may be augmented by photographs, videotapes, slides, sample assemblies, and sample finished devices. All of these DMR documents and records must be identified, current, correct and approved for their intended use. Review, approval, signatures, and dates should control any list or index referring to the location of DMR documents and their latest versions.

Please refer to Figure 13.1, page 157, for a detailed list of "Documents That May Appear in a Device Master Record."

What the FDA Investigator wants to see during an inspection

FDA Investigators expect to find a device master record (DMR) for each regulated device manufactured. Investigators know a DMR may be:

- One or more files or volumes, or
- A list or index referring to the location of all documentation required by the DMR, or
- A combination of files, volumes, and list or index

Investigators will specifically look for (among other things):

- Device specifications
- Production process specifications
- Quality assurance procedures and specifications
- Packaging and labeling specifications
- Installation procedures
- Maintenance procedures
- Servicing procedures

1.0 Device Master Record Index
The device master record Index is a table of contents, which is used for convenience. It may be known as a:
Device Master Record Index
Documentation or Device Master Record Unit
Documentation Plan
Product Tree
Documentation Index
Product Structure or
Bill of Materials (if it also lists the device master record documents).

2.0 Device Specifications

3.0 Manufacturing Information
  3.1 Index
  3.2 Formulation or top-assembly drawing
  3.3 List of components
    a. List of ingredients (including grade or type)
    b. Bill of materials (i.e., component list usually arranged by subassembly or other sub-product level or by process steps)
    c. Formula
  3.4 Purchasing documentation
    a. Specifications
    b. Drawings
    c. Certificate of compliance requirements
    d. Supplier assessment procedures
  3.5 Device documentation
    a. Fabrication drawings
    b. Surface finish procedures
    c. Subassembly drawings
    d. Wiring and piping diagrams
    e. Assembly procedures
    f. Assembly drawings
    g. Reference documentation
      1) Wiring and piping schematics
        a) Test specifications
    h. Sub-batch procedures
    i. Blending or mixing procedures
    j. Solution procedures
    k. Final formulation procedures
    l. Software packages
  3.6 Precautions and special notations
    a. Apparel
    b. Cleaning
    c. Storage conditions
    d. Filling and mixing conditions
    e. Hazards and safety precautions
  3.7 Equipment, lines, and procedures
    a. Process lines
    b. Assembly lines
    c. Vessels
    d. Mixers and tools
    e. Molds
    f. Machine maintenance procedures
    g. Calibration procedures
    h. Setup procedures
    i. Operating procedures
    j. Process flow charts

  3.8 Sterilization procedures
    a. Procedures for ethylene oxide, radiation, filtration, steam, and so on
    b. Handling and flow procedures
    c. Cycle parameter specifications
    d. Diagrams for loading products in the chamber
  3.9 Production control documentation
    a. Inspection procedures
    b. Test procedures
    c. Blank job travelers
    d. Blank inspection/test forms
    e. Instrument charts
    f. Reporting forms
    g. Approved deviations

4.0 Labeling and Packaging
  4.1 Index
  4.2 Labeling
    a. Label drawings
    b. Labeling drawings
    c. Label/labeling review procedures and forms
    d. Production control procedures and history record forms
    e. Instruction manuals
    f. Service manuals
    g. Customer software
    h. Customer feedback forms
  4.3 Packaging
    a. Package drawings (usually includes labeling information)
    b. Closure drawings
    c. Filling and/or packaging procedures
    d. Packing procedures
    e. Special shipment procedures
  4.4 Storage requirements
    a. Temperature
    b. Humidity
    c. Shelf life

5.0 Control Procedures and Activities
  5.1 Index
  5.2 Inspection procedures
    a. Incoming
    b. In-process
    c. Finished devices
    d. Process control charts
    e. Blank data reporting forms
  5.3 Test procedures
    a. Incoming
    b. In-process
    c. Pretest conditioning
    d. Finished device
    e. Process control charts
    f. Blank device history record forms
    g. Automated test programs and/or software

6.0 Final Release
  6.1 Release document review list
  6.2 Distribution procedures
  6.3 Blank device history record forms

Figure 13.1. Documents That May Appear in a Device Master Record

Experience has taught FDA Investigators to pay particular attention to changes in any part of the DMR, and Investigators can be expected to critically review any changes to a device's design or the manufacturing process. These reviews may start during assessments of activities associated with:

- Complaints
- Service
- Repair
- Failure investigations
- In-process or finished device inspection
- Rework or
- Reinspection

However, they will focus on the manufacturer's state of control over these changes, including any appropriate verification and validation activities and any nonconformities that resulted from the changes.

Whenever changes have been made to the DMR that may reflect a broader problem, Inspectors will expect that the DMR will reflect an investigation that covers appropriate similar devices or processes to ensure any similar issues are resolved.

---

*Note: The Tables on pages 154 and 155 and in Figure 13.1 were recreated from FDA's **Quality Systems Regulation Manual, A Small Entity Compliance Guide for Medical Device Manufacturers,** 1st Edition, 1997.*

14

Labeling and Packaging

INTRODUCTION

This chapter of **Mastering and Managing the FDA Maze: Medical Device Overview Training and Management Desk Reference** discusses FDA oversight of medical device labeling and packaging.

SCOPE

The goal of this chapter is to provide an overview of FDA regulations for labeling and packaging for medical device manufacturers. Significant detail has been omitted, and further training to ensure proficiency and understanding to the level required for FDA compliance will be needed.

Assuming that a firm can provide appropriate design controls to a device and manufacture it under proper controls, unless appropriate labeling and packaging controls are implemented, there will be an unreasonable risk that the device will fail to meet specifications, be improperly labeled and/or packaged and will not be distributed and supported in a manner that meets FDA expectations.

To ensure that finished devices are suitable for release and distribution, each step in the labeling and packaging process must fulfill its quality system role.

It should be emphasized that this discussion is *basic.* Individuals will require significant additional study and implementation before they can be assured that the manufacturing controls they establish and maintain meet FDA expectations. The definitions, unless followed by an asterisk, are quoted from FDA's Quality System Regulations.

LABELING

Definitions   *Design History File* (DHF) means a compilation of records which describe the design history of a finished device.

Device History Record (DHR) means a compilation of records containing the production history of a finished device.

Device Master Record (DMR) means a compilation of records containing the procedures and specifications for a finished device.

Directions for use provides directions under which the practitioner or layperson (e.g., patient or unlicensed health care provider), as appropriate, can use the device safely and for the purposes for which it is intended. Directions for use also include indications for use and appropriate contraindications, warnings, precautions, and adverse reaction information. Directions for use requirements applicable to prescription and over-the-counter devices appear throughout 21 CFR Part 801.*

Intended uses refers to the objective intent of the persons legally responsible for the labeling of the device. The intent is determined by their expressions or may be shown by the circumstances surrounding the distribution of the device. This objective intent may, for example, be shown by labeling claims, advertising matter, or oral or written statements by such representatives. It may be shown by the offering or the using of the device, with the knowledge of such persons or their representatives, for a purpose for which it is neither labeled nor advertised. [21 CFR 801.4]*

Label is a display of written, printed, or graphic matter upon the immediate container of any article. [Act, section 201(k).]*

Labeling includes all labels and other written, printed or graphic matter (1) upon any article or any of its containers or wrappers, or (2) accompanying such article. [Act, section 201(m).]*

Misbranded means a device's labeling provides false or misleading information in any particular.*

Misleading mean that labeling is deceptive if it creates or leads to a false impression in the mind of a reader.*

Specification means any requirement with which a product, process, service, or other activity must conform.

Labeling Regulations other than QS Regulations– Identified for Additional Study

Something to note!

Specific FDA labeling requirements are found in a variety of federal laws and FDA regulations in addition to 21 CFR 820 Quality System Regulations, including:

- The Federal Food, Drug, and Cosmetic Act
- The Fair Packaging and Labeling Act
- The Radiation Control for Health and Safety Act
- Title 21 CFR, Part 801 for general devices
- Title 21 CFR, Part 812.5 for investigational devices
- Title 21 CFR, Part 1010 performance standards for electrical products

These other regulations, applicable to medical devices, provide that the inclusion of any of the following representations in device labeling constitutes misbranding of the device:

- 21 CFR 801.6 False or misleading representation with respect to another device or a drug
- 21 CFR 807.39 Any representation that creates an impression of official approval because of registration or possession of a registration number (e.g., inclusion of FDA establishment registration number)
- 21 CFR 807.97 Any representation that creates an impression of official approval because of complying with the premarket notification regulations (e.g., inclusion of premarket notification reference number)

Labeling Discussion—Other Regulations

Labeling regulations are fundamental to FDA's regulation of medical devices and the agency's other regulatory mandates. However, the above-cited regulations, among others, control device labels or labeling by making any of the following actions "misbranding" of any device:

- Making any "false or misleading representations" [21 CFR 801.6]
- Creating any "impression of official approval because of registration or possession of a registration number" [21 CFR 807.39] or
- Creating any impression of official approval because of complying with premarket notification regulations" [21 CFR 807.97]

Remember!

Sales and marketing department staff must be made aware of these and other regulatory requirements. Most firms require that all advertising and promotional literature must include an in-house or third-party expert "regulatory review" to ensure compliance.

Misbranding actions can cause FDA to declare a device "misbranded" and force a recall or take other administrative actions against identified firms.

Don't forget!   Misbranding is a term frequently used by FDA to describe labeling noncompliance and may include:

- False or misleading labeling
- Packaging does not bear a label containing the name and place of business of the manufacturer and an accurate statement of the quantity of contents.
- Words, statements, or other required information not prominent on the labeling or not stated clearly.

- Label does not contain adequate directions for use. These include warnings against use in certain pathological conditions; warnings against use by children where its use may be dangerous to health; and warnings against unsafe dosage, methods, duration of administration or application unless exempt as unnecessary to protect the public health.
- The device's established name (if it has one), name in an official compendium, or including common or usual name is not printed prominently in type at least half as large as used for any proprietary name
- The device is subject to a performance standard and does not bear the labeling requirements prescribed in that standard.
- The device is commercially distributed without FDA concurrence on a 510(k) premarket notification submission.

Something   *False* or *misleading labeling* are two other terms frequently used by FDA to
to note!   describe labeling noncompliance "in any particular" and may include:

- Incorrect, inadequate, or incomplete identification
- Unsubstantiated claims of therapeutic value
- Inaccuracies concerning condition, state, treatment, size, shape, or style
- Substitution of parts or material

- Subjective or unsubstantiated quality or performance claims
- Use of the prefix U.S. or other similar indication suggesting government or agency approval or endorsement of the product

---

Required   FDA requires that labeling provide "adequate directions for use," meaning
procedure(s),   "directions under which the layman can use a device safely and for the purpose
document(s),   for which it is intended."
and record(s)   Adequate directions for medical device use require:

- Statement of all conditions, purposes, or uses for which the device is intended. This includes conditions, purposes, or uses for which it is prescribed, recommended, or suggested in its oral, written, printed, or graphic advertising. This statement also includes conditions, purposes, or uses for which the device is commonly used. These statements should not refer to conditions, uses, or purposes for which the device can be used safely only under the supervision of a practitioner licensed by law; those conditions, uses, and purposes may be referred to only in advertisements directed to a licensed practitioner.
- Frequency of administration or application
- Duration of administration or application
- Time of administration or application in relation to meals, onset of symptoms, or other time factors
- Preparation for use, adjustment of temperature, or other manipulation or process

FDA has identified the following sections to be included in medical device labeling and are typically provided with any premarket submission:

Section of Information for Prescribers	Device Directions for use Known to an Ordinary Individual	Device with Minimal Labeling	Clinical Data Not the Basis of Device Marketing	Clinical Data Supporting Device Marketing
Essential Prescribing Information	-	as needed	yes	yes
1. Brief device description	Name	yes	yes	yes
2. Intended use / indications	-	yes	yes	yes
3. Contraindications	-	if any	yes	yes
4. Warnings	-	-	yes	yes
5. Precautions	-	-	yes	yes
6. Adverse events	-	-	yes	yes
7. Clinical studies	-	-	-	yes
8. Individualization of treatment	-	-	as needed	yes
9. Patient counseling information	-	as needed	as needed	as needed
10. Conformance to standards	-	if any	yes	yes
11. How supplied	-	as needed	as needed	as needed
12. Operator's manual	-		as needed	as needed
13. Patient's manual	-	-	as needed	as needed
14. References	-	-	as needed	as needed

*Table redrawn from FDA's **Quality Systems Regulation Manual, A Small Entity Compliance Guide for Medical Device Manufacturers**, 1st Edition, 1997.*

Devices marketed with approved premarket approvals (PMAs) will require completion of all 14 sections. Devices with "Clinical Data Are Not the Basis of Device Marketing" may omit section 7. Other sections' inclusion or exclusion should be reflective of each device's safety, effectiveness, and performance characteristics.

Don't forget!

FDA proposes that manufacturers avoid including any disclaimer regarding the safety and effectiveness of the device for its indicated or intended use. The agency requests that labeling be balanced to "include an objective and accurate representation of the clinical experience with the device whereby the practitioner and patient are made aware not to expect a completely safe and effective outcome with the use of the device in all cases." All of the above sections of labeling should reflect this balance.

Remember!

It must be emphasized that FDA medical device labeling regulations are potential sources of major noncompliance actions, and this labeling discussion identifies only basic regulatory background. Not discussed in this training material are labeling activities associated with prescription devices, sterile devices, and labeling design and transfer. Do not assume that understanding this basic information will prepare anyone to successfully create, edit, finalize, and appropriately implement medical device labeling to FDA compliance.

SUBPART K–LABELING AND PACKAGING CONTROL

LABELING CONTROL § 820.120

**What the
regulation states**

§ 820.120

Each manufacturer shall establish and maintain procedures to control labeling activities.

§ 820.120 Discussion

Don't forget!

FDA requires device manufacturers to fully control all labeling activities. That means that labeling, from concept to shipment, must be controlled by designated individuals. FDA's goal with these activities is to ensure that users and patients are accurately and completely informed about each device's intended uses, identity, warnings, and any contraindications.

**Something
to note!**

Labels should be scrutinized to ensure they accurately contain the following:

- Expiration date
- Control number (when required)
- Storage instructions
- Handling instructions
- Any additional processing instructions

**Required
procedure(s),
document(s),
and record(s)**

Labeling specifications of the content and physical design parameters are part of the device master record (DMR), while control activity such as proofreading, review, approval, and testing of labels and labeling is included in design history file (DHF) documentation.

The table provided in Figure 14.1, page 165, summarizes the "Typical Sequence of the Control of Labels." To ensure control by designated individuals, all of the activities identified on this checklist should be documented with written procedures and associated forms, tags, and appropriate checklists.

**What the
regulation states**

§ 820.120 (a)

(a) *Label integrity.* Labels shall be printed and applied so as to remain legible and affixed during the customary conditions of processing, storage, handling, distribution, and where appropriate use.

Label Phase	QS Regulation Section	Control Activity
1. Design	820.30, 820.120 & 820.130	Meets needs of user and intended use. Text review. Quality of mounting such as rivets, adhesives, etc. Quality of ink, anodize, etc. Content per 21 CFR 801 and 809, company claims and standards.
2. Verification/ validation	820.120, 820.75 & 820.30	Simulated or actual processing such as sterilization, shipping tests, label affixing, etc. Saline, alcohol, and coffee spill tests?
3. Changes	820.30 & 820.75	Establish and maintain approval procedures.
4. Documentation	820.30, 820.181 & 820.120(e)	Approve, date, and change control label drawings. A key label shall contain the control number of the finished device either on or accompanying device.
5. Procurement	820.120(b), 820.180	Proofread before release to inventory stock. Record signature of proofreader and date.
6. Storage	820.120(c) & (d)	Store labels to prevent mix-ups. Restrict access to authorized persons.
7. Separate operations	820.120(d)	Separate multiple operations to prevent mix-ups.
8. Area inspection	820.120(d)	Before beginning labeling operations, designee to inspect area and remove extraneous devices and labels.
9. Issuance	820.120(b), 820.120(e) & 820.65	Examine for identity and, where appropriate, expiration date and control number. Record date and person examining labels.
10. File Sample	820.184(e)	Copy of primary ID label shall be in the device history record.
11. Inspection	820.80(d), 820.86 & 820.80(e)	Inspect finished device per written procedure. Designee shall check all acceptance records test results and see that requirements are met and records are present and complete.

Table redrawn from FDA's **Quality Systems Regulation Manual, A Small Entity Compliance Guide for Medical Device Manufacturers,** 1st Edition, 1997.

Figure 14.1.   Typical Sequence of the Control of Labels

§ 820.120 (a) Discussion

Required procedure(s), document(s), and record(s)

Labeling must be produced in a manner that ensures it remains legible, and labels must remain attached during normal processing, storage, handling, distribution, and use. That means that labels must be tested to ensure and validate that they will meet that regulatory requirement from initial processing to use. This testing should be documented, reviewed, and approved and becomes part of the DHF.

Labeling integrity must address issues of appropriate paper, plastic, sizes, inks, coatings, etching, adhesives, fasteners, machinery, and validation.

What the regulation states

§ 820.120 (b)

(b) *Labeling inspection.* Labeling shall not be released for storage or use until a designated individual(s) has examined the labeling for accuracy including, where applicable, the correct expiration date, control number, storage instructions, handling instructions, and any additional processing instructions. The release, including the date and signature of the individual(s) performing the examination, shall be documented in the DHR.

§ 820.120 (b) Discussion

Inspection activities should be documented with one or more forms or tags and a checklist to ensure compliance with FDA expectations.

What the regulation states

§ 820.120 (c)

(c) *Labeling storage.* Each manufacturer shall store labeling in a manner that provides proper identification and is designed to prevent mix-ups.

§ 820.120 (c) Discussion

Storage activities should be documented with one or more forms, tags, and a checklist to ensure compliance with FDA expectations.

What the regulation states

§ 820.120 (d)

(d) *Labeling operations.* Each manufacturer shall control labeling and packaging operations to prevent labeling mix-ups. The label and labeling used for each production unit, lot, or batch shall be documented in the DHR.

§ 820.120 (d) Discussion

Required procedure(s), document(s), and record(s)

Labeling operations activities should be documented with forms and checklists to ensure compliance with FDA expectations.

What the regulation states

§ 820.120 (e)

(e) *Control number.* Where a control number is required by § 820.65, that control number shall be on or shall accompany the device through distribution.

§ 820.120 (e) Discussion

Control numbers are required on some devices to facilitate tracing and must be on or accompany the finished device through distribution.

Required procedure(s), document(s), and record(s)

FDA expects control of labeling activities. This means that there should be procedures and/or work instructions that ensure that labeling operations are controlled to prevent labeling mix-ups. The procedures and/or work instructions should be sufficiently detailed to identify all the labeling associated with each device or device family, identify storage requirements, labeling operations, and control number requirement. Label and labeling use with each device are documented for the DHR. Written records should document that labels and labeling are designed to ensure they remain legible and affixed during normal use. Records must also document that labels and labeling were examined, approved for accuracy, and released by designated individuals. When complaints or returns identify problems with labels or labeling materials, investigations should document any appropriate corrective and preventive actions.

What the FDA Investigator wants to see during an inspection

FDA Investigators expect that manufacturers will provide procedural documentation and records that clearly demonstrate that the firm's labeling operations are in a state of control. They will check that these procedures and records ensure:

- Label legibility.
- Release from storage only after accuracy examination by designated individuals.
- Firm's examination includes:
  — Correct expiration date
  — Correct control number (when required)
  — Storage instruction
  — Handling instructions
  — Any added processing instructions needed
- Release is documented in DHR with date and signatures.
- Labels are stored to ensure proper identification and prevent mix-ups.
- Labeling operations are controlled to prevent mix-ups.
- Label and labeling for each production unit, lot, or batch are documented in DHR.
- Whenever a control number is required, that number is on or accompanies the device.
- Labeling for devices labeled as sterile will be validated and that documentation reviewed and approved.

PACKAGING

Definitions

Test plan is a step-by-step plan to be followed during the verification or validation of a product or process.

SUBPART K–LABELING AND PACKAGING CONTROL

Packaging Control

What the
regulation states

§ 820.130

Each manufacturer shall ensure that device packaging and shipping containers are designed and constructed to protect the device from alteration or damage during the customary conditions of processing, storage, handling, and distribution.

§ 820.130–Packaging Discussion

FDA oversight requires manufacturers to ensure that device packaging and shipping containers are designed to protect each device from "alteration or damage" during "customary conditions of processing, storage, handling, and distribution."

Required
procedure(s),
document(s),
and record(s)

This means that manufacturers should have identified a specification for appropriate packaging and shipping containers during the design control process. See Chapter 4 Design Controls. Appropriate packaging design typically requires packaging expertise to consider each device's end use; ranges of temperature and moisture expected; device size, shape, and composition; adhesives; and local, regional, national and international shipping criteria, among others.

Additionally, manufacturers should create and execute a test plan to verify that the packaging and shipping specifications meet requirements. The test plan should include actual shipment of the device in the packaging and shipping containers. That documentation should be reviewed and approved prior to final acceptance of the finished medical device.

Control of packaging activities means that there should be procedures and/or work instructions that ensure that packaging operations are controlled to prevent packaging mix-ups. The work instructions should be sufficiently detailed to identify all the packaging associated with each device or device family. Written records should document that the packaging and shipping container's design and construction protect devices from alteration and damage during their normal use. When complaints or returns identify problems with packaging and shipping materials, investigations should document any appropriate corrective and preventive actions.

What the FDA
Investigator
wants to see
during an
inspection

FDA expects control of packaging operations. This means that there should be procedures and/or work instructions that ensure that packaging operations are controlled and packaging is designed to protect each device from alteration or damage during its customary conditions of processing, handling, storage, and distribution.

Investigators will review packaging operations to ensure that:

- Packaging operations are controlled to prevent mix-ups.
- Packaging and shipping containers are designed and constructed to protect the device from alteration or damage.
- If there is a sterilization requirement, validation includes packaging and shipping conditions.
- Review of complaints and returns to assess packaging and shipping operations is implemented.

15

Handling, Storage, and Distribution

INTRODUCTION

This chapter of **Mastering and Managing the FDA Maze: Medical Device Overview Training and Management Desk Reference** discusses FDA oversight of medical device handling, storage and distribution of medical devices.

SCOPE

The goal of this chapter is to provide an overview of FDA regulations on handling, storage, and distribution of medical devices. Significant detail has been omitted, and further training to ensure proficiency and understanding to the level required for FDA compliance will be needed.

Assuming that a firm can provide appropriate design, manufacturing, approvals, labeling, and packaging controls for a device, unless appropriate handling, storage, and distribution are implemented, there will be an unreasonable risk that the device will not be distributed in a manner that meets FDA expectations.

To ensure that finished devices are suitable for release and distribution, each step in the handling, storage, and distribution of devices must fulfill its quality system role.

This discussion is *basic.* Individuals will require significant additional study and implementation before they can be assured that the manufacturing controls they establish and maintain meet FDA expectations. The definitions, unless followed by an asterisk, are quoted from FDA's Quality System Regulations.

HANDLING

SUBPART L—HANDLING

Definitions   *Quality System Inspection Technique* (QSIT) is FDA's latest inspection strategy. QSIT involves what FDA calls "top-down" inspections of the four major subsystems of each device manufacturer's quality system, that is, their management controls, design controls, corrective and preventive actions, and production and process controls.*

Specification means any requirement with which a product, process, service, or other activity must conform.

Handling Regulation—§ 820.140

What the regulation states

§ 820.140

Each manufacturer shall establish and maintain procedures to ensure that mix-ups, damage, deterioration, contamination, or other adverse effects to product do not occur during handling.

§ 820.140 Discussion

FDA oversight requires manufacturers to ensure that device packaging and shipping containers are designed to protect each device from "alteration or damage" during all phases of "handling."

Required procedure(s), document(s), and record(s)

This means that manufacturers should have identified a specification for appropriate packaging and shipping containers during the design control process. See Chapter 4 Design Controls. Appropriate packaging design typically requires packaging expertise to consider (1) ranges of temperature and moisture expected; (2) device size, shape, and composition; (3) adhesives; and (4) local, regional, national, and international shipping criteria, among others, to ensure problems or failures, including contamination associated with handling, do not occur.

Remember!

Additionally, manufacturers should create and execute a test plan to verify that the packaging and shipping specifications meet handling requirements. The test plan should include actual shipment of the device in the packaging and shipping containers. That documentation should be reviewed and approved prior to final acceptance of the finished medical device.

What the FDA Investigator wants to see during an inspection

Under the new QSIT inspectional strategy, FDA Investigators can be expected to focus on handling issues during their investigation of both a firm's corrective and preventive action subsystem and its production and process controls subsystem. See Chapter 8 Production and Process Controls and Chapter 11 Corrective and Preventive Action.

FDA Investigators will review procedures related to handling each firm's medical devices or, if appropriate, review any procedure written for specific handling requirements of an individual device. They will assess those procedures' ability to ensure that the devices associated with them are protected from mixups, damage, deterioration and contamination or any other adverse effects.

For example, Investigators may inspect areas identified and designed to provide electrostatic discharge (ESD) protection to a device's components, a finished device, or warehouse areas controlled by special storage conditions, shelving, or cabinets.

Investigators will closely review records of products that deteriorate over time, making sure that any special handling specifications required by the manufacture are followed and documented.

Warehouse cleanliness is also evaluated by Investigators to ensure that reasonable in-process product and finished product are handled in a manner appropriate with their packaging, handling, and storage requirements.

STORAGE

SUBPART L–STORAGE

Definitions

Device history record (DHR) means a compilation of records containing the production history of a finished device.

Finished device means any device or accessory to any device that is suitable for use or capable of functioning, whether or not it is packaged, labeled, or sterilized.

Quality System Inspection Technique (QSIT) is FDA's latest inspection strategy. QSIT involves what FDA calls "top-down" inspections of the four major subsystems of each device manufacturer's quality system, that is, their management controls, design controls, corrective and preventive actions, and production and process controls.*

§ 820.150

What the regulation states

§ 820.150 (a)

(a) Each manufacturer shall establish and maintain procedures for the control of storage areas and stock rooms for product to prevent mix-ups, damage, deterioration, contamination, or other adverse effects pending use or distribution and to ensure that no obsolete, rejected, or deteriorated product is used or distributed. When the quality of product deteriorates over time, it shall be stored in a manner to facilitate proper stock rotation, and its condition shall be assessed as appropriate.

§ 820.150 (a) Discussion

Required procedure(s), document(s), and record(s)

FDA expects to find that medical device manufacturers have written procedures that control access to storage areas and stock rooms. Control measures are to ensure there are no mix-ups, damage, deterioration, contamination, or other adverse effects as well as to ensure that no obsolete, rejected, or deteriorated manufacturing materials are used or distributed.

Remember!

For any manufacturing material that deteriorates over time, FDA also expects that stock rotation strategies and systems are used and that such manufacturing material is periodically assessed at defined intervals.

What the regulation states

§ 820.150 (b)

(b) Each manufacturer shall establish and maintain procedures that describe the methods for authorizing receipt from and dispatch to storage areas and stock rooms.

§ 820.150 (b) Discussion

Required procedure(s), document(s), and record(s)

Manufacturing material receipt and issuance must be controlled by written procedures that identify the methods for authorizing the receipt and issuance. Mechanisms to control manufacturing materials will require limiting access and identifying the individuals with authorized access.

Finally, the procedures must identify the steps to be followed by the authorized individuals to properly remove manufacturing material from any storage area.

What the FDA Investigator will expect to see during an inspection

Under the new QSIT inspectional strategy, FDA Investigators can be expected to focus on handling issues during their investigation of both a firm's corrective and preventive action subsystem and production and process controls subsystem. See Chapter 8 Production and Process Controls and Chapter 11 Corrective and Preventive Action.

FDA Investigators will review procedures related to storing each firm's medical devices or, if appropriate, review any procedure written for specific storing requirements of an individual device. They will assess those procedures' ability to ensure that the devices associated with them are protected from mix-ups, damage, deterioration, and contamination or any other adverse effects.

For example, Investigators may inspect areas identified and designed to provide electrostatic discharge (ESD) protection to a device's components, a finished device, or warehouse areas controlled by special storage conditions, shelving, or cabinets.

Investigators will closely review records of products that deteriorate over time, making sure that those requiring special storage are stored as the manufacturer specifies. Warehouse cleanliness is also evaluated by Investigators to ensure that reasonable in-process product and finished product are stored in a manner appropriate with their packaging, handling and storage requirements.

DISTRIBUTION

Definitions

Device history record (DHR) means a compilation of records containing the production history of a finished device.

Finished device means any device or accessory to any device that is suitable for use or capable of functioning, whether or not it is packaged, labeled, or sterilized.

Quality System Inspection Technique (QSIT) is FDA's latest inspection strategy. QSIT involves what FDA calls "top-down" inspections of the four major subsystems of each device manufacturer's quality system, that is, their management controls, design controls, corrective and preventive actions, and production and process controls.*

<u>SUBPART L—DISTRIBUTION</u>

Distribution—§ 820.160

What the regulation states

§ 820.160

(a) Each manufacturer shall establish and maintain procedures for control and distribution of finished devices to ensure that only those devices approved for release are distributed and that purchase orders are reviewed to ensure that ambiguities and errors are resolved before devices are released for distribution. Where a device's fitness for use or quality deteriorates over time, the procedures shall ensure that expired devices or devices deteriorated beyond acceptable fitness for use are not distributed.

§ 820.160 (a) Discussion

Remember!

FDA fully expects that purchase orders are reviewed to resolve "ambiguities and errors" and that only approved finished devices are released for distribution after such review. Further, those finished devices that have expiration dates or deteriorate and become unfit must be controlled by written procedures.

What the regulation states

§ 820.160 (b)

(b) Each manufacturer shall maintain distribution records which include or refer to the location of:

(1) The name and address of the initial consignee;
(2) The identification and quantity of devices shipped;
(3) The date shipped; and
(4) Any control number(s) used.

§ 820.160 (b) Discussion

Required procedure(s), document(s), and record(s)

Distribution records that identify the name and address of the initial consignee, what and how many were shipped, the shipping dates, and any control numbers used must be maintained. Those distribution records can be the manufacturer's normal business records but must be kept at the same location as the DHR. Electronically retrievable records are acceptable, assuming they can be retrieved at the location of the DHR.

What the FDA Investigator wants to see during an inspection

Under the new QSIT inspectional strategy, FDA Investigators can be expected to focus on distribution issues during their investigation of both a firm's corrective and preventive action subsystem and production and process controls subsystem. See Chapter 8 Production and Process Controls and Chapter 11 Corrective and Preventive Action.

FDA Investigators will review procedures related to the distribution of each firm's medical devices or, if appropriate, review any procedure written for specific distribution requirements of an individual device. They will assess those procedures' ability to ensure that the devices associated with them are protected from mix-ups, damage, deterioration, and contamination or any other adverse effects.

They will make sure these procedures and their associated records contain or make reference to the location of:

- Name and address of the initial consignee
- Identification and quantity of devices shipped
- Date shipped
- Any control numbers used.

Additionally, Investigators will assess distribution procedures to ensure that they are being followed and that they prohibit the use or distribution of obsolete, rejected, or deteriorated in-process products or finished devices. They expect to find that these procedures describe how product will be authorized as received from and dispatched to storage areas, stock rooms, or any special storage areas.

Investigators are instructed to review distribution records and cross-reference them to final inspection, release and quarantine records and verify that no obsolete, rejected, or deteriorated in-process or finished device was used or distributed.

Investigators will closely review records of products that deteriorate over time. They will make sure that only those products approved for release are distributed.

16

Installation and Servicing

INTRODUCTION

This chapter of **Managing and Mastering the FDA Maze: Medical Device Overview Training and Management Desk Reference** discusses FDA oversight of medical device installation and servicing.

SCOPE

The goal of this chapter is to provide an overview of FDA installation and servicing regulations for medical device manufacturers. Significant detail has been omitted, and further training to ensure proficiency and understanding to the level required for FDA compliance will be needed.

Assuming that a firm can provide appropriate design and manufacturing controls to a device, unless appropriate installation and service controls are implemented, there will be an unreasonable risk that the device will fail to meet specifications and will not be installed and supported in a manner that meets FDA expectations.

To ensure that finished devices are suitable for release and distribution, each step in the installation and service support must fulfill its quality system role.

It should be emphasized that this discussion is *basic*. Individuals will require significant additional study and implementation before they can be assured that the manufacturing controls they establish and maintain meet FDA expectations. The definitions, unless followed by an asterisk, are quoted from FDA's Quality System Regulations.

INSTALLATION

SUBPART L—INSTALLATION § 820.170

Definitions

Quality System Inspection Technique (QSIT) is FDA's latest inspection strategy. QSIT involves what FDA calls "top-down" inspections of the four major subsystems of each device manufacturer's quality system, that is, their management controls, design controls, corrective and preventive actions, and production and process controls.*

Specification means any requirement with which a product, process, service, or other activity must conform.

What the regulation states

§820.170 (a)

(a) Each manufacturer of a device requiring installation shall establish and maintain adequate installation and inspection instructions, and where appropriate test procedures. Instructions and procedures shall include directions for ensuring proper installation so that the device will perform as intended after installation. The manufacturer shall distribute the instructions and procedures with the device or otherwise make them available to the person(s) installing the device.

§ 820.170 (a) Discussion

FDA's goal with respect to installation regulations is to ensure that installation is correctly performed and verified to manufacturer's specifications and that installation information is collected and analyzed to aid in the correction of any device design, manufacturing, labeling, or packaging problems.

Required procedure(s), document(s), and record(s)

For devices that require installation or reinstallation, FDA requires manufacturers to establish and maintain written procedures and instructions controlling the installation activities and verifying that the installation meets specifications. Often with software upgrades, "bug" fixes, or enhancements, a partial or complete reinstallation is required.

Remember!

Manufacturers must specify which, if any, of their devices require manufacturer-controlled installation and any required reinstallation activity. If manufacturer-controlled installation is required, manufacturers may charge a department or group with that activity or may contract with a third party to provide required installation or reinstallation.

Any third-party installation or reinstallation activity must be controlled and in conformance with § 820.50 Purchasing regulations. See Chapter 6 Purchasing Controls.

Don't forget!

Installation regulations may link back to § 820.30 (b), Design and Development Planning, which requires manufacturers to identify and describe interfaces with individuals, groups, or activities that provide or result in input to the design and development process.

What the regulation states

§ 820.170 (b)

(b) The person installing the device shall ensure that the installation, inspection, and any required testing are performed in accordance with the manufacturer's instructions and procedures and shall document the inspection and any test results to demonstrate proper installation.

§ 820.170 (b) Discussion

Required procedure(s), document(s), and record(s)

FDA requires that installation records establish that each device's required installation or reinstallation was performed according to manufacturer's instructions and procedures and verified, with test results when appropriate, to document proper installation. When a third party performs any required installation, the manufacturer must implement control procedures that ensure proper installation or reinstallation.

These records should be routinely reviewed and assessed to ensure proper installation, to identify any apparent nonconformances, and to provide any appropriate feedback with an interface to design control and design change activities. If appropriate, statistical methodologies should be implemented to assist in the review of installation activities.

The review of installation records should result in periodic reports to appropriate individuals and management with the findings of those records detailing their analysis for nonconforming product or other quality problems, any statistical data obtained, and any corrective or preventive actions recommended or made.

What the FDA Investigator wants to see during an inspection

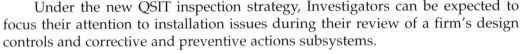

Under the new QSIT inspection strategy, Investigators can be expected to focus their attention to installation issues during their review of a firm's design controls and corrective and preventive actions subsystems.

FDA Investigators will review written installation procedures to ensure that they describe the installation and inspection instructions, and, whenever appropriate, any testing procedures. They will assess the instructions to ensure that they are sufficient to ensure proper installation and, subsequently, each device's ability to perform as intended.

Investigators will review service records, checking to see if additional service activity was required immediately after installation to correct failures or problems during installation.

Finally, Investigators will ensure that personnel who are installing devices document their inspection and any test results demonstrating proper installation in accordance with the manufacturer's written instructions and procedures.

SERVICING

Definitions

End of life means an established time-to-failure period, determined by the original device manufacturer, based upon reliability data and analysis to characterize nonrepairable product.*

Quality System Inspection Technique (QSIT) is FDA's latest inspection strategy. QSIT involves what FDA calls "top-down" inspections of the four major subsystems of each device manufacturer's quality system, that is, their management controls, design controls, corrective and preventive actions, and production and process controls.*

Servicing means maintenance or repair of a finished device after distribution for purposes of returning it to its safety and performance specifications established by the original finished device manufacturer and to meet its original intended use, prior to the device's established end of life or before it is considered to be nonrepairable.*

Subpart N–Servicing § 820.200

What the regulation states

§ 820.200 (a)

(a) Where servicing is a specified requirement, each manufacturer shall establish and maintain instructions and procedures for performing and verifying that the servicing meets the specified requirements.

§ 820. 200 (a) Discussion

Something to note!

FDA's goal with respect to servicing regulations is to ensure that servicing is correctly performed and verified to manufacturer's specifications (the intended use of the device) and that service information is collected and analyzed to aid in the correction of any device design, manufacturing, labeling, or packaging problems.

Required procedure(s), document(s), and record(s)

For those devices that require servicing, FDA requires manufacturers to establish and maintain written procedures and instructions controlling the service activities and verifying that the servicing meets specifications.

Manufacturers must specify which, if any, of their devices require manufacturer-controlled servicing. If manufacturer-controlled servicing is required, manufacturers may charge a department or group with that activity or may contract with a third party to provide required servicing. Some manufacturer's service personnel are charged with installation and/or reinstallation activities.

Any third-party service activity must be controlled and in conformance with § 820.50 Purchasing regulations. See Chapter 6 Purchasing Controls.

Remember!

Servicing regulations link back to § 820.30 (b) Design and Development Planning, which requires manufacturers to identify and describe interfaces with individuals, groups, or activities that provide or result in input to the design and development process.

What the regulation states

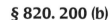

§ 820. 200 (b)

(b) Each manufacturer shall analyze service reports with appropriate statistical methodology in accordance with § 820.100.

§ 820. 200 (b) Discussion

Don't forget!

FDA requires manufacturers who identify a manufacturer-supplied service activity to analyzed service reports, among other records and "to identify existing and potential causes of nonconforming product or other quality problems." Manufacturers are expected to identify appropriate statistical methods to be used to detect recurring quality problems.

In many cases, reasonably detailed classifications of service activities and their root causes can provide the capability to count service classifications and their root causes, providing firms with one measure of required statistical analysis. In other cases, more sophisticated statistical analysis will be required to identify problems with specific design elements, manufacturing materials and components, manufacturing equipment, production employees, storage conditions, environmental conditions, packaging or shipping activities, and even service personnel.

Required procedure(s), document(s), and record(s)

Any manufacturer should implement forms documenting the information required in § 820.200 (d), below, and any other appropriate information, providing required service. These forms must be routinely reviewed and assessed for compliance with these servicing regulations. Reports should be made and distributed to appropriate staff and management, detailing (1) their analysis for nonconforming product or other quality problems, (2) any Medical Device Reportable event, (3) any statistical data obtained, and (4) any corrective or preventive actions recommended or made. See Chapter 12 Statistical Techniques.

What the regulation states

§ 820. 200 (c)

(c) Each manufacturer who receives a service report that represents an event which must be reported to FDA under part 803 or 804 of this chapter shall automatically consider the report a complaint and shall process it in accordance with the requirements of § 820.198.

§ 820. 200 (c) Discussion

Required procedure(s), document(s), and record(s)

FDA's expectation is that any Medical Device Report failure event from any source must be reported as required by § 803 or § 804 of the regulations. See Chapter 19 Medical Device Reporting. The review of service reports should indicate that an assessment was made to determine if any event could be identified as a Medical Device Report failure. This review might be noted on the Service Manager's copy of each report and that manager's assessment required for all or certain types of reports.

What the regulation states

§ 820. 200 (d)

(d) Service reports shall be documented and shall include:

(1) The name of the device serviced;
(2) Any device identification(s) and control number(s) used;
(3) The date of service;
(4) The individual(s) servicing the device;
(5) The service performed; and
(6) The test and inspection data.

§ 820. 200 (d) Discussion

***Required
procedure(s),
document(s),
and record(s)***

Manufacturers identifying a servicing requirement they provide are required to document service reports that detail the following:

- Device name
- Device ID and any control numbers
- Date of service
- Service personnel
- Service activity
- Test and inspection data.

***What the FDA
Investigator
wants to see
during an
inspection***

Under FDA's new QSIT inspection strategy, firms should expect FDA Investigators to focus their review of servicing during corrective and preventive actions subsystem and follow-up that leads them back to the firm's design control and production and process controls subsystems for issues surrounding servicing specifications and production failures. Some attention may be focused on servicing during management controls subsystem review if device failure service records were not reviewed appropriately by management.

FDA Investigators will review manufacturer's procedures to ensure that, when appropriate, there are written service procedures.

They will review service records to ensure that service personnel are performing their service tasks in accordance with the manufacturer's procedures and regulatory requirements. This review will also include an assessment of any service problems that should also have been documented as a complaint and any that should have been investigated as a Medical Device Reporting (MDR) reportable event. Probable MDR events must have been considered complaints and fully investigated, including a determination of whether the event requires reporting to FDA.

FDA will also review the manufacturer's records associated with the analysis of service records by appropriate statistical methods.

Failures to implement cross-checks of service records for complaints, possible MDR events, and statistical analysis will probably lead to FDA Form 483 observations and may result in a Warning Letter.

17

Records–General Requirements, Device History Record (DHR), and Quality System Record (QSR)

INTRODUCTION

This chapter of **Mastering and Managing the FDA Maze: Medical Device Overview Training and Management Desk Reference** discusses FDA oversight of the following records: general requirements, device history records (DHR), and the quality system records.

SCOPE

The goal of this chapter is to provide an overview of FDA regulations related to the following records: general requirements, the device history records (DHR), and quality system records for medical device manufacturers. Significant detail has been omitted, and further training to ensure proficiency and understanding to the level required for FDA compliance will be needed.

Assuming that a firm can provide appropriate design and manufacturing controls to a device, unless appropriate document and record controls are implemented, there will be an unreasonable risk that the device will fail to meet specifications, will not be properly distributed or supported, or will fail in some other in a manner to meet FDA expectations.

To ensure that finished devices are suitable for release and distribution, all record requirements must fulfill their quality system role.

It should be emphasized that this discussion is *basic*. Individuals will require significant additional study and implementation before they can be assured that the manufacturing controls they establish and maintain meet FDA expectations. The definitions, unless followed by an asterisk, are quoted from FDA's Quality System Regulations.

DEVICE HISTORY RECORD

Definitions   *Device history record* (DHR) means a compilation of records containing the complete production history of a finished device.

Documentation means any records, written, electronic, or automated that provide information describing, defining, specifying, reporting, certifying, or auditing any manufacturer's FDA regulatory activities, requirements, verifications, or validations.*

Label is a display of written, printed or graphic matter upon the immediate container of any article. [Act, section 201(k).]*

Labeling includes all labels and other written, printed or graphic matter (1) upon any article or any of its containers or wrappers, or (2) accompanying such article. [Act, section 201(m).]*

Quality system means the organizational structure, responsibilities, procedures, processes, and resources for implementing quality management.

Quality System Inspection Technique (QSIT) is FDA's latest inspection strategy. QSIT involves what FDA calls "top-down" inspections of the four major subsystems of each device manufacturer's quality system, that is, their management controls, design controls, corrective and preventive actions, and production and process controls.*

Record means any written, electronic, or automated document, including books, manuals, papers, photographs, and machine-readable materials, which contain specifications, procedures, work instructions, protocols, standards, methods, plans, files, notes, reviews, analyses, corrections or changes, checklists, reports, training materials, or instructions, regardless of their physical form or characteristics, made during the design, development, change, testing, manufacture, review, approval, labeling, packaging, promotion, shipment, distribution, service, or support of any regulated medical device.*

SUBPART M–GENERAL REQUIREMENTS

§ 820.180 General Requirements

What the regulation states

§ 820.180

All records required by this part shall be maintained at the manufacturing establishment or other location that is reasonably accessible to responsible officials of the manufacturer and to employees of FDA designated to perform inspections. Such records, including those not stored at the inspected establishment, shall be made readily available for review and copying by FDA employee(s). Such records shall be legible and shall be stored to minimize deterioration and to prevent loss. Those records stored in automated data processing systems shall be backed up.

§ 820.180 General Requirements Discussion

The Quality System Regulations, 21 CFR 820, created new record-keeping requirements for medical device manufacturers while at the same time expanding the scope of the records required under the previous good manufacturing practice regulations.

Remember!

FDA firmly believes that compliance with its record-keeping regulations will provide device manufacturers with a state of control and a level of accountability that provides significant assurance that in-process products and finished devices will conform to their specifications.

FDA requires that its mandated records be maintained at the manufacturer's establishment and any other appropriate location and that these records be "reasonably accessible" to responsible officials of both the manufacturer and employees of the FDA designated to perform inspections.

Typically, this means that these records must be available during the manufacturer's normal business hours. If the manufacturer is open for business only between 8 AM and 5 PM, those are the hours they must be available for Investigators. However, if the business operates 24 hours a day, five or seven days a week, Investigators could request access during those business hours. Records that are stored off-site should be retrievable within one or two working days.

FDA expects that all quality system records to be legible and stored in a manner that ensures their safekeeping, reasonable retrieval and anticipated use. Any records stored in any electronic system must be backed up, and FDA would expect that there are written procedures to manage electronic storage and back-up of records.

What the regulation states

§ 820.180 (a)

(a) *Confidentiality.* Records deemed confidential by the manufacturer may be marked to aid FDA in determining whether information may be disclosed under the public information regulation in part 20 of this chapter.

§ 820.180 (a) Discussion

FDA understands that many of the procedures, documents, and records associated with any device manufacturer contain confidential information. That information may be any of the following:

- Trade secrets
- Formulas

- Proprietary designs
- Proprietary algorithms
- Proprietary software
- Proprietary specifications
- Proprietary patient or test data
- Patient administrative data (that is, name, address, age, sex, and so on)

Something to note!   Under the Freedom of Information Act (FOIA or FOI), that is, part 20 of this chapter, FDA is charged with protecting such information from public disclosure. FDA welcomes manufacturer's assistance in marking such procedures, documents, and records as "confidential or proprietary—not for public disclosure" or some similar marking when appropriate.

However, manufacturers must use discretion when applying such markings; they should be used only when the information requires confidential or proprietary treatment. Blanket markings on all procedures, documents, or records will significantly dilute any confidential or proprietary claim.

What the regulation states

§ 820.180 (b)

(b) *Record retention period.* All records required by this part shall be retained for a period of time equivalent to the design and expected life of the device, but in no case less than 2 years from the date of release for commercial distribution by the manufacturer.

§ 820.180 (b) Discussion

All quality system records must be retained for a minimum of two years. Longer retention is required based on the design and expected life of each device.

Required procedure(s), document(s), and record(s)

Manufacturers should establish procedures and requirements regarding their retention of quality system records. This is particularly important as devices are dropped from manufacturing, distribution, and service. Manufacturers should consider retaining legal counsel to assist them in establishing these procedures and requirements. This will help ensure that they meet FDA requirements, business, and any appropriate state or federal legal requirements.

What the regulation states

§ 820.180 (c)

(c) *Exceptions.* This section does not apply to the reports required by § 820.20(c) Management review, § 820.22 Quality audits, and supplier audit reports used to meet the requirements of § 820.50(a) Evaluation of suppliers, contractors, and consultants, but does apply to procedures established under these provisions. Upon request of a designated employee of FDA, an employee in management with executive responsibility shall certify in writing that the management reviews and quality audits required under this part, and supplier audits where applicable, have been performed and documented, the dates on which they were performed, and that any required corrective action has been undertaken.

§ 820.180 (c) Discussion

Don't forget!

Although FDA's oversight of quality system records is broad, there are notable exceptions to the agency's access to and record-keeping requirement of records:

- Management review reports
- Quality audit reports
- Supplier audit reports, any supplier, contractor, or consultant

---

Required procedure(s), document(s), and record(s)

FDA can review any procedures or blank forms related to these activities, but unless there is some overriding judicial issue, the agency will not request access to these records.

The agency may request that the manufacturer's executive with quality system responsibility provide written certification that these reviews and audits have been performed, documented, their dates have been specified, and that any required corrective actions are or have been implemented. See Chapter 3 Quality System Requirements, Management Responsibilities, and Personnel and Chapter 20 Quality Audit.

What the FDA Investigator wants to see during an inspection

Under FDA's new QSIT inspection strategy, significant emphasis will be place on a firm's records through out the FDA Investigator's assessment of the firm's four subsystems: management control, design control, corrective and preventative actions and production and process controls.

FDA Investigators expect and will take any appropriate administrative and judicial steps necessary to gain access to the procedures, documents, and records the federal law and regulations afford the agency. That access includes the right to copy those records.

FDA Investigators understand that determinations of the "expected life of the device" may be made by a number of methods, including the following:

- Stability data
- Service records
- Marketing analysis
- Component manufacturer's claims

Investigators will expect stability studies are available to document any label expiration dates.

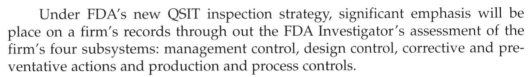

SUBPART M–DEVICE HISTORY RECORD (DHR)

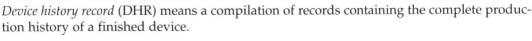

§ 820.184 Device History Record

Definitions

Device history record (DHR) means a compilation of records containing the complete production history of a finished device.

Documentation means any records, written, electronic, or automated that provide information describing, defining, specifying, reporting, certifying, or auditing any manufacturer's FDA regulatory activities, requirements, verifications, or validations.*

Label is a display of written, printed or graphic matter upon the immediate container of any article. [Act, section 201(k).]*

Labeling includes all labels and other written, printed or graphic matter (1) upon any article or any of its containers or wrappers, or (2) accompanying such article. [Act, section 201(m).]*

Quality system means the organizational structure, responsibilities, procedures, processes, and resources for implementing quality management.

Quality System Inspection Technique (QSIT) is FDA's latest inspection strategy. QSIT involves what FDA calls "top-down" inspections of the four major subsystems of each device manufacturer's quality system, that is, their management controls, design controls, corrective and preventive actions, and production and process controls.*

Record means any written, electronic, or automated document, including books, manuals, papers, photographs, and machine-readable materials that contain specifications, procedures, work instructions, protocols, standards, methods, plans, files, notes, reviews, analyses, corrections or changes, checklists, reports, training materials, or instructions, regardless of their physical form or characteristics, made during the design, development, change, testing, manufacture, review, approval, labeling, packaging, promotion, shipment, distribution, service, or support of any regulated medical device.*

What the regulation states

§ 820.184

Each manufacturer shall maintain device history records (DHR's). Each manufacturer shall establish and maintain procedures to ensure that DHR's for each batch, lot, or unit are maintained to demonstrate that the device is manufactured in accordance with the DMR and the requirements of this part.

§ 820.184 Discussion

Manufacturers must maintain a device history record (DHR) and establish and maintain DHR procedures that ensure that these records for "each batch, lot, or unit" are "maintained to demonstrate" that each device is manufactured according to its DMR and the Quality System Regulations. The DHR is a compilation of all of the manufacturing and testing processes of the DMR.

§ 820.184 (continued)

The DHR shall include, or refer to the location of, the following information:

What the regulation states

(a) The dates of manufacture;
(b) The quantity manufactured;
(c) The quantity released for distribution;
(d) The acceptance records which demonstrate the device is manufactured in accordance with the DMR;
(e) The primary identification label and labeling used for each production unit; and
(f) Any device identification(s) and control number(s) used.

§ 820.184 (a)–(f) Discussion

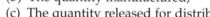
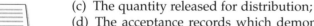

Required procedure(s), document(s), and record(s)

DHR documents must identify the manufacturing dates, quantity manufactured, and quantity released for distribution and must record the acceptance records that demonstrate each device's conformance with its DMR. Additionally, the primary identification label and labeling for each production unit and any device identification and/or control numbers used shall be included.

An efficient mechanism to control DHR compliance is to establish a checklist of all the manufacturing and testing process records or their location required in the DHR.

DHR Activities Requiring Identification of an Individual for Review

Regulatory Reference	Activity
820.70(g)	Equipment maintenance and inspection activities performed
820.72(b)	Calibration performed
820.80(d)	Release of finished devices
820.90(b)	Authorization to use nonconforming product
820.120(b)	Labeling inspection
820.160	Distribution

*Table recreated from FDA's **Quality Systems Regulation Manual, A Small Entity Compliance Guide for Medical Device Manufacturers,** 1st Edition, 1997.*

Remember!

Some of the information required in § 820.160 Distribution is duplicated in the DHR requirement. Many firms combine both requirements in a single file and file-referencing record location, identifying this file as an "Expanded DHR File" including the required distribution elements.

What the FDA Investigator wants to see during an inspection

Under the QSIT inspection strategy, FDA Investigators will expect to review a DHR for each finished device or family of finished devices. They will expect that these DHRs accurately reflect that all operations and processes described in the device master record (DMR) have been completed. Additionally, they will expect the DHR to contain or refers to the location of the following:

- Dates of manufacturing
- Quantity manufactured
- Quantity approved and released for distribution
- Any device identifications and required control numbers used
- The primary identification label and labeling used for each production unit
- The acceptance records documenting that the device is manufactured in accordance with the DMR

Investigators will expect to see DHR documentation that shows labels and labeling were examined prior to acceptance and actual use with finished devices.

Investigators understand that the DHRs may not be maintained at one location; however, they will expect that these records are maintained in a manner that allows them reasonable access to all appropriate individuals, including Investigators. They also will expect that the DHRs were reviewed and approved with signatures and dates prior to distribution of any finished devices.

QUALITY SYSTEM RECORD

SUBPART M—QUALITY SYSTEM RECORD

§ 820.186 Quality System Record

Definitions

Device history record (DHR) means a compilation of records containing the complete production history of a finished device.

Documentation means any records, written, electronic, or automated, that provide information describing, defining, specifying, reporting, certifying, or auditing any manufacturer's FDA regulatory activities, requirements, verifications, or validations.*

Label is a display of written, printed or graphic matter upon the immediate container of any article. [Act, section 201(k).]*

Labeling includes all labels and other written, printed or graphic matter (1) upon any article or any of its containers or wrappers, or (2) accompanying such article. [Act, section 201(m).]*

Quality system means the organizational structure, responsibilities, procedures, processes, and resources for implementing quality management.

Quality System Inspection Technique (QSIT) is FDA's latest inspection strategy. QSIT involves what FDA calls "top-down" inspections of the four major subsystems of each device manufacturer's quality system, that is, their management controls, design controls, corrective and preventive actions, and production and process controls.*

Record means any written, electronic, or automated document, including books, manuals, papers, photographs, and machine-readable materials, which contain specifications, procedures, work instructions, protocols, standards, methods, plans, files, notes, reviews, analyses, corrections or changes, checklists, reports, training materials, or instructions, regardless of their physical form or characteristics, made during the design, development, change, testing, manufacture, review, approval, labeling, packaging, promotion, shipment, distribution, service, or support of any regulated medical device.*

What the regulation states

§ 820.186

Each manufacturer shall maintain a quality system record (QSR). The QSR shall include, or refer to the location of, procedures and the documentation of activities required by this part that are not specific to a particular type of device(s), including, but not limited to, the records required by § 820.20. Each manufacturer shall ensure that the QSR is prepared and approved in accordance with § 820.40.

§ 820.186 Quality System Record Discussion

FDA identifies the quality system record (QSR) as the entirety of procedures that are required to operate a medical device establishment. The QSR is composed of the procedures that are often enterprisewide or certainly multidepartmental and not specific to any one device.

Required procedure(s), document(s), and record(s)

The QSR must include procedures and records required for compliance with § 820.20 Management Responsibility, including the quality policy, establishment organization, responsibility and authority, resources, management representative, management review, quality planning, and quality system procedures. FDA expects that the volume of these documents will increase as the size of the establishment increases. FDA identifies some typical QSR documents as follows:

- SOP creation and numbering procedures
- SOP deviation procedure
- Employee training procedures
- General design control procedures
- Drawing numbering system procedure
- Design review procedure
- Change control procedure
- Purchasing procedures
- Supplier assessment procedures
- Component inspection procedures
- Calibration policy
- Sterile water system maintenance
- Workmanship standards
- Label review procedure
- Insecticide—Pest removal procedures
- AC—Heating procedures
- Safety procedures
- Tool kit/use procedures
- Cleaning procedures
- Service policy
- Complaint handling procedure
- Return goods procedure
- Recall procedure
- Medical device reporting procedure

Typically, the original of each of these QSR documents is filed with a department or activity specified by management as having responsibility for maintaining all of these procedures or specific QSR procedures. Often firms post these procedures in SOP or QA manuals or electronically on an establishment-controlled intranet.

What the FDA Investigator wants to see during an inspection

Under the new QSIT inspection strategy, FDA Investigators will expect to see a quality system record that includes or makes reference to the location of all of the procedures and documents required by the QSR and are not specific to any one device. Of particular interest to Investigators are the following:

- Procedures and records related to management responsibility, exclusive of those records beyond their review, that is, management review reports
- Procedures for all phases of design control
- Procedures and records for complaints and Medical Device Reporting
- Procedures for preventive and corrective action
- Procedures and records for cleaning
- Procedures and records for maintenance activity

Investigators should also recognize that it is not significant in which record, DMR, or QSR a particular procedure, document, or record resides. What is most important is that the manufacturer has the procedure, document, or record and that it is readily available for their review.

18

Complaint Files

INTRODUCTION

This chapter of **Mastering and Managing the FDA Maze: Medical Device Overview Training and Management Desk Reference** discusses FDA oversight of device complaint files.

SCOPE

The goal of this chapter is to provide an overview of medical device compliance with FDA complaint regulations for device manufacturers. Significant detail has been omitted, and further training to ensure proficiency and understanding to the level required for FDA compliance will be needed.

Assuming that a firm can provide appropriate design and manufacturing controls to a device, unless appropriate complaint controls are implemented, there will be an unreasonable risk that the device will fail to meet specifications and are will not be distributed and supported in a manner that meets FDA expectations.

To ensure that finished devices are suitable for release and distribution, each step in the complaint process must fulfill its quality system role.

It should be emphasized that this discussion is *basic.* Individuals will require significant additional study and implementation before they can be assured that the manufacturing controls they establish and maintain meet FDA expectations. The definitions, unless followed by an asterisk, are quoted from FDA's Quality System Regulations.

COMPLAINT FILES

Definitions   *Complaint* means any written, electronic, or oral communication that alleges deficiencies related to the identity, quality, durability, reliability, safety, effectiveness, or performance of a device.

SUBPART M–RECORDS–COMPLAINT FILES

What the regulation states

§ 820.198 (a)

(a) Each manufacturer shall maintain complaint files. Each manufacturer shall establish and maintain procedures for receiving, reviewing, and evaluating complaints by a formally designated unit. Such procedures shall ensure that:

(1) All complaints are processed in a uniform and timely manner;
(2) Oral complaints are documented upon receipt; and
(3) Complaints are evaluated to determine whether the complaint represents an event which is required to be reported to FDA under part 803 or 804 of this chapter, Medical Device Reporting.

§ 820.198 (a) Discussion

Required procedure(s), document(s), and record(s)

Manufacturers' complaint procedures should identify a "formally designated" complaint unit. This can be done with a textual description and/or a diagram that identifies the individuals, activities, and departments charged with "receiving, reviewing and evaluating complaints." Manufacturers must maintain FDA complaint files based on their written complaint procedures.

The manufacturer must retain complaint files for a period of time equivalent to the design and expected life of any device but in all cases no less than two years from the date of commercial distribution release.

Remember!

FDA takes medical device complaints very seriously. Complaint files can be reviewed during an inspection. Failures or nonconformances with complaints and complaint files will usually result in one or more "Observations" on Form FDA 483. Complaint failures and nonconformances can also result in a "Warning Letter."

FDA expects that all complaints will be consistently handled in a regulatory complaint manner, according to a written complaint procedure. Failures to handle complaints in a uniform and timely manner can be cited as a nonconformance.

Required procedure(s), document(s), and record(s)

The complaint procedure must identify what is and what is not a complaint. Customer calls that are not complaints should be documented as "NOT A COMPLAINT," with the individual making that determination and date. This means that returned, failed devices are complaints. Some, perhaps many or most, repair requests are complaints. Some, but not all, service requests are complaints. A salesman talking to a customer at the customer's facility can be a complaint.

A discussion with a customer at a trade show can be a complaint. A journal article describing a problem with your device can be a complaint.

Complaints must be assessed to determine whether each complaint represents an event requiring a Medical Device Report (MDR) to be filed with the agency. See Chapter 19 Medical Device Reporting.

Complaint responsibility and oversight must be assigned to knowledgeable, trained personnel. As with all issues of responsibility, qualifications, and training, complaint compliance in these areas must also be documented. Because complaints may come from many different sources, employees in sales, marketing, engineering, manufacturing, regulatory affairs, installation, service, and support must be properly trained in identifying and reporting complaints. See Figure 18.1, page 198.

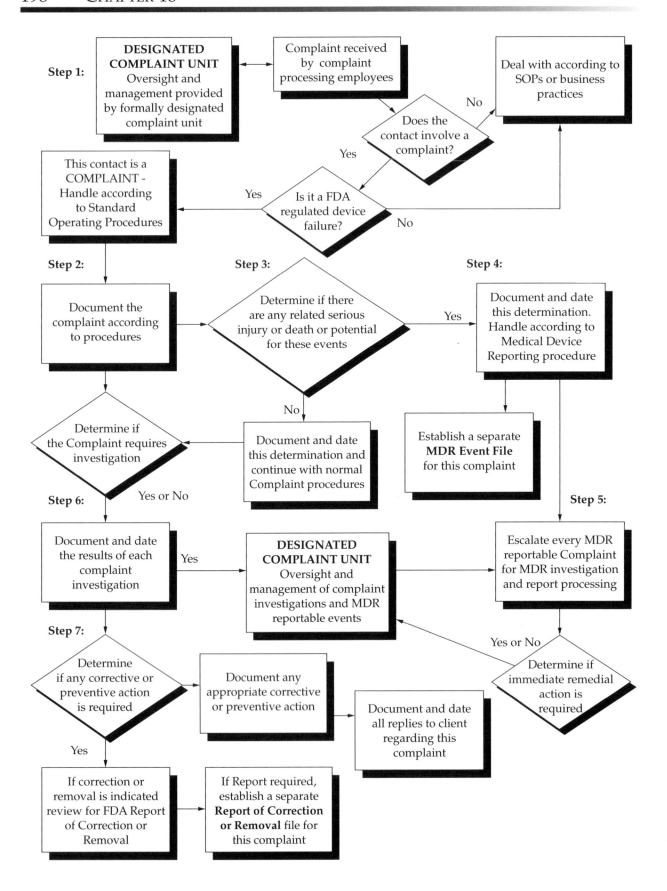

Figure 18.1.   Complaint Handling Flowsheet

What the regulation states

§ 820.198 (b)

(b) Each manufacturer shall review and evaluate all complaints to determine whether an investigation is necessary. When no investigation is made, the manufacturer shall maintain a record that includes the reason no investigation was made and the name of the individual responsible for the decision not to investigate.

§ 820.198 (b) Discussion

Don't forget!

The requirement to review and assess all complaints means "complaints" in terms of the broad definition FDA gives complaints: "Any written, electronic, or oral communication that alleges deficiencies related to the identity, quality, durability, reliability, safety, effectiveness, or performance of a device."

Complaints may be received from the following sources:

- Customers—by letter, credit memo, returned goods, phone, personal conversations, or e-mail
- Manufacturer's representative or other employees
- FDA or MDR report—a MedWatch report or other FDA contact
- Service report or repair request
- Journal article

Required procedure(s), document(s), and record(s)

The assessment must follow a written procedure and be documented. Paper forms are typically required. Many firms implement an electronic complaint-handling system. Manufacturers often imbed their complaint procedures with assessment models or tables developed by the manufacturer to provide a standardized mechanism for complaint assessments. These models or tables aid in ensuring that complaints assessed by different individuals will result in the same or nearly the same assessment.

Complaint assessment models or tables also aid employees in creating a hierarchy of complaint investigations and further actions, that is, those with the greatest risk to patient or user receive the most resources from the "complaint unit."

Something to note!

The implementation of an electronic complaint record system must be done cautiously. On March 20, 1997, FDA published finalized "21 CFR Part 11 Electronic Records and Electronic Signatures" regulations, which have provided the agency with authority and oversight with electronic records and electronic signatures. Any electronic system must be able to withstand FDA's expectation of security and an audit trail of electronic records and electronic signatures.

Remember!

These electronic records regulations mean that using any word processing, flat file database, or even relational database software applications as an electronic record for complaints are not permitted. None of these systems provides the security and audit trail 21 CFR Part 11 mandates.

Manufacturers wisely make 21 CFR Part 11 compliance a requirement of any purchase and implementation agreement with a supplier of a complaint-handling system. Obviously, any electronic system implemented must be fully validated for its intended use and that validation fully documented prior to final implementation.

What the regulation states

§ 820.198 (c)

(c) Any complaint involving the possible failure of a device, labeling, or packaging to meet any of its specifications shall be reviewed, evaluated, and investigated, unless such investigation has already been performed for a similar complaint and another investigation is not necessary.

§ 820.198 (c) Discussion

Don't forget!

FDA understands that a device manufacturer experiences many complaints more than once. When the second, third, or 50th complaint is documented, the review, evaluation, and, when performed, investigation of the earlier complaint can be referenced. However, if earlier corrective or preventive actions implemented as results of earlier complaints are obviously not working, a new investigation and new corrective or preventive actions will be necessary.

FDA also understands that isolated event complaints are difficult to investigate and resolve. In some cases, no satisfactory final resolution occurs. The event leading to the complaint cannot be reproduced, and no other similar complaints have been received.

Complaint personnel must be excellent analysts, piecing together bits of information from a variety of sources, and, in some cases, discovering obscure causes of device failures. Good complaint personnel are also excellent at documentation detail, providing the information necessary for later review and investigation.

What the regulation states

§ 820.198 (d)

(d) Any complaint that represents an event which must be reported to FDA under part 803 or 804 of this chapter shall be promptly reviewed, evaluated, and investigated by a designated individual(s) and shall be maintained in a separate portion of the complaint files or otherwise clearly identified. In addition to the information required by § 820.198(e), records of investigation under this paragraph shall include a determination of:

(1) Whether the device failed to meet specifications;
(2) Whether the device was being used for treatment or diagnosis; and
(3) The relationship, if any, of the device to the reported incident or adverse event.

§ 820.198 (d) Discussion

21 CFR § 803 and § 804 involve FDA's Medical Device Reporting regulations. These complaints involve an event in which a device caused or was implicated in a patient's or user's death or serious injury *or* the threat of a patient's or user's death or serious injury.

Something to note!

These events require more assessment, more documentation, and more and broader investigations and are typically pushed "upstairs" to a management level of oversight and documentation. When accurate, they also require one or more reports to FDA (some in a matter of days from first reporting).

A complete discussion of FDA oversight and expectations for compliance with § 803 or § 804 is provided in Chapter 19 Medical Device Reporting.

What the regulation states

§ 820.198 (e)

(e) When an investigation is made under this section, a record of the investigation shall be maintained by the formally designated unit identified in paragraph (a) of this section. The record of investigation shall include:

(1) The name of the device;
(2) The date the complaint was received;
(3) Any device identification(s) and control number(s) used;
(4) The name, address, and phone number of the complainant;
(5) The nature and details of the complaint;
(6) The dates and results of the investigation;
(7) Any corrective action taken; and
(8) Any reply to the complainant.

§ 820.198 (e) Discussion

Required procedure(s), document(s), and record(s)

Complaint procedures must require the recording of the specific information the regulation details for each complaint. Complaint forms or electronic complaint systems that require responses to each of these items help ensure compliance. See Figure 18.2, page 202.

Remember!

Complaints, as noted in § 820.198 (a) (1), must be "timely." However, FDA understands that hours or days and, in some cases, weeks can go by from the first report of a complaint until any corrective action is taken and a reply provided to the complainant. In some cases, the sequence of these events will not follow the sequence of § 820.198 (d).

For example, a correct reply to the complainant with a low-priority, low-risk problem might be as follows: "That defect will be corrected in the next version of the device." The corrective action taken, "the next version of the device," might be weeks or months later. However, upon later final corrective action, the originating complaint should be updated with information on the final corrective action and closed.

What the regulation states

§ 820.198 (f) (g)

(f) When the manufacturer's formally designated complaint unit is located at a site separate from the manufacturing establishment, the investigated complaint(s) and the record(s) of investigation shall be reasonably accessible to the manufacturing establishment.
(g) If a manufacturer's formally designated complaint unit is located outside of the United States, records required by this section shall be reasonably accessible in the United States at either:

(1) A location in the United States where the manufacturer's records are regularly kept; or
(2) The location of the initial distributor.

Date: _____

Customer Contact No.: (forms could be sequentially numbered) _____
Device Name: _____   Model No.: _____
Catalog No.: _____   Serial/Lot No.: _____
Name of Complainant: _____   Phone No.: _____
Complainant Address: _____
Complaint Received by: _____   Employee No.: _____
Complaint source: ❏ Visit ❏ Phone ❏ Letter ❏ Sales ❏ Service ❏ Credit Memo ❏ Other: _____

COMPLAINT INFORMATION
❏ Sterility _____   ❏ Particulate matter _____
❏ Defect: _____
❏ Packaging: _____   ❏ Labeling: _____
❏ Patient death: _____   ❏ User death: _____
❏ Patient injury: _____   ❏ User injury: _____
❏ Product malfunction: _____
❏ Other (detail): _____
Comments/Description of Event: _____

ATTACHMENTS
❏ Implicated device _____   ❏ Associated device_____
❏ Other: _____

INVESTIGATION
Received by QA: _____   Date: _____
Assigned to: _____   ❏ Response due date: _____
Instructions: _____   Date: _____
_____   Date: _____
Comments: _____   Date: _____
_____   Date: _____
Tests: _____   Date: _____
_____   Date: _____
❏ Copy of test attached   Findings: _____
                                                                                  Date: _____

CONCLUSION(S)
❏ Improper use _____   ❏ Shipping damage ❏ Yes ❏ No ❏ ? ❏ Repair request
❏ Device defective: _____
❏ Device Failed to meet Specifications: _____
❏ Other: _____

ACTION/REPLY TO COMPLAINANT
❏ No action: (reason) _____
❏ Recalled FDA phoned on—Date: _____   FDA contact: _____
❏ Complaint Committed Informed on—Date: _____   ❏ MDR filed on—Date: _____
❏ Referred to: _____   for further Investigation or Correction
❏ Reportable Corrective Action   ❏ Reportable Removal   ❏ Report ID _____
❏ Replaced ❏ Repaired ❏ Credited ❏ Letter Sent—Date: _____   Reference: _____
❏ Sales Follow-up   **❏ No reply necessary**
❏ Reason for no reply: _____

FINAL DISPOSITION
Reviewed by ❏ QA Date: _____ ❏ Engineering Date: _____ ❏ Mfging Date: _____
Distribution: ❏ Quality Control ❏ Engineering ❏ Manufacturing ❏ QA ❏ Sales ❏ Service ❏ Other _____

SIGNATURES:
❏ Quality Review (Name) _____ Title_____ Date: _____
❏ Management Review (Name) _____ Title_____ Date: _____

Figure 18.2.   Sample Complaint Record Form

§ 820.198 (f) and (g) Discussion

Required procedure(s), document(s), and record(s)

In these situations, FDA fully expects that the "formally designated complaint unit" will create mechanisms that ensure that complaint investigations and records are available to the manufacturing activity or, when outside the United States, available at a standard U.S. record location. The activity involved in ensuring those investigations and records are available should be documented.

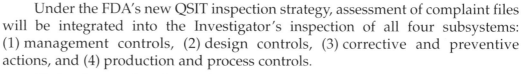

On May 17, 1998, FDA's Reports of Corrections and Removals regulations, 21 CFR 806, became effective. These regulations require manufacturers to report device corrections and removals in a specific format. See Chapter 11 Corrective and Preventive Action for a brief description and Attachment B, page 239, for 21 CFR 806 in its entirety.

What the FDA Investigator wants to see during an inspection

Under the FDA's new QSIT inspection strategy, assessment of complaint files will be integrated into the Investigator's inspection of all four subsystems: (1) management controls, (2) design controls, (3) corrective and preventive actions, and (4) production and process controls.

Under the previous inspection strategy, FDA trained Investigators that complaint files "should be the beginning point of every inspection." Investigators are well trained and experienced in determining whether a firm's complaints are the result of possible or potential defective devices.

During the Investigators review of management controls, management's review of complaints and any lack of or appropriate corrective or preventive action can be assessed. During the review of design controls, complaints may be assessed for their affect or lack of effect on appropriate changes to failed devices. During the review of corrective and preventive actions, records will be assess to document that all complaints are:

- Reviewed
- Evaluated
- Maintained by a "formally designated unit"

Investigators know that, depending upon the device manufacturer's operations, the "unit" can be one individual, a department, or multiple departments.

Investigators will expect to review written procedures for processing complaints, focusing on those complaints received after June 1, 1997. However, the Investigators can be expected to review many complaints, including those received prior to that date as well as those open and still under investigation.

Investigators are trained to identify deficiencies in the complaint-handling process as a source of possible quality system problems that are not being adequately addressed by the manufacturer.

Their review focuses on identifying existing or potential causes of the following:

- Nonconforming products
- Quality problems with similar products
- Enterprise-wide failure modes
- Environmental-related problems

The review will determine whether the manufacturer has:

- Performed sufficient complaint investigation
- Provided appropriately trained complaint reviewers
- Established appropriate mechanisms for determining complaint significance
- Ensured that oral and telephone complaints are documented

Please review the **FDA Investigator Icon** comments made in Chapter 11 Correction and Preventive Action, pages 142 and 143, concerning anticipated FDA Investigator activity regarding FDA's Reports of Corrections and Removals regulations, 21 CFR 806.

19

Medical Device Reporting

INTRODUCTION

This chapter of **Mastering and Managing the FDA Maze: Medical Device Overview Training and Management Desk Reference** discusses Medical Device Reporting (MDR) regulations.

SCOPE

Even though the Medical Device Reporting regulations are separate from the Quality System Regulations, that is, 21 CFR 803 vs. 21 CFR 820, they are referenced in the Quality System Regulations and play a significant role in compliance with 21 CFR 820. Therefore, a discussion of 21 CFR 803 is included in this training and management desk reference. 21 CFR 803 is provided in its entirety as Attachment D, page 253.

Significant detail has been omitted, and further training to ensure proficiency and understanding to the level required for FDA compliance will be needed.

Assuming that a firm can provide appropriate design controls, manufacturing, packaging, handling, storage, distribution, service and support, without adequate notification to FDA of significant device failures and malfunctions, there will be an unreasonable risk that, during those events, the device will not be serviced, supported, and managed in a manner that meets FDA requirements. To ensure that finished devices are suitable for continued release and distribution, compliance with FDA's Medical Device Reporting must occur and fulfill its quality system role.

It should be emphasized that this discussion is *basic*. Significant additional study and implementation will be required by individuals before they can be assured that the reporting practices manufacturers establish and maintain meet FDA expectations. The definitions, unless followed by an asterisk, are quoted from the Quality System Regulations.

MEDICAL DEVICE REPORTING

Definitions   *Become aware* means that an employee of the entity required to report has acquired information reasonably suggesting a reportable adverse event has occurred. Device user facilities are considered to have "become aware" when medical personnel, who are employed by or otherwise formally affiliated with the facility, acquire such information about a reportable event. Manufacturers are considered to have "become aware" of an event when:

(1) Any employee becomes aware of a reportable event that is required to be reported within 30 days, or that is required to be reported within 5 days pursuant to a written request from FDA under 803.53(b); and

(2) Any employee, who is a person with management or supervisory responsibilities over persons with regulatory, scientific, or technical responsibilities, or a person whose duties relate to the collection and reporting of adverse events, becomes aware that a reportable MDR event or events, from any information, including any trend analysis, necessitate remedial action to prevent an unreasonable risk of substantial harm to the public health.*

Caused or contributed means that a death or serious injury was or may have been attributed to a medical device, or that a medical device was or may have been a factor in a death or serious injury, including events occurring as a result of:

(1) Failure
(2) Malfunction
(3) Improper or inadequate design
(4) Manufacture
(5) Labeling or
(6) User error.*

Expected life of a device (required on the manufacturer's baseline report) means the time that a device is expected to remain functional after it is placed into use. Certain implanted devices have specified "end of life" (EOL) dates. Other devices are not labeled as to their respective EOL, but are expected to remain operational through maintenance, repair, upgrades, etc., for an estimated period of time.*

Five-day report means a medical device report that must be submitted by a manufacturer to FDA pursuant to § 803.53, on FDA Form 3500A or electronic equivalent as approved under § 803.14, within 5 workdays.*

Malfunction means the failure of a device to meet its performance specifications or otherwise perform as intended. Performance specifications include all claims made in the labeling for the device. The intended performance of a device refers to the intended use for which the device is labeled or marketed, as defined in § 801.4 of this chapter.*

MDR means medical device report or medical device reporting.*

MDR reportable event (or reportable event) means:

(1) An event about which user facilities become aware of information that reasonably suggests that a device has or may have caused or contributed to a death or serious injury; or
(2) An event about which manufacturers have received or become aware of information that reasonably suggests that one of their marketed devices:
   (a) May have caused or contributed to a death or serious injury or
   (b) Has malfunctioned and that the device or a similar device marketed by the manufacturer would be likely to cause or contribute to a death or serious injury if the malfunction were to recur.*

Permanent means, for purposes of this subpart, irreversible impairment or damage to a body structure or function, excluding trivial impairment or damage.*

Remedial action means, for the purposes of this subpart, any action other than routine maintenance or servicing, of a device where such action is necessary to prevent recurrence of a reportable event.*

Serious injury means an injury or illness that:

(1) Is life threatening
(2) Results in permanent impairment of a body function or permanent damage to body structure or
(3) Necessitates medical or surgical intervention to preclude permanent impairment of a body function or permanent damage to a body structure.*

21 CFR § 803—Medical Device Reporting

What the regulation states

21 CFR § 803

The Medical Device Reporting (MDR) regulation 21 CFR 803 is provided in its entirety as Attachment C, page 242.

This is not a full discussion of the MDR regulations. This is a brief treatment of those regulations to provide readers and FDA regulatory students with a basic understanding of these regulations and their interrelationship with FDA's complaint regulations.

Part 803 Medical Device Reporting regulation subpart and section titles are listed below to aid the reader and student in understanding the MDR regulation's depth and sophistication.

Subpart A—General Provisions
Sec.
803.1 Scope
803.3 Definitions
803.9 Public availability of reports
803.10 General description of reports required from user facilities and manufacturers
803.11 Obtaining the forms
803.12 Where to submit reports
803.13 English reporting requirement
803.14 Electronic reporting
803.15 Requests for additional information
803.16 Disclaimers
803.17 Written MDR procedures
803.18 Files
803.19 Exemptions, variances, and alternative reporting requirements

Subpart B—Generally Applicable Requirements for Individual Adverse Event Reports
803.20 How to report
803.21 Reporting codes
803.22 When not to file

Subpart C—User Facility Reporting Requirements
803.30 Individual adverse event reports; user facilities
803.31 Individual adverse event report data elements
803.33 Semiannual reports

Subpart D—[Reserved]

Subpart E—Manufacturer Reporting Requirements
803.50 Individual adverse event reports; manufacturers
803.52 Individual adverse event report data elements
803.53 Five-day reports
803.55 Baseline reports
803.56 Supplemental reports
803.57 Annual certification
803.58 Foreign manufacturers

Medical Device Reporting Discussion

Remember!

FDA's Medical Device Reporting (MDR) regulation was not implemented to replace the Quality System Regulation complaint and failure investigation requirements, **§ 820.198 Complaint Files,** but are intended to significantly supplement them.

MDR regulations are proscriptive for both device users and manufacturers. There are specific time limits within which MDR reports shall be made:

• Any report of a device-related death, serious injury, and malfunction shall be submitted within 30 calendar days from becoming aware of an MDR reportable event.
• Any MDR reportable event that requires remedial action to prevent an unreasonable risk of substantial harm to public health shall be submitted within 5 work days.
• FDA notification to any manufacturer that a 5-day report is required shall be submitted within 5 work days.

***Required
procedure(s),
document(s),
and record(s)***

Manufacturers are responsible for maintaining written MDR procedures, training employees on MDR requirements, and training complaint-handling employees on recognizing MDR reportable events. MDR procedures must work in harmony with complaint procedures to ensure that appropriate complaints are evaluated for an MDR event.

Manufacturers are also required to maintain "MDR Event Files," which may be part of, but separate from, other complaint files containing:

- The original or a copy of the initial complaint record of the complaint or event
- Copies of any records documenting the manufacturer's attempts to follow up and obtain missing or additional information about the event. Problems associated with these attempts must be explained.
- Copies of any test reports, laboratory reports, service records and reports, and records of investigations
- Copies of all documentation involving the final assessment of the event, deliberations, and/or decision-making processes and any corrective and/or preventive actions taken.
- Copies of all FDA 3500A forms, or "MedWatch Reports," submitted to FDA or received from any user or distributor
- Documents and records that verify the event has been evaluated in accordance with applicable requirements of the Quality System Regulations, § 820.100 and § 820.198
- References to any other relevant documents or information used during the investigation and assessment

As with complaint files, MDR Event Files must be retained for 2 years from the date of the event or a period of time equivalent to the expected life of the device, whichever is greater. An excellent practice associated with managing an MDR event is the use of an MDR Checklist. An example is provided in the Figure 19.1, pages 210 and 211.

Don't forget!

After an MDR event is identified, a key result of the event's investigation will be the determination of appropriate corrective or preventive action. If the event requires "remedial action," what FDA defines as "any action other than routine maintenance or servicing of a device where such action is necessary to prevent recurrence of a reportable event," the event becomes a 5-day reportable event. FDA notes that "actions taken to fix a single device involved in the MDR reportable event are not remedial actions."

In some cases, it could be that the determination of "remedial action" comes later in the investigation. In those cases, what appeared to be a 30-day reportable event may suddenly become a 5-day reportable event. Obviously, MDR events and situations must be properly investigated and well documented and all parties involved, typically the formally designated complaint unit, must work together to ensure MDR compliance.

In addition to 30-day and 5-day reports, manufacturers are required to submit a baseline report on FDA Form 3417 with an initial MDR report on a device model. The baseline report provides FDA with information the device's distribution and number of device's in use. Baseline reports are used by FDA to assess adverse event reports, their level of risk, and any appropriate FDA response. FDA also requires supplemental MDR reports within 30 days when important additional information is received that was not included in the initial report.

Potential MDR Event ID Number: (mm/yy-sequential no): _____

Potential MDR Event Identification/Brief Description: _____

_____

_____

_____

_____

Report: ❏ Form FDA 3500A ❏ Initial 5-day ❏ Initial 30-day ❏ Supplemental
❏ Initial Form FDA 3417 Baseline ❏ Supplemental Baseline (omit items 15 & 16)
❏ Annual Certification Form FDA 3381

❏ Reviewed **"Instructions for Completing Form 3500A with Coding Manual for Form 3500A,"** 12/1995 ❏ Yes ❏ No
❏ Reviewed **"Medical Device Reporting for Manufacturers,"** 3/1997 ❏ Yes ❏ No

❏ Patient information, including name or other identifier, age or date of birth, gender, and weight:
❏ Yes ❏ In File ❏ No

❏ Documentation of adverse event or product problem, including description of event or problem, outcomes attributed to event or problem, specifying, if applicable, death, serious injury or life threatening injury or illness, disability resulting from permanent impairment of a body function or permanent damage to a body structure:
❏ Yes ❏ In File ❏ No

❏ Adverse event or product problem description including date, date of report by initial reporter, description of how device was involved, nature of the problem, patient follow-up or required treatment, and any environmental conditions that may have influenced the event or problem: ❏ Yes ❏ In File ❏ No

❏ Any relevant tests, including data and laboratory data? ❏ Yes ❏ In File ❏ No
❏ Any relevant patient history, including pre-existing medical conditions? ❏ Yes ❏ In File
❏ No _____
❏ Device brand name: ❏ Yes ❏ In File ❏ No ❏ Model number: ❏ Yes ❏ In File ❏ No
❏ Catalog number: ❏ Yes ❏ In File ❏ No ❏ Type of device: ❏ Yes ❏ In File ❏ No
❏ Serial number, lot number or other ID no: ❏ Yes ❏ In File ❏ No
❏ Any expiration date? ❏ Yes ❏ In File ❏ No Date: ❏ Yes ❏ In File ❏ No
❏ Operator of the device: ❏ Yes ❏ In File ❏ No
❏ Device implantation: ❏ Yes ❏ In File ❏ No Explanation: ❏ Yes ❏ In File ❏ No
❏ Is device available for evaluation? ❏ Yes ❏ In File ❏ No
❏ Date of return to manufacturer: ❏ Yes ❏ In File ❏ No
❏ Any concomitant medical products and therapy dates: ❏ Yes ❏ In File ❏ No
❏ Initial reporter's name: ❏ Yes ❏ In File ❏ No
❏ Status, title or occupation: ❏ Yes ❏ In File ❏ No ❏ Address: ❏ Yes ❏ In File ❏ No
❏ Initial reporter's phone number: ❏ Yes ❏ In File ❏ No
❏ Did initial reporter also sent a copy of the report to FDA? ❏ Yes ❏ In File ❏ No
❏ Is this reported event addressed in the device labeling? ❏ Yes ❏ In File ❏ No
❏ Contact device office name, address, device manufacturing site, and appropriate phone numbers:
❏ Yes ❏ In File ❏ No
❏ Report sources and date received by manufacturer: ❏ Yes ❏ In File ❏ No
❏ Use of device was ❏ initial, ❏ reuse, or ❏ unknown.
❏ Manufacturer report number: ❏ Yes ❏ In File ❏ No
❏ Death? ❏ Yes ❏ No Serious injury? ❏ Yes ❏ No ❏ Malfunction? ❏ Yes ❏ No
❏ Follow-up report of any correction? ❏ Yes ❏ In File ❏ No
❏ Response to FDA request? ❏ Yes ❏ No FDA request letter: ❏ In File
❏ Device returned? ❏ Yes ❏ In File ❏ No
❏ Evaluation by manufacturer? ❏ Yes ❏ In File ❏ No
❏ Summary of the evaluation? ❏ Yes ❏ In File ❏ No
❏ If no evaluation was performed, an explanation of why none was performed? ❏ Yes ❏ In File ❏ No

Figure 19.1. MDR Event Checklist

❏ Device's date of manufacturer: ❏ In File   ❏ Labeled for single use: ❏ Yes   ❏ In File   ❏ No
❏ Evaluation codes, see "**Coding Manual for Form 3500A**": ❏ In File
❏ Method of evaluation: ❏ In File   ❏ Result and conclusion codes: ❏ In File
❏ Single, isolated device failure, corrective action not considered "remedial action."
❏ Remedial action taken and type, including if remedial action taken was reported as a removal or correction:
   ❏ Yes   ❏ In File   ❏ No   ❏ Number of devices in Remedial Action _____
❏ Was remedial action taken to prevent an unreasonable risk of substantial harm to the public health? *If no remedial action was taken for such prevention, no 5-day report is required however, 30-day report may be required.*
   ❏ Yes   ❏ In File   ❏ No
❏ Known missing information, not submitted: ❏ Yes   ❏ In File   ❏ No
❏ Why the information was not submitted: ❏ Yes   ❏ In File   ❏ No
❏ Steps taken to obtain such information: ❏ Yes   ❏ In File   ❏ No
❏ Corrected data, including any information missing on previously submitted reports, missing event codes, or information corrected, after manufacturer verification, on previously submitted forms: ❏ Yes   ❏ In File   ❏ No
❏ Event or problem investigation completed?   ❏ Yes   ❏ In File   ❏ No
❏ Event or problem a reportable event?   ❏ Yes   ❏ In File   ❏ No

Comments: _____
_____
_____
_____
_____

I have reviewed the MDR event or problem identified above and, to the best of my knowledge, this checklist reflects the status of this potential event at the date and time listed below.

Printed Name	Signature	Title	Date

Figure 19.1.–*Continued*

Something to note!

In the original regulations, FDA required that all manufacturers certify and submit annually on Form FDA 3381, that they have filed MDR reports on all reportable events, the number of MDR reports submitted to FDA, or that no MDR reportable events were documented for the previous 12 months. The certification required the certifying official to attest that:

- The official has read the requirements of the MDR regulations
- The firm has a system to comply with MDR regulations and reporting
- The firm has complied with its MDR procedures
- The firm has submitted "n" MDR reports, or the firm has submitted no MDR reports
- The certification is made to the best of the official's "knowledge or belief"

Remember!

However, the FDA Modernization Act (FDAMA) of 1997 FDA Modernization Act of 1997 (FDAMA of '97) amended the Food, Drug, and Cosmetic Act to eliminate manufacturers' requirement to submit Form FDA 3381.

Section 211 of FDAMA of '97, also amends the Food, Drug, and Cosmetic Act to eliminate mandatory tracking requirements to **only Class II and III devices:**

- Whose failure would be reasonably likely to have serious adverse health consequences
- Intended to be implanted for over one year or
- Life-sustaining or life-supporting devices intended for use outside the device user facility.

The following table provides a synopsis of **Manufacturer's MDR Activities and Responsibilities:**

Report Requirement	Report to?	Report when?	Report what?
Deaths, serious injuries, and malfunctions reporting	FDA	Within 30 days of becoming aware	FDA Form 3500A or FDA approved electronic equivalent
Identify and provide distribution and use data on any device subject to an MDR report	FDA	With the 30-day report when any device is reported for the first time	FDA Form 3417 or FDA approved electronic equivalent
MDR reportable events that require immediate remedial action to prevent an unreasonable risk to public health and other events designated by FDA	FDA	Within 5 work days of becoming aware immediate remedial action is required	FDA Form 3500A or FDA approved electronic equivalent
Repealed by FDAMA of '97 Annual certification of all reportable events for the previous 12 months, the number of reports or statement that no reports were filed.	FDA	***Repealed by FDAMA of '97*** With firm's annual registration	***Repealed*** FDA Form 3381 or FDA approved electronic equivalent

*This table was modified by the author from an original in FDA's **Medical Device Reporting for Manufacturers**, March 1997.*

The following table provides a **Summary of Manufacturer's Other MDR Requirements:**

Manufacturer's Requirement	Summary
MDR Event Files 21 CFR § 803.18	Records of complaints investigated as MDR reports must be kept in MDR Event Files for 2 years.
Written MDR Procedures 21 CFR § 803.17	Written procedures established, maintained, and implemented to: (1) identify potential MDR reportable events (2) evaluate potential MDR reportable events (3) make timely MDR reports on MDR reportable events (4) comply with FDA record-keeping regulations
Exemptions, Variances, and Alternate Reporting 21 CFR § 80319	Investigational devices are exempt. Other exemptions, variances, or alternatives of MDR regulations may be granted upon request or at FDA's discretion.
Designation of U.S. Agent* 21 CFR § 803.58 *Requirement under review, not currently enforced	Foreign manufacturers must designate an agent in the United States who will register and submit MDR reports, conduct or obtain information about investigations, forward reports to manufacturer, and maintain complaint files on behalf of manufacturer.

*This table was modified by the author from an original in FDA's **Medical Device Reporting for Manufacturers**, March 1997.*

What the FDA Investigator wants to see during an inspection

Under FDA's new QSIT inspection strategy, Investigators can be expected to assess a firm's MDR compliance early when reviewing the management controls subsystem. Investigators will quickly assess the level of interaction between the appointed management representative and the firm's quality system through that individual's interaction with MDRs, among other elements. Later assessments can be expected during the Investigator's evaluation of the firm's corrective and preventive actions.

Because FDA's compliance program requires an MDR inspection with each quality system inspection, FDA Investigators will access FDA CDRH Information Retrieval System (CIRS) and review a manufacturer's Medical Device Reporting data immediately prior to any inspection. The Establishment Inspection Report (EIR) should document that the Inspector reviewed complaints and service records for MDR reportable events and MDR procedures for compliance with MDR regulations.

Also reviewed at that time are the firm's FDA registration and listing data and any 510(k) and PMA summary data. Some of these databases are accessible only to users with "individual accounts."

In some cases involving MDRs and device failures, FDA Investigators will make "Directed Device Inspections." For these inspections, FDA Investigators have a shopping list that may include MDR reports, and they focus on specific areas known to be routinely implicated in device failures.

FDA Investigators will consider the failure of any firm to have documents or data related to MDR reports on file involving that firm to be in "significant non-compliance" with FDA regulations.

If MDR reports are found that provide evidence that any unsafe and/or unreliable product was or may have been distributed, the Investigator will focus on the firm's complaint records, service records, past, present, and incomplete corrective and preventive actions, and distribution records. That investigation will also determine whether any other nonconforming product may have been released.

Investigators finding any service record that represented an MDR reportable event will also assess the event to ensure it was considered a complaint and received appropriate follow-up under § 820.198.

Inspectors will also focus on process problems, reviewing procedures in detail to determine whether problems are related to processes that are "people dependent." The documentation Inspectors retain in these cases typically become inspectional observations of training issues, the use of unqualified personnel, or process validation problems.

When these types of inspectional observations are made, they often result in an additional inspectional observation of failure of the firm's management and management responsibility to comply with regulations.

Noncompliances associated with any of these activities, particularly those associated with MDRs or potential MDRs, will be considered as significant risks and will have a high likelihood of becoming inspectional observations and result in a Warning Letter and potentially other FDA actions.

20

Quality Audit

INTRODUCTION

This chapter of **Mastering and Managing the FDA Maze: Medical Device Overview Training and Management Desk Reference** discusses FDA's quality audit regulation.

SCOPE

The goal of this chapter is to provide an overview of FDA regulations for quality audits for medical device manufacturers. Significant detail has been omitted, and further training to ensure proficiency and understanding to the level required for FDA compliance will be needed.

Assuming that a firm can provide appropriate design, manufacturing, acceptance and corrective and preventive action controls to a device, unless appropriate quality auditing techniques are implemented with those activities, there will be an unreasonable risk that the manufacturing of the device will result in devices that fail to meet specifications and are unsuitable for release as finished devices.

To ensure that finished devices meet specifications and are suitable for release and distribution, the use of quality auditing throughout the design, manufacturing and remaining processes helps ensure manufacturers fulfill their quality system role.

It should be emphasized that this discussion is *basic*. Significant additional study and implementation will be required by individuals before they can be assured that the manufacturing controls they establish and maintain meet FDA expectations. The definitions, unless followed by an asterisk, are quoted from FDA's Quality System Regulation.

QUALITY AUDIT

§ 820.22 QUALITY AUDIT

Definitions   *Design history file* (DHF) means a compilation of records which describes the design history of a finished device.

Device history record (DHR) means a compilation of records containing the production history of a finished device.

Device master record (DMR) means a compilation of records containing the procedures and specifications for a finished device.

Establish means define, document (in writing or electronically), and implement.

Finished device means any device or accessory to any device that is suitable for use or capable of functioning, whether or not it is packaged, labeled, or sterilized.

Lead auditor is the individual responsible for auditing management and finalization of audit findings and reports.*

Management with executive responsibility means those senior employees of a manufacturer who have the authority to establish or make changes to the manufacturer's quality policy and quality system.

Manufacturer means any person who designs, manufactures, fabricates, assembles, or processes a finished device. Manufacturer includes but is not limited to those who perform the functions of contract sterilization, installation, relabeling, remanufacturing, repacking, or specification development, and initial distributors of foreign entities performing these functions.

Nonconformity means the nonfulfillment of a specified requirement.

Product means components, manufacturing materials, in-process devices, finished devices, and returned devices.

Quality means the totality of features and characteristics that bear on the ability of a device to satisfy fitness-for-use, including safety and performance.

Quality audit means a systematic, independent examination of a manufacturer's quality system that is performed at defined intervals and at sufficient frequency to determine whether both quality system activities and the results of such activities comply with quality system procedures, that these procedures are implemented effectively, and that these procedures are suitable to achieve quality system objectives.

Quality policy means the overall intentions and direction of an organization with respect to quality, as established by management with executive responsibility.

Quality system means the organizational structure, responsibilities, procedures, processes, and resources for implementing quality management.

Record means any written or electronic document, including specifications, procedures, protocols, standards, methods, instructions, plans, files, forms, notes, reviews, analyses, data, and reports.

Root cause is the most basic cause of any undesirable condition or problem, which when eliminated or mitigated, will prevent or significantly reduce the effect of the condition or problem.*

Specification means any requirement with which a product, process, service, or other activity must conform.

§ 820.22 Quality Audit

What the regulation states

§ 820.22

Each manufacturer shall establish procedures for quality audits and conduct such audits to assure that the quality system is in compliance with the established quality system requirements and to determine the effectiveness of the quality system. Quality audits shall be conducted by individuals who do not have direct responsibility for the matters being audited. Corrective action(s), including a reaudit of deficient matters, shall be taken when necessary. A report of the results of each quality audit, and reaudit(s) where taken, shall be made and such reports shall be reviewed by management having responsibility for the matters audited. The dates and results of quality audits and reaudits shall be documented.

§ 820.22 Discussion

Performing quality system audits requires an understanding of what auditing entails. Auditing is the following things:

- A management tool to ensure organizations meet established objectives
- An assessment of an organization's documents and records to demonstrate effective and suitable conformance with established objectives
- A mechanism to provide organizations with objective evidence, where needed, of the requirement to reduce, eliminate, and/or prevent nonconformities

FDA fully expects that manufacturers will provide quality audits of their quality system. If there is no trained auditor on staff, a training resource for one or more employees must be obtained. Alternately, with written procedural documentation, and, after assessment, review, and approval, a contract or purchase of the services of a qualified third-party auditor can be substituted.

Don't forget!

Make sure that all quality auditing activities, even those associated with suppliers, contractors and consultants, are protected from FDA oversight and copying. Subpart M Records of the Quality System Regulations, specifically, § 820.180 (c) *Exceptions*, exempts these records and documents from FDA oversight and copying. However, FDA may review audit procedures and schedules and may request that manufacturers "certify in writing that the management reviews and quality audits required" have been "performed and documented," identify the dates of those audits, and certify "that any required corrective action has been undertaken." See Chapter 17 Records—General Requirements, Device History Record (DHR), and Quality System Record (QSR).

Something to note!

Good auditing techniques are learned. These skills require attention to detail, good documentation, and an investigative perspective. A good auditor can adequately audit almost any kind of organization. Specific organizational "domain" knowledge is not required although it can be helpful. Good auditing technique requires that the auditors have independence from the activities being audited to ensure that their audits are not unduly influenced. Good auditors must be free from bias and influences that could affect their objectivity.

Remember!

Management must demonstrate respect and support for all auditing activities throughout their organization. Management should:

- Determine the need for and purpose of audits
- Initiate the audit process
- Identify the auditors and lead auditor, if appropriate
- Determine the general scope and objectives of the audit
- Inform appropriate staff about the objectives and scope of the audits
- If appropriate, appoint appropriate staff members to accompany individual auditors
- Provide all the necessary resources to ensure an effective and efficient audit
- Ensure audit objectives are met
- Receive the audit reports
- Ensure that any follow-up, corrective, or preventive actions taken are appropriate.

Don't forget!

Stated quality system audit objectives should include the following:

- The need to determine the conformity or nonconformity of the quality system, or its parts, including any third-party standards or regulations
- The need to determine the effectiveness of the implemented quality system
- The need to provide the individual, department, or activity being audited with the objective evidence necessary to improve their quality system

Audits are typically conducted for one or more of the following reasons:

- To perform an initial evaluation of a potential supplier, contractor or consultant.
- To perform a periodic evaluation of an existing supplier, contractor or consultant.
- To verify an organization's quality system has implemented and continues to meet established, specified requirements.
- To verify an organization's quality system has implemented and continues to meet a specific quality system standard or regulatory requirement.

Audits may be:

- Scheduled and routine
- Unscheduled and prompted by significant changes in an organization's:
  — Quality system
  — Process
  — Product
  — Service quality
- Scheduled and a follow-up of a corrective action.

FDA requires that audits be performed at a "defined interval" and "at sufficient frequency to determine whether both quality system activities and the results of such activities comply with quality system procedures, and that these procedures are suitable to achieve quality system objectives."

The organization's management and complexity of their quality system determine auditing frequency. In smaller organizations, semiannual or annual audits are appropriate. Medium size organizations typically require quarterly or semiannual audits. Larger organizations typically require monthly audits.

Auditing activities may, in and of themselves, trigger additional audits. If audit findings indicate the potential for similar findings in other activities, good auditing practice **requires** that audits be scheduled to assess these activities for those and other nonconformances and noncompliances.

Whenever required, audit teams should be created to:

- Ensure independence
- Provide any required "domain" expertise
- Provide audit training
- Provide for audit observers from management or staff

Whenever an audit is conducted by more than one individual, a "lead auditor" who is responsible for audit management should be identified. The lone auditor or lead auditor is responsible for the following activities:

- Overseeing all phases of the audit
- Providing demonstrated experience and management capability
- Reviewing previous audits, their observations, and nonconformities
- Assisting with team member selection
- Finalizing the audit format and form
- Interfacing with management at any appropriate phase of the audit
- Submitting the final audit report

Auditors are responsible for the following activities:

- Complying with applicable written audit requirements
- Communicating and clarifying audit requirements
- Planning and fulfilling assigned responsibilities effectively and efficiently
- Documenting observations of both conformances and nonconformances
- Reporting audit results
- Verifying the effectiveness of corrective actions taken as a result of an audit

- Retaining and safeguarding audit documents and records
  - Submitting documents and records as required
  - Ensuring documents and records remain confidential
  - Treating privileged and confidential information appropriately
  - Cooperating with and supporting the lead auditor

Where and when appropriate, auditing activities should be initiated with a brief opening meeting to do the following:

- Introduce members of the audit team or auditors
- Review the scope and objectives of the audit
- Provide a short summary of the methods and procedures used to conduct the audit
- Establish a communication link between the auditors and the auditees
- Confirm that appropriate resources and facilities have been provided the auditors
- Confirm the date and time for the closing meeting and any interim meetings of the audits and senior management
- Provide a mechanism for answering questions about the auditing activities

A closing meeting with senior management might:

- Be held prior to finalization of the audit report and include senior management and managers of audited activities
- Focus on providing senior management with audit observations so that they clearly understand the results of the audit
- Provide the auditors assessment of the significance of each observation
- Provide the auditors with conclusions regarding the quality system's effectiveness in ensuring that the organization's quality objectives are being met
- Provide a documented record of the closing meeting
- Provide nonbinding recommendations to auditees for improvements to their quality system (auditors might do this upon request).

Required procedure(s), document(s), and record(s)

FDA requires manufacturers to create procedures that require and detail defined intervals of quality audits. Those procedures may identify a standard audit plan that directs the actions and activities of the auditors but is flexible enough to allow for changes in emphasis based on information gathered during any audit. These procedures should identify all audit output documents as confidential, proprietary, and not to be provided to unauthorized individuals, including FDA Investigators. Audit plans might include the following:

- Audit objectives and scope
- Identification of responsibilities and, where appropriate, lead auditors, audit teams, or third-party auditors
- Identification of reference documents, for example, quality system standards, quality manual, and appropriate regulations
- Audit schedules
- Expected times and durations of scheduled audits
- Identification of appropriate meetings with management and audited activities
- Confidentiality requirements
- Audit opening, interim, and closing meeting requirements and format
- Audit report issuance dates and distribution

Audit working documents might include the following:

- Checklists for evaluating quality system elements
- Forms for reporting audit observations
- Forms for documenting supporting evidence of conclusions reached by auditors

A number of audit working document examples are provided in Figures 20.1, 20.2, 20.3, 20.4, and 20.5, pages 222–227.

Audit reports should include the following:

- A brief statement of the scope and objectives of the audit
- Dates of the auditing activities
- Details of the audit plan, identification of the auditors, and activities audited
- Identification of audit reference documents
- Observations of nonconformities
- The auditor's assessment of the extent of the organization's compliance with their quality system, applicable standards, regulations, previous audits' observations, and corrective and preventive actions

The audit report should be made as a single copy to the senior management of the organization audited or, for supplier, contractor, or consultant audits, to the organization sponsoring the audit. Any additional distribution of the final audit report is the responsibility of that organization. Audit reports that contain confidential or proprietary information must be appropriately safeguarded by all parties. Audit records should be retained in accordance with regulatory requirements or as identified by the organization's auditing procedures.

Remember!

A major reason quality audits are performed is to identify nonconformances and root causes that require corrective and preventive actions. To ensure that those activities are understood, please review Chapter 11 Corrective and Preventive Action.

What the FDA Inspector wants to see during an inspection

Under the new QSIT inspection strategy, FDA Investigators will want to review and copy the manufacturer's auditing procedures. Currently, FDA does not require manufacturers to provide the documents associated with audits to FDA considers them to be subject to agency review only when firms are undergoing severe administrative or judicial actions. [See §820.180 (c) Exceptions.]

However, Investigators may request that senior management certify, that is, provide a certified or sworn document that states that required quality audits, including any supplier, contractor, or consultant audits, have been performed and documented, the dates they were performed, and that any required corrective action has been undertaken.

If Investigators' findings document that any audit certification is false or misleading, FDA could be expected to take severe actions against those attempting to deceive the agency, both the individuals making the certification and their firm.

Date: _____ Internal Audit No.: _____

Activity/Department: _____ Auditor: _____

§ 820.5 Quality System

Compliance: S = Satisfactory   D = Deficient   NA = Not applicable   NAv = Not available
Comments: Write comments on deficiency, verification, objective evidence, names, doc #'s, revision #'s, etc.

S,D, NA, NAv	Requirements	Comments
	Has the organization established a quality system?	
	Has the organization maintained a quality system?	
	Is the quality system appropriate for the specific medical devices designed or manufactured?	
	Where are company policies and procedures for quality documented?	
	Are documented quality system procedures identified or referred to in a quality manual?	
	Is the documentation's structure outlined in that manual?	
	Is the documentation maintained to ensure the quality system complies with FDA regulations?	
	Is the documentation maintained to ensure the quality system complies with ISO 9000? [Note: When applicable]	

Reviewed on: _____ Reviewed by: _____ Auditor's initials: _____

Subpart B   Quality Management Requirements

§ 820.20 Management responsibility

Compliance: S = Satisfactory   D = Deficient   NA = Not applicable   NAv = Not available
Comments: Write comments on deficiency, verification, objective evidence, names, doc #'s, revision #'s, etc.

S,D, NA, NAv	Requirements	Comments
	(a) Quality Policy	
	Does the staff, at all levels, know and understand the quality policy and supporting procedures?	
	Are the firm's organizational goals, expectations, and needs integral to the quality policy?	
	(b) (1), (2), (3) Organization	
	Is the firm's organizational structure produced and distributed?	
	Is the organizational structure current?	
	Does that structure ensure devices are designed & produced with appropriate management, auditing and personnel?	
	Have the actions of personnel with the responsibility and authority that may affect quality been defined and documented?	

Reviewed on: _____ Reviewed by: _____ Auditor's initials: _____

Subpart B   Quality Management Requirements

§ 820.20 Management responsibility

Figure 20.1. Sample Audit Checklist (Partial)

	Where are those responsibilities documented?	
	Is there definition and documentation of the interrelationship of individuals and activities?	
	Where are the responsibilities for solving identified quality problems documented?	
	Ditto . . . records documented?	
	Ditto . . . problem solving documented?	
	Ditto . . . prevention documented?	
	(c) Management review	
	What documents identify management review?	
	At what intervals does management review occur?	
	Who is authorized to conduct these reviews?	
	Are the effectiveness and efficiency of the quality system reviewed by executive management?	
	Are appropriate support and direction, e.g., people and budgets, provided by executive management?	
	(d) Quality planning	
	Are the requirements of how quality will be met defined and documented?	
	Do these planning requirements include documentation on product design, production processes, inspection, test, installation, and support?	
	Do the planning requirements include documentation for implementing new procedures in QC, inspection, testing, new equipment, & measurement requirements?	
	Are these activities identified, developed, and implemented prior to their need?	
	(e) Quality system procedures	
	Does it appear that sufficient procedures are in place to ensure a quality system? Note: Effective implementation of procedures will be assessed during activity audits of the enterprise.	

Reviewed on: _____ Reviewed by: _____ Auditor's initials: _____

Figure 20.1.–*Continued*

[Note: This completed form is a controlled document and may not be provided to unauthorized individuals.]

Complete this form in pen or as a word-processing printed document.

Activity/Department: _____   Audit Date: _____

Report Date: _____   Item Number: _____

Auditor: _____

Deficiency Description:

Requirement Source(s):

Requirement Description(s):

Auditor's Signature: _____

Figure 20.2.   Quality Assurance Audit Deficiency Report Form

[Note: This completed form is a controlled document and may not be provided to unauthorized individuals.]

Complete this form in pen or as a word-processing printed document.

Date: _____   Item Number: _____

Brief Description of Deficiency:

Follow-up Corrective Actions

Manager Name: _____

Manager Title: _____

Manager Signature: _____   Date: _____

Auditor's Review:

❐ Auditor Rejection   ❐ Auditor Acceptance   Date: _____

Signature: _____   Auditor's Name: _____

Figure 20.3.   Response to Reported Deficiency Report Form

[Note: This completed form is a controlled document and may not be provided to unauthorized individuals.]

Complete this form in pen or as a word-processing printed document.

Activity/Department: _____   Audit Date: _____

Report Date: _____   Item Number: _____

Auditor: _____   Item Number: _____

Reasons for Deficiency Response Rejection:

Signature: _____

Auditor's Name: _____

Figure 20.4. Audit Deficiency Response Rejection Report Form

[Note: This completed report is a controlled document and may not be provided to unauthorized individuals.]

Distribution is to the Activity/Department Manager and Management Representative; additional distribution is precluded except by approval of the Management Representative.

NOTE: THE FIRST PAGE OF THIS *AUDIT FINAL REPORT TO RESPONSIBLE MANAGEMENT* MAY BE PROVIDED TO FDA INVESTIGATORS TO DOCUMENT OUR FIRM'S COMPLIANCE WITH FDA REGULATIONS.

HOWEVER, NO OTHER PART OF THIS REPORT OR ANY OF ITS ATTACHED DOCUMENTS ARE TO BE SHARED WITH THE FDA.

Audit dates from _____ to _____

Activity/Department audited: _____

Auditors: _____

SCOPE: The scope of this audit was:

FOLLOW-UP CORRECTIVE ACTIONS ❐ WERE   ❐ WERE NOT IDENTIFIED

The audit's purpose was to identify problems, deficiencies, and nonconformities for the activity listed above. Those situations were assessed by the auditors using the following Level of Severity strategy:

Level of Severity: P = Problem, a failure of record-keeping or document control that needs to be addressed, that is a minor failure and is not severe enough to be labeled a Deficiency but requires corrective action. D = Deficiency, a failure to accurately follow written procedures, work instructions, or forms that needs to be addressed, that is a significant failure, and is not severe enough to be labeled a Nonconformity, but requires corrective action.
N = Nonconformity, a failure to follow written procedures, work instructions or forms, or a failure of a process that is a major failure of the quality system and requires corrective action.

QUALITY SYSTEM STRENGTHS ❐ WERE   ❐ WERE NOT IDENTIFIED

One or more areas of audited activities' quality system were found to be above the norm and reflect exemplary efforts by the activities' quality system management.

FUTURE AUDIT FREQUENCY ASSESSMENT:
The audit team has determined that this activities' audit frequency should

❐ Remain unchanged from _____ times per year
❐ Follow-up audit within _____
❐ Be increased to _____ times per year

❐ This certifies that I have reviewed the audit records of the activity listed above and have found them to be
❐ **incomplete** and require that they be revised as identified on a separate sheet.

❐ This certifies that I have reviewed the audit records of the activity listed above and have found them to be
❐ **complete** and accept them as final.

_____   _____   _____
Management Representative Signature   Management Representative Name, Title   Date

Figure 20.5. Audit Final Report to Responsible Management

Attachments

ATTACHMENT A

DEPARTMENT OF HEALTH AND HUMAN SERVICES

FOOD AND DRUG ADMINISTRATION

QUALITY SYSTEM REGULATION

1996: 21 CFR §820

FINAL RULE

October 7, 1996

PART 820—QUALITY SYSTEM REGULATION

Subpart A—General Provisions

Sec.
820.1 Scope.
820.3 Definitions.
820.5 Quality system.

Subpart B—Quality System Requirements

820.20 Management responsibility.
820.22 Quality audit.
820.25 Personnel.

Subpart C—Design Controls

820.30 Design controls.

Subpart D—Document Controls

820.40 Document controls.

Subpart E—Purchasing Controls

820.50 Purchasing controls.

Subpart F—Identification and Traceability

820.60 Identification.
820.65 Traceability.

Subpart G—Production and Process Controls

820.70 Production and process controls.
820.72 Inspection, measuring, and test equipment.
820.75 Process validation.

Subpart H—Acceptance Activities

820.80 Receiving, in-process, and finished device acceptance.
820.86 Acceptance status.

Subpart I—Nonconforming Product

820.90 Nonconforming product.

Subpart J—Corrective and Preventive Action

820.100 Corrective and preventive action.

Subpart K—Labeling and Packaging Control

820.120 Device labeling.
820.130 Device packaging.

Subpart L—Handling, Storage, Distribution, and Installation

820.140 Handling.
820.150 Storage.
820.160 Distribution.
820.170 Installation.

Subpart M—Records

820.180 General requirements.
820.181 Device master record.
820.184 Device history record.
820.186 Quality system record.
820.198 Complaint files.

Subpart N—Servicing

820.200 Servicing.

Subpart O—Statistical Techniques

820.250 Statistical techniques.
Authority: Secs. 501, 502, 510, 513, 514, 515, 518, 519, 520, 522, 701, 704, 801, 803 of the Federal Food, Drug, and Cosmetic Act (21 U.S.C. 351, 352, 360, 360c, 360d, 360e, 360h, 360i, 360j, 360l, 371, 374, 381, 383).

Subpart A—General Provisions

§ 820.1 Scope.

(a) *Applicability.*

(1) Current good manufacturing practice (CGMP) requirements are set forth in this quality system regulation. The requirements in this part govern the methods used in, and the facilities and controls used for, the design, manufacture, packaging, labeling, storage, installation, and servicing of all finished devices intended for human use. The requirements in this part are intended to ensure that finished devices will be safe and effective and otherwise in compliance with the Federal Food, Drug, and Cosmetic Act (the act). This part establishes basic requirements applicable to manufacturers of finished medical devices. If a manufacturer engages in only some operations subject to the requirements in this part, and not in others, that manufacturer need only comply with those requirements applicable to the operations in which it is engaged. With respect to class I devices, design controls apply only to those devices listed in § 820.30(a)(2). This regulation does not apply to manufacturers of components or parts of finished devices, but such manufacturers

are encouraged to use appropriate provisions of this regulation as guidance. Manufacturers of human blood and blood components are not subject to this part, but are subject to part 606 of this chapter.

(2) The provisions of this part shall be applicable to any finished device as defined in this part, intended for human use, that is manufactured, imported, or offered for import in any State or Territory of the United States, the District of Columbia, or the Commonwealth of Puerto Rico.

(3) In this regulation the term "where appropriate" is used several times. When a requirement is qualified by "where appropriate," it is deemed to be "appropriate" unless the manufacturer can document justification otherwise. A requirement is "appropriate" if nonimplementation could reasonably be expected to result in the product not meeting its specified requirements or the manufacturer not being able to carry out any necessary corrective action.

(b) *Limitations.* The quality system regulation in this part supplements regulations in other parts of this chapter except where explicitly stated otherwise. In the event that it is impossible to comply with all applicable regulations, both in this part and in other parts of this chapter, the regulations specifically applicable to the device in question shall supersede any other generally applicable requirements.

(c) *Authority.* Part 820 is established and issued under authority of sections 501, 502, 510, 513, 514, 515, 518, 519, 520, 522, 701, 704, 801, 803 of the act (21 U.S.C. 351, 352, 360, 360c, 360d, 360e, 360h, 360i, 360j, 360l, 371, 374, 381, 383). The failure to comply with any applicable provision in this part renders a device adulterated under section 501(h) of the act. Such a device, as well as any person responsible for the failure to comply, is subject to regulatory action.

(d) *Foreign manufacturers.* If a manufacturer who offers devices for import into the United States refuses to permit or allow the completion of a Food and Drug Administration (FDA) inspection of the foreign facility for the purpose of determining compliance with this part, it shall appear for purposes of section 801(a) of the act, that the methods used in, and the facilities and controls used for, the design, manufacture, packaging, labeling, storage, installation, or servicing of any devices produced at such facility that are offered for import into the United States do not conform to the requirements of section 520(f) of the act and this part and that the devices manufactured at that facility are adulterated under section 501(h) of the act.

(e) *Exemptions or variances.*

(1) Any person who wishes to petition for an exemption or variance from any device quality system requirement is subject to the requirements of section 520(f)(2) of the act. Petitions for an exemption or variance shall be submitted according to the procedures set forth in § 10.30 of this chapter, the FDA"s administrative procedures. Guidance is available from the Center for Devices and Radiological Health, Division of Small Manufacturers Assistance, (HFZ–220), 1350 Piccard Dr., Rockville, MD 20850, U.S.A., telephone 1–800–638–2041 or 1–301–443–6597, FAX 301–443–8818.

(2) FDA may initiate and grant a variance from any device quality system requirement when the agency determines that such variance is in the best interest of the public health. Such variance will remain in effect only so long as there remains a public health need for the device and the device would not likely be made sufficiently available without the variance.

§ 820.3 Definitions.

(a) *Act* means the Federal Food, Drug, and Cosmetic Act, as amended (secs. 201–903, 52 Stat. 1040 et seq., as amended (21 U.S.C. 321–394)). All definitions in section 201 of the act shall apply to the regulations in this part.

(b) *Complaint* means any written, electronic, or oral communication that alleges deficiencies related to the identity, quality, durability, reliability, safety, effectiveness, or performance of a device after it is released for distribution.

(c) *Component* means any raw material, substance, piece, part, software, firmware, labeling, or assembly which is intended to be included as part of the finished, packaged, and labeled device.

(d) *Control* number means any distinctive symbols, such as a distinctive combination of letters or numbers, or both, from which the history of the manufacturing, packaging, labeling, and distribution of a unit, lot, or batch of finished devices can be determined.

(e) *Design history file (DHF)* means a compilation of records which describes the design history of a finished device.

(f) *Design input* means the physical and performance requirements of a device that are used as a basis for device design.

(g) *Design output* means the results of a design effort at each design phase and at the end of the total design effort. The finished design output is the basis for the device master record. The total finished design output consists of the device, its packaging and labeling, and the device master record.

(h) *Design review* means a documented, comprehensive, systematic examination of a design to evaluate the adequacy of the design requirements, to evaluate the capability of the design to meet these requirements, and to identify problems.

(i) *Device history record (DHR)* means a compilation of records containing the production history of a finished device.

(j) *Device master record (DMR)* means a compilation of records containing the procedures and specifications for a finished device.

(k) *Establish* means define, document (in writing or electronically), and implement.

(l) *Finished device* means any device or accessory to any device that is suitable for use or capable of functioning, whether or not it is packaged, labeled, or sterilized.

(m) *Lot or batch* means one or more components or finished devices that consist of a single type, model, class, size, composition, or software version that are manufactured under essentially the same conditions and that are intended to have uniform characteristics and quality within specified limits.

(n) *Management with executive responsibility* means those senior employees of a manufacturer who have the authority to establish or make changes to the manufacturer's quality policy and quality system.

(o) *Manufacturer* means any person who designs, manufactures, fabricates, assembles, or processes a finished device. Manufacturer includes but is not limited to those who perform the functions of contract sterilization, installation, relabeling, remanufacturing, repacking, or specification development, and initial distributors of foreign entities performing these functions.

(p) *Manufacturing material* means any material or substance used in or used to facilitate the manufacturing process, a concomitant constituent, or a byproduct constituent produced during the manufacturing process, which is present in or on the finished device as a residue or impurity not by design or intent of the manufacturer.

(q) *Nonconformity* means the nonfulfillment of a specified requirement.

(r) *Product* means components, manufacturing materials, in-process devices, finished devices, and returned devices.

(s) *Quality* means the totality of features and characteristics that bear on the ability of a device to satisfy fitness-for-use, including safety and performance.

(t) *Quality audit* means a systematic, independent examination of a manufacturer's quality system that is performed at defined intervals and at sufficient frequency to determine whether both quality system activities and the results of such activities comply with quality system procedures, that these procedures are implemented effectively, and that these procedures are suitable to achieve quality system objectives.

(u) *Quality policy* means the overall intentions and direction of an organization with respect to quality, as established by management with executive responsibility.

(v) *Quality system* means the organizational structure, responsibilities, procedures, processes, and resources for implementing quality management.

(w) *Remanufacturer* means any person who processes, conditions, renovates, repackages, restores, or does any other act to a finished device that significantly changes the finished device's performance or safety specifications, or intended use.

(x) *Rework* means action taken on a nonconforming product so that it will fulfill the specified DMR requirements before it is released for distribution.

(y) *Specification* means any requirement with which a product, process, service, or other activity must conform.

(z) *Validation* means confirmation by examination and provision of objective evidence that the particular requirements for a specific intended use can be consistently fulfilled.

(1) *Process validation* means establishing by objective evidence that a process consistently produces a result or product meeting its predetermined specifications.

(2) *Design validation* means establishing by objective evidence that device specifications conform with user needs and intended use(s).

(aa) *Verification* means confirmation by examination and provision of objective evidence that specified requirements have been fulfilled.

§ 820.5 Quality system.

Each manufacturer shall establish and maintain a quality system that is appropriate for the specific medical device(s) designed or manufactured, and that meets the requirements of this part.

Subpart B—Quality System Requirements

§ 820.20 Management responsibility.

(a) *Quality policy.* Management with executive responsibility shall establish its policy and objectives for, and commitment to, quality. Management with executive responsibility shall ensure that the quality policy is understood, implemented, and maintained at all levels of the organization.

(b) *Organization.* Each manufacturer shall establish and maintain an adequate organizational structure to ensure that devices are designed and produced in accordance with the requirements of this part.

(1) *Responsibility and authority.* Each manufacturer shall establish the appropriate responsibility, authority, and interrelation of all personnel who manage, perform, and assess work affecting quality, and provide the independence and authority necessary to perform these tasks.

(2) *Resources.* Each manufacturer shall provide adequate resources, including the assignment of trained personnel, for management, performance of work, and assessment activities, including internal quality audits, to meet the requirements of this part.

(3) *Management representative.* Management with executive responsibility shall appoint, and document such appointment of, a member of management who, irrespective of other responsibilities, shall have established authority over and responsibility for:

(i) Ensuring that quality system requirements are effectively established and effectively maintained in accordance with this part; and

(ii) Reporting on the performance of the quality system to management with executive responsibility for review.

(c) *Management review.* Management with executive responsibility shall review the suitability and effectiveness of the quality system at defined intervals and with sufficient frequency according to established procedures to ensure that the quality system satisfies the requirements of this part and the manufacturer's established quality policy and objectives. The dates and results of quality system reviews shall be documented.

(d) *Quality planning.* Each manufacturer shall establish a quality plan which defines the quality practices, resources, and activities relevant to devices that are designed and manufactured. The manufacturer shall establish how the requirements for quality will be met.

(e) *Quality system procedures.* Each manufacturer shall establish quality system procedures and instructions. An outline of the structure of the documentation used in the quality system shall be established where appropriate.

§ 820.22 Quality audit.

Each manufacturer shall establish procedures for quality audits and conduct such audits to assure that the quality system is in compliance with the established quality system requirements and to determine the effectiveness of the quality system. Quality audits shall be conducted by individuals who do not have direct responsibility for the matters being audited. Corrective action(s), including a reaudit of deficient matters,

shall be taken when necessary. A report of the results of each quality audit, and reaudit(s) where taken, shall be made and such reports shall be reviewed by management having responsibility for the matters audited. The dates and results of quality audits and reaudits shall be documented.

§ 820.25 Personnel.

(a) *General.* Each manufacturer shall have sufficient personnel with the necessary education, background, training, and experience to assure that all activities required by this part are correctly performed.

(b) *Training.* Each manufacturer shall establish procedures for identifying training needs and ensure that all personnel are trained to adequately perform their assigned responsibilities. Training shall be documented.

(1) As part of their training, personnel shall be made aware of device defects which may occur from the improper performance of their specific jobs.

(2) Personnel who perform verification and validation activities shall be made aware of defects and errors that may be encountered as part of their job functions.

Subpart C—Design Controls

§ 820.30 Design controls.

(a) General.

(1) Each manufacturer of any class III or class II device, and the class I devices listed in paragraph (a)(2) of this section, shall establish and maintain procedures to control the design of the device in order to ensure that specified design requirements are met.

(2) The following class I devices are subject to design controls:

(i) Devices automated with computer software; and

(ii) The devices listed in the following chart.

Section	Device
868.6810	Catheter, Tracheobronchial Suction.
878.4460	Glove, Surgeon's.
880.6760	Restraint, Protective.
892.5650	System, Applicator, Radionuclide, Manual.
892.5740	Source, Radionuclide Teletherapy.

(b) *Design and development planning.* Each manufacturer shall establish and maintain plans that describe or reference the design and development activities and define responsibility for implementation. The plans shall identify and describe the interfaces with different groups or activities that provide, or result in, input to the design and development process. The plans shall be reviewed, updated, and approved as design and development evolves.

(c) *Design input.* Each manufacturer shall establish and maintain procedures to ensure that the design requirements relating to a device are appropriate and address the intended use of the device, including the needs of the user and patient. The procedures shall include a mechanism for addressing incomplete, ambiguous, or conflicting requirements. The design input requirements shall be documented and shall be reviewed and approved by a designated individual(s). The approval, including the date and signature of the individual(s) approving the requirements, shall be documented.

(d) *Design output.* Each manufacturer shall establish and maintain procedures for defining and documenting design output in terms that allow an adequate evaluation of conformance to design input requirements. Design output procedures shall contain or make reference to acceptance criteria and shall ensure that those design outputs that are essential for the proper functioning of the device are identified. Design output shall be documented, reviewed, and approved before release. The approval, including the date and signature of the individual(s) approving the output, shall be documented.

(e) *Design review.* Each manufacturer shall establish and maintain procedures to ensure that formal documented reviews of the design results are planned and conducted at appropriate stages of the device's design development. The procedures shall ensure that participants at each design review include representatives of all functions concerned with the design stage being reviewed and an individual(s) who does not have direct responsibility for the design stage being reviewed, as well as any specialists needed. The results of a design review, including identification of the design, the date, and the individual(s) performing the review, shall be documented in the design history file (the DHF).

(f) *Design verification.* Each manufacturer shall establish and maintain procedures for verifying the device design. Design verification shall confirm that the design output meets the design input requirements. The results of the design verification, including identification of the design, method(s), the date, and the individual(s) performing the verification, shall be documented in the DHF.

(g) *Design validation.* Each manufacturer shall establish and maintain procedures for validating the device design. Design validation shall be performed under defined operating conditions on initial production units, lots, or batches, or their equivalents. Design validation shall ensure that devices conform to defined user needs and intended uses and shall include testing of production units under actual or simulated use conditions. Design validation shall include software validation and risk analysis, where appropriate. The results of the design validation, including identification of the design, method(s), the date, and the individual(s) performing the validation, shall be documented in the DHF.

(h) *Design transfer.* Each manufacturer shall establish and maintain procedures to ensure that the device design is correctly translated into production specifications.

(i) *Design changes.* Each manufacturer shall establish and maintain procedures for the identification, documentation, validation or where appropriate verification, review, and approval of design changes before their implementation.

(j) *Design history file.* Each manufacturer shall establish and maintain a DHF for each type of device. The DHF shall contain or reference the records necessary to demonstrate that the design was developed in accordance with the approved design plan and the requirements of this part.

Subpart D—Document Controls

§ 820.40 Document controls.
Each manufacturer shall establish and maintain procedures to control all documents that are required by this part. The procedures shall provide for the following:

(a) *Document approval and distribution.* Each manufacturer shall designate an individual(s) to review for adequacy and approve prior to issuance all documents established to meet the requirements of this part. The approval, including the date and signature of the individual(s) approving the document, shall be documented. Documents established to meet the requirements of this part shall be available at all locations for which they are designated, used, or otherwise necessary, and all obsolete documents shall be promptly removed from all points of use or otherwise prevented from unintended use.

(b) *Document changes.* Changes to documents shall be reviewed and approved by an individual(s) in the same function or organization that performed the original review and approval, unless specifically designated otherwise. Approved changes shall be communicated to the appropriate personnel in a timely manner. Each manufacturer shall maintain records of changes to documents. Change records shall include a description of the change, identification of the affected documents, the signature of the approving individual(s), the approval date, and when the change becomes effective.

Subpart E—Purchasing Controls

§ 820.50 Purchasing controls.
Each manufacturer shall establish and maintain procedures to ensure that all purchased or otherwise received product and services conform to specified requirements.

(a) *Evaluation of suppliers, contractors, and consultants.* Each manufacturer shall establish and maintain the requirements, including quality requirements, that must be met by suppliers, contractors, and consultants. Each manufacturer shall:

(1) Evaluate and select potential suppliers, contractors, and consultants on the basis of their ability to meet specified requirements, including quality requirements. The evaluation shall be documented.

(2) Define the type and extent of control to be exercised over the product, services, suppliers, contractors, and consultants, based on the evaluation results.

(3) Establish and maintain records of acceptable suppliers, contractors, and consultants.

(b) Purchasing data. Each manufacturer shall establish and maintain data that clearly describe or reference the specified requirements, including quality requirements, for purchased or otherwise received product and services. Purchasing documents shall include, where possible, an agreement that the suppliers, contractors, and consultants agree to notify the manufacturer of changes in the product or service so that manufacturers may determine whether the changes may affect the quality of a finished device. Purchasing data shall be approved in accordance with § 820.40.

Subpart F—Identification and Traceability

§ 820.60 Identification.
Each manufacturer shall establish and maintain procedures for identifying product during all stages of receipt, production, distribution, and installation to prevent mixups.

§ 820.65 Traceability.
Each manufacturer of a device that is intended for surgical implant into the body or to support or sustain life and whose failure to perform when properly used in accordance with instructions for use provided in the labeling can be reasonably expected to result in a significant injury to the user shall establish and maintain procedures for identifying with a control number each unit, lot, or batch of finished devices and where appropriate components. The procedures shall facilitate corrective action. Such identification shall be documented in the DHR.

Subpart G—Production and Process Controls

§ 820.70 Production and process controls.
(a) *General.* Each manufacturer shall develop, conduct, control, and monitor production processes to ensure that a device conforms to its specifications. Where deviations from device specifications could occur as a result of the manufacturing process, the manufacturer shall establish and maintain process control procedures that describe any process controls necessary to ensure conformance to specifications. Where process controls are needed they shall include:

(1) Documented instructions, standard operating procedures (SOP's), and methods that define and control the manner of production;

(2) Monitoring and control of process parameters and component and device characteristics during production;

(3) Compliance with specified reference standards or codes;

(4) The approval of processes and process equipment; and

(5) Criteria for workmanship which shall be expressed in documented standards or by means of identified and approved representative samples.

(b) *Production and process changes.* Each manufacturer shall establish and maintain procedures for changes to a specification, method, process, or procedure. Such changes shall be verified or where appropriate validated according to § 820.75, before implementation and these activities shall be documented. Changes shall be approved in accordance with § 820.40.

(c) *Environmental control.* Where environmental conditions could reasonably be expected to have an adverse effect on product quality, the manufacturer shall establish and maintain procedures to adequately control these environmental conditions. Environmental control system(s) shall be periodically inspected to verify that the system, including necessary equipment, is adequate and functioning properly. These activities shall be documented and reviewed.

(d) *Personnel.* Each manufacturer shall establish and maintain requirements for the health, cleanliness, personal practices, and clothing of personnel if contact between such personnel and product or environment could reasonably be expected to have an adverse effect on product quality. The manufacturer shall ensure that maintenance and other personnel who are required to work temporarily under special environmental conditions are appropriately trained or supervised by a trained individual.

(e) *Contamination control.* Each manufacturer shall establish and maintain procedures to prevent contamination of equipment or product by substances that could reasonably be expected to have an adverse effect on product quality.

(f) *Buildings.* Buildings shall be of suitable design and contain sufficient space to perform necessary operations, prevent mixups, and assure orderly handling.

(g) *Equipment.* Each manufacturer shall ensure that all equipment used in the manufacturing process meets specified requirements and is appropriately designed, constructed, placed, and installed to facilitate maintenance, adjustment, cleaning, and use.

(1) *Maintenance schedule.* Each manufacturer shall establish and maintain schedules for the adjustment, cleaning, and other maintenance of equipment to ensure that manufacturing specifications are met. Maintenance activities, including the date and individual(s) performing the maintenance activities, shall be documented.

(2) *Inspection.* Each manufacturer shall conduct periodic inspections in accordance with established procedures to ensure adherence to applicable equipment maintenance schedules. The inspections, including the date and individual(s) conducting the inspections, shall be documented.

(3) *Adjustment.* Each manufacturer shall ensure that any inherent limitations or allowable tolerances are visibly posted on or near equipment requiring periodic adjustments or are readily available to personnel performing these adjustments.

(h) *Manufacturing material.* Where a manufacturing material could reasonably be expected to have an adverse effect on product quality, the manufacturer shall establish and maintain procedures for the use and removal of such manufacturing material to ensure that it is removed or limited to an amount that does not adversely affect the device's quality. The removal or reduction of such manufacturing material shall be documented.

(i) *Automated processes.* When computers or automated data processing systems are used as part of production or the quality system, the manufacturer shall validate computer software for its intended use according to an established protocol. All software changes shall be validated before approval and issuance. These validation activities and results shall be documented.

§ 820.72 Inspection, measuring, and test equipment.

(a) *Control of inspection, measuring, and test equipment.* Each manufacturer shall ensure that all inspection, measuring, and test equipment, including mechanical, automated, or electronic inspection and test equipment, is suitable for its intended purposes and is capable of producing valid results. Each manufacturer shall establish and maintain procedures to ensure that equipment is routinely calibrated, inspected, checked, and maintained. The procedures shall include provisions for handling, preservation, and storage of equipment, so that its accuracy and fitness for use are maintained. These activities shall be documented.

(b) *Calibration.* Calibration procedures shall include specific directions and limits for accuracy and precision. When accuracy and precision limits are not met, there shall be provisions for remedial action to reestablish the limits and to evaluate whether there was any adverse effect on the device's quality. These activities shall be documented.

(1) *Calibration standards.* Calibration standards used for inspection, measuring, and test equipment shall be traceable to national or international standards. If national or international standards are not practical or available, the manufacturer shall use an independent reproducible standard. If no applicable standard exists, the manufacturer shall establish and maintain an in-house standard.

(2) *Calibration records.* The equipment identification, calibration dates, the individual performing each calibration, and the next calibration date shall be documented. These records shall be displayed on or near each piece of equipment or shall be readily available to the personnel using such equipment and to the individuals responsible for calibrating the equipment.

§ 820.75 Process validation.

(a) Where the results of a process cannot be fully verified by subsequent inspection and test, the process shall be validated with a high degree of assurance and approved according to established procedures. The validation activities and results, including the date and signature of the individual(s) approving the validation and where appropriate the major equipment validated, shall be documented.

(b) Each manufacturer shall establish and maintain procedures for monitoring and control of process parameters for validated processes to ensure that the specified requirements continue to be met.

(1) Each manufacturer shall ensure that validated processes are performed by qualified individual(s).

(2) For validated processes, the monitoring and control methods and data, the date performed, and, where appropriate, the individual(s) performing the process or the major equipment used shall be documented.

(c) When changes or process deviations occur, the manufacturer shall review and evaluate the process and perform revalidation where appropriate. These activities shall be documented.

Subpart H—Acceptance Activities

§ 820.80 Receiving, in-process, and finished device acceptance.

(a) *General.* Each manufacturer shall establish and maintain procedures for acceptance activities. Acceptance activities include inspections, tests, or other verification activities.

(b) *Receiving acceptance activities.* Each manufacturer shall establish and maintain procedures for acceptance of incoming product. Incoming product shall be inspected, tested, or otherwise verified as conforming to specified requirements. Acceptance or rejection shall be documented.

(c) *In-process acceptance activities.* Each manufacturer shall establish and maintain acceptance procedures, where appropriate, to ensure that specified requirements for in-process product are met. Such procedures shall ensure that in-process product is controlled until the required inspection and tests or other verification activities have been completed, or necessary approvals are received, and are documented.

(d) *Final acceptance activities.* Each manufacturer shall establish and maintain procedures for finished device acceptance to ensure that each production run, lot, or batch of finished devices meets acceptance criteria. Finished devices shall be held in quarantine or otherwise adequately controlled until released. Finished devices shall not be released for distribution until:

(1) The activities required in the DMR are completed;

(2) the associated data and documentation is reviewed;

(3) the release is authorized by the signature of a designated individual(s); and

(4) the authorization is dated.

(e) *Acceptance records.* Each manufacturer shall document acceptance activities required by this part. These records shall include:

(1) The acceptance activities performed;

(2) the dates acceptance activities are performed;

(3) the results;

(4) the signature of the individual(s) conducting the acceptance activities; and

(5) where appropriate the equipment used. These records shall be part of the DHR.

§ 820.86 Acceptance status.

Each manufacturer shall identify by suitable means the acceptance status of product, to indicate the conformance or nonconformance of product with acceptance criteria. The identification of acceptance status shall be maintained throughout manufacturing, packaging, labeling, installation, and servicing of the product to ensure that only product which has passed the required acceptance activities is distributed, used, or installed.

Subpart I—Nonconforming Product

§ 820.90 Nonconforming product.

(a) *Control of nonconforming product.* Each manufacturer shall establish and maintain procedures to control product that does not conform to specified requirements. The procedures shall address the identification, documentation, evaluation, segregation, and disposition of nonconforming product. The evaluation of nonconformance shall include a determination of the need for an investigation and notification of the persons or organizations responsible for the nonconformance. The evaluation and any investigation shall be documented.

(b) *Nonconformity review and disposition.*

(1) Each manufacturer shall establish and maintain procedures that define the responsibility for review and the authority for the disposition of nonconforming product. The procedures shall set forth the review and disposition process. Disposition of nonconforming product shall be documented. Documentation shall include the justification for use of nonconforming product and the signature of the individual(s) authorizing the use.

(2) Each manufacturer shall establish and maintain procedures for rework, to include retesting and reevaluation of the nonconforming product after rework, to ensure that the product meets its current approved specifications. Rework and reevaluation activities, including a determination of any adverse effect from the rework upon the product, shall be documented in the DHR.

Subpart J—Corrective and Preventive Action

§ 820.100 Corrective and preventive action.

(a) Each manufacturer shall establish and maintain procedures for implementing corrective and preventive action. The procedures shall include requirements for:

(1) Analyzing processes, work operations, concessions, quality audit reports, quality records, service records, complaints, returned product, and other sources of quality data to identify existing and potential causes of nonconforming product, or other quality problems. Appropriate statistical methodology shall be employed where necessary to detect recurring quality problems;

(2) Investigating the cause of nonconformities relating to product, processes, and the quality system;

(3) Identifying the action(s) needed to correct and prevent recurrence of nonconforming product and other quality problems;

(4) Verifying or validating the corrective and preventive action to ensure that such action is effective and does not adversely affect the finished device;

(5) Implementing and recording changes in methods and procedures needed to correct and prevent identified quality problems;

(6) Ensuring that information related to quality problems or nonconforming product is disseminated to those directly responsible for assuring the quality of such product or the prevention of such problems; and

(7) Submitting relevant information on identified quality problems, as well as corrective and preventive actions, for management review.

(b) All activities required under this section, and their results, shall be documented.

Subpart K—Labeling and Packaging Control

§ 820.120 Device labeling.
Each manufacturer shall establish and maintain procedures to control labeling activities

(a) *Label integrity.* Labels shall be printed and applied so as to remain legible and affixed during the customary conditions of processing, storage, handling, distribution, and where appropriate use.

(b) *Labeling inspection.* Labeling shall not be released for storage or use until a designated individual(s) has examined the labeling for accuracy including, where applicable, the correct expiration date, control number, storage instructions, handling instructions, and any additional processing instructions. The release, including the date and signature of the individual(s) performing the examination, shall be documented in the DHR.

(c) *Labeling storage.* Each manufacturer shall store labeling in a manner that provides proper identification and is designed to prevent mixups.

(d) *Labeling operations.* Each manufacturer shall control labeling and packaging operations to prevent labeling mixups. The label and labeling used for each production unit, lot, or batch shall be documented in the DHR.

(e) *Control number.* Where a control number is required by § 820.65, that control number shall be on or shall accompany the device through distribution.

§ 820.130 Device packaging.
Each manufacturer shall ensure that device packaging and shipping containers are designed and constructed to protect the device from alteration or damage during the customary conditions of processing, storage, handling, and distribution.

Subpart L—Handling, Storage, Distribution, and Installation

§ 820.140 Handling.
Each manufacturer shall establish and maintain procedures to ensure that mixups, damage, deterioration, contamination, or other adverse effects to product do not occur during handling.

§ 820.150 Storage.
(a) Each manufacturer shall establish and maintain procedures for the control of storage areas and stock rooms for product to prevent mixups, damage, deterioration, contamination, or other adverse effects pending use or distribution and to ensure that no obsolete, rejected, or deteriorated product is used or distributed. When the quality of product deteriorates over time, it shall be stored in a manner to facilitate proper stock rotation, and its condition shall be assessed as appropriate.

(b) Each manufacturer shall establish and maintain procedures that describe the methods for authorizing receipt from and dispatch to storage areas and stock rooms.

§ 820.160 Distribution.
(a) Each manufacturer shall establish and maintain procedures for control and distribution of finished devices to ensure that only those devices approved for release are distributed and that purchase orders are reviewed to ensure that ambiguities and errors are resolved before devices are released for distribution. Where a device's fitness for use or quality deteriorates over time, the procedures shall ensure that expired devices or devices deteriorated beyond acceptable fitness for use are not distributed.

(b) Each manufacturer shall maintain distribution records which include or refer to the location of:

(1) The name and address of the initial consignee;

(2) The identification and quantity of devices shipped;

(3) The date shipped; and

(4) Any control number(s) used.

§ 820.170 Installation.
(a) Each manufacturer of a device requiring installation shall establish and maintain adequate installation and inspection instructions, and where appropriate test procedures. Instructions and procedures shall include directions for ensuring proper installation so that the device will perform as intended after installation. The manufacturer shall distribute the instructions and procedures with the device or otherwise make them available to the person(s) installing the device.

(b) The person installing the device shall ensure that the installation, inspection, and any required testing are performed in accordance with the manufacturer's instructions and procedures and shall document the inspection and any test results to demonstrate proper installation.

Subpart M—Records

§ 820.180 General requirements.
All records required by this part shall be maintained at the manufacturing establishment or other location that is reasonably accessible to responsible officials of the manufacturer and to employees of FDA designated to perform inspections. Such records, including those not stored at the

inspected establishment, shall be made readily available for review and copying by FDA employee(s). Such records shall be legible and shall be stored to minimize deterioration and to prevent loss. Those records stored in automated data processing systems shall be backed up.

(a) *Confidentiality.* Records deemed confidential by the manufacturer may be marked to aid FDA in determining whether information may be disclosed under the public information regulation in part 20 of this chapter.

(b) *Record retention period.* All records required by this part shall be retained for a period of time equivalent to the design and expected life of the device, but in no case less than 2 years from the date of release for commercial distribution by the manufacturer.

(c) *Exceptions.* This section does not apply to the reports required by § 820.20(c) Management review, § 820.22 Quality audits, and supplier audit reports used to meet the requirements of § 820.50(a) Evaluation of suppliers, contractors, and consultants, but does apply to procedures established under these provisions. Upon request of a designated employee of FDA, an employee in management with executive responsibility shall certify in writing that the management reviews and quality audits required under this part, and supplier audits where applicable, have been performed and documented, the dates on which they were performed, and that any required corrective action has been undertaken.

§ 820.181 Device master record.

Each manufacturer shall maintain device master records (DMR's). Each manufacturer shall ensure that each DMR is prepared and approved in accordance with § 820.40. The DMR for each type of device shall include, or refer to the location of, the following information:

(a) Device specifications including appropriate drawings, composition, formulation, component specifications, and software specifications;

(b) Production process specifications including the appropriate equipment specifications, production methods, production procedures, and production environment specifications;

(c) Quality assurance procedures and specifications including acceptance criteria and the quality assurance equipment to be used;

(d) Packaging and labeling specifications, including methods and processes used; and

(e) Installation, maintenance, and servicing procedures and methods.

§ 820.184 Device history record.

Each manufacturer shall maintain device history records (DHR's). Each manufacturer shall establish and maintain procedures to ensure that DHR's for each batch, lot, or unit are maintained to demonstrate that the device is manufactured in accordance with the DMR and the requirements of this part. The DHR shall include, or refer to the location of, the following information:

(a) The dates of manufacture;

(b) The quantity manufactured;

(c) The quantity released for distribution;

(d) The acceptance records which demonstrate the device is manufactured in accordance with the DMR;

(e) The primary identification label and labeling used for each production unit; and

(f) Any device identification(s) and control number(s) used.

§ 820.186 Quality system record.

Each manufacturer shall maintain a quality system record (QSR). The QSR shall include, or refer to the location of, procedures and the documentation of activities required by this part that are not specific to a particular type of device(s), including, but not limited to, the records required by § 820.20. Each manufacturer shall ensure that the QSR is prepared and approved in accordance with § 820.40.

§ 820.198 Complaint files.

(a) Each manufacturer shall maintain complaint files. Each manufacturer shall establish and maintain procedures for receiving, reviewing, and evaluating complaints by a formally designated unit. Such procedures shall ensure that:

(1) All complaints are processed in a uniform and timely manner;

(2) Oral complaints are documented upon receipt; and

(3) Complaints are evaluated to determine whether the complaint represents an event which is required to be reported to FDA under part 803 or 804 of this chapter, Medical Device Reporting.

(b) Each manufacturer shall review and evaluate all complaints to determine whether an investigation is necessary. When no investigation is made, the manufacturer shall maintain a record that includes the reason no investigation was made and the name of the individual responsible for the decision not to investigate.

(c) Any complaint involving the possible failure of a device, labeling, or packaging to meet any of its specifications shall be reviewed, evaluated, and investigated, unless such investigation has already been performed for a similar complaint and another investigation is not necessary.

(d) Any complaint that represents an event which must be reported to FDA under part 803 or 804 of this chapter shall be promptly reviewed, evaluated, and investigated by a designated individual(s) and shall be maintained in a separate portion of the complaint files or otherwise clearly identified. In addition to the information required by § 820.198(e), records of investigation under this paragraph shall include a determination of:

(1) Whether the device failed to meet specifications;

(2) Whether the device was being used for treatment or diagnosis; and

(3) The relationship, if any, of the device to the reported incident or adverse event.

(e) When an investigation is made under this section, a record of the investigation shall be maintained by the formally designated unit identified in paragraph (a) of this section. The record of investigation shall include:

(1) The name of the device;

(2) The date the complaint was received;

(3) Any device identification(s) and control number(s) used;

(4) The name, address, and phone number of the complainant;

(5) The nature and details of the complaint;

(6) The dates and results of the investigation;

(7) Any corrective action taken; and

(8) Any reply to the complainant.

(f) When the manufacturer's formally designated complaint unit is located at a site separate from the manufacturing establishment, the investigated complaint(s) and the record(s) of investigation shall be reasonably accessible to the manufacturing establishment.

(g) If a manufacturer's formally designated complaint unit is located outside of the United States, records required by this section shall be reasonably accessible in the United States at either:

(1) A location in the United States where the manufacturer's records are regularly kept; or

(2) The location of the initial distributor.

Subpart N—Servicing

§ 820.200 Servicing.

(a) Where servicing is a specified requirement, each manufacturer shall establish and maintain instructions and procedures for performing and verifying that the servicing meets the specified requirements.

(b) Each manufacturer shall analyze service reports with appropriate statistical methodology in accordance with § 820.100.

(c) Each manufacturer who receives a service report that represents an event which must be reported to FDA under part 803 or 804 of this chapter shall automatically consider the report a complaint and shall process it in accordance with the requirements of § 820.198.

(d) Service reports shall be documented and shall include:

(1) The name of the device serviced;

(2) Any device identification(s) and control number(s) used;

(3) The date of service;

(4) The individual(s) servicing the device;

(5) The service performed; and

(6) The test and inspection data.

Subpart O—Statistical Techniques

§ 820.250 Statistical techniques.

(a) Where appropriate, each manufacturer shall establish and maintain procedures for identifying valid statistical techniques required for establishing, controlling, and verifying the acceptability of process capability and product characteristics.

(b) Sampling plans, when used, shall be written and based on a valid statistical rationale. Each manufacturer shall establish and maintain procedures to ensure that sampling methods are adequate for their intended use and to ensure that when changes occur the sampling plans are reviewed. These activities shall be documented.

Dated: October 1, 1996. David A. Kessler, Commissioner of Food and Drugs.
Donna E. Shalala, Secretary of Health and Human Services.

ATTACHMENT B

DEPARTMENT OF HEALTH AND HUMAN SERVICES

FOOD AND DRUG ADMINISTRATION
21 CFR Part 806
Medical Devices; Reports of Corrections and Removals
AGENCY: Food and Drug Administration, HHS.

PART 806—MEDICAL DEVICE CORRECTIONS AND REMOVALS

Subpart A—General Provisions

Sec.
806.1 Scope.
806.2 Definitions.

Subpart B—Reports and Records

806.10 Reports of corrections and removals.

806.20 Records of corrections and removals not required to be reported.

806.30 FDA access to records.
806.40 Public availability of reports.
Authority: Secs. 502, 510, 519, 520, 701, and 704 of the Federal Food, Drug, and Cosmetic Act (21 U.S.C. 352, 360, 360i, 360j, 371, 374).

Subpart A—General Provisions

Sec. 806.1 Scope.

(a) This part implements the provisions of section 519(f) of the Federal Food, Drug, and Cosmetic Act (the act) requiring device manufacturers and distributors, including importers, to report promptly to the Food and Drug

Administration (FDA) certain actions concerning device corrections and removals, and to maintain records of all corrections and removals regardless of whether such corrections and removals are required to be reported to FDA.

(b) The following actions are exempt from the reporting requirements of this part:

(1) Actions undertaken by device manufacturers and distributors, including importers, to improve the performance or quality of a device but that do not reduce a risk to health posed by the device or remedy a violation of the act caused by the device.

(2) Market withdrawals as defined in Sec. 806.2(h).

(3) Routine servicing as defined in Sec. 806.2(k).

(4) Stock recoveries as defined in Sec. 806.2(l).

Sec. 806.2 Definitions.

As used in this part:

(a) "Act" means the Federal Food, Drug, and Cosmetic Act.

(b) "Agency" or ``FDA'' means the Food and Drug Administration.

(c) "Consignee" means any person or firm that has received, purchased, or used a device subject to correction or removal.

(d) "Correction" means the repair, modification, adjustment, relabeling, destruction, or inspection (including patient monitoring) of a device without its physical removal from its point of use to some other location.

(e) "Correction or removal report number" means the number that uniquely identifies each report submitted.

(f) "Distributor" means any person, including any person who imports a device into the United States, who furthers the marketing of a device from the original place of manufacture to the person who makes final delivery or sale to the ultimate user, but who does not repackage or otherwise change the container, wrapper, or labeling of the device or device package.

(g) "Manufacturer" means any person who manufactures, prepares, propagates, compounds, assembles, or processes a device by chemical, physical, biological, or other procedures. The term includes any person who:

(1) Repackages or otherwise changes the container, wrapper, or labeling of a device in furtherance of the distribution of the device from the original place of manufacture to the person who makes final delivery or sale to the ultimate user or consumer;

(2) Initiates specifications for devices that are manufactured by a second party for subsequent distribution by the person initiating the specifications; or

(3) Manufactures components or accessories which are devices that are ready to be used and are intended to be commercially distributed and are intended to be used as is, or are processed by a licensed practitioner or other qualified person to meet the needs of a particular patient.

(h) "Market withdrawal" means a correction or removal of a distributed device that involves a minor violation of the act that would not be subject to legal action by FDA or that involves no violation of the act, e.g., normal stock rotation practices.

(i) "Removal" means the physical removal of a device from its point of use to some other location for repair, modification, adjustment, relabeling, destruction, or inspection.

(j) "Risk to health" means

(1) A reasonable probability that use of, or exposure to, the product will cause serious adverse health consequences or death; or

(2) That use of, or exposure to, the product may cause temporary or medically reversible adverse health consequences, or an outcome where the probability of serious adverse health consequences is remote.

(k) "Routine servicing" means any regularly scheduled maintenance of a device, including the replacement of parts at the end of their normal life expectancy, e.g., calibration, replacement of batteries, and responses to normal wear and tear. Repairs of an unexpected nature, replacement of parts earlier than their normal life expectancy, or identical repairs or replacements of multiple units of a device are not routine servicing.

(l) "Stock recovery" means the correction or removal of a device that has not been marketed or that has not left the direct control of the manufacturer, i.e., the device is located on the premises owned, or under the control of, the manufacturer, and no portion of the lot, model, code, or other relevant unit involved in the corrective or removal action has been released for sale or use.

Subpart B—Reports and Records

Sec. 806.10 Reports of corrections and removals.

(a) Each device manufacturer, importer, or distributor shall submit a written report to FDA of any correction or removal of a device initiated by such manufacturer or distributor if the correction or removal was initiated:

(1) To reduce a risk to health posed by the device; or

(2) To remedy a violation of the act caused by the device which may present a risk to health unless the information has already been provided as set forth in paragraph (f) of this section or the corrective or removal action is exempt from the reporting requirements under Sec. 806.1(b).

(b) The manufacturer, importer, or distributor shall submit any report required by paragraph (a) of this section within 10-working days of initiating such correction or removal. The report shall be submitted to the appropriate FDA district office listed in Sec. 5.115 of this chapter. A foreign manufacturer or owner or operator of devices must submit reports of corrective or removal actions.

(c) The manufacturer, importer, or distributor shall include the following information in the report:

(1) The seven digit registration number of the entity responsible for submission of the report of corrective or removal action (if applicable), the month, day, and year that the report is made, and a sequence number (i.e., 001 for the first report, 002 for the second report, 003 etc.), and the report type designation "C" or "R". For example, the complete number for the first correction report submitted on June 1, 1997, will appear as follows for a firm with the

registration number 1234567: 1234567-6/1/97-001-C. The second correction report number submitted by the same firm on July 1, 1997, would be 1234567-7/1/97-002-C etc. For removals, the number will appear as follows: 1234567-6/1/97-001-R and 1234567-7/1/97-002-R, etc. Firms that do not have a seven digit registration number may use seven zeros followed by the month, date, year, and sequence number (i.e. 0000000-6/1/97-001-C for corrections and 0000000-7/1/97-001-R for removals). Reports received without a seven digit registration number will be assigned a seven digit central file number by the district office reviewing the reports.

(2) The name, address, and telephone number of the manufacturer, importer, or distributor and the name, title, address, and telephone number of the manufacturer, importer, or distributor's representative responsible for conducting the device correction or removal.

(3) The brand name and the common name, classification name, or usual name of the device and the intended use of the device.

(4) Marketing status of the device, i.e., any applicable premarket notification number, premarket approval number, or indication that the device is a preamendments device, and the device listing number. A manufacturer, importer, or distributor that does not have an FDA establishment registration number shall indicate in the report whether it has ever registered with FDA.

(5) The model, catalog, or code number of the device and the manufacturing lot or serial number of the device or other identification number.

(6) The manufacturer's name, address, telephone number, and contact person if different from that of the person submitting the report.

(7) A description of the event(s) giving rise to the information reported and the corrective or removal actions that have been, and are expected to be taken.

(8) Any illness or injuries that have occurred with use of the device. If applicable, include the medical device report numbers.

(9) The total number of devices manufactured or distributed subject to the correction or removal and the number in the same batch, lot, or equivalent unit of production subject to the correction or removal.

(10) The date of manufacture or distribution and the device's expiration date or expected life.

(11) The names, addresses, and telephone numbers of all domestic and foreign consignees of the device and the dates and number of devices distributed to each such consignee.

(12) A copy of all communications regarding the correction or removal and the names and addresses of all recipients of the communications not provided in accordance with paragraph (c)(11) of this section.

(13) If any required information is not immediately available, a statement as to why it is not available and when it will be submitted.

(d) If, after submitting a report under this part, a manufacturer, distributor, or importer determines that the same correction or removal should be extended to additional lots or batches of the same device, the manufacturer,

distributor, or importer shall within 10-working days of initiating the extension of the correction or removal, amend the report by submitting an amendment citing the original report number assigned according to paragraph (c)(1) of this section, all of the information required by paragraph (c)(2), and any information required by paragraphs (c)(3) through (c)(12) of this section that is different from the information submitted in the original report. The manufacturer, distributor, or importer shall also provide a statement in accordance with paragraph (c)(13) of this section for any required information that is not readily available.

(e) A report submitted by a manufacturer, distributor, or importer under this section (and any release by FDA of that report or information) does not necessarily reflect a conclusion by the manufacturer, distributor, importer, or FDA that the report or information constitutes an admission that the device caused or contributed to a death or serious injury. A manufacturer, distributor, or importer need not admit, and may deny, that the report or information submitted under this section constitutes an admission that the device caused or contributed to a death or serious injury.

(f) No report of a correction or removal is required under this part, if a report of the correction or removal is required and has been submitted under parts 803, 804, or 1004 of this chapter.

Sec. 806.20 Records of corrections and removals not required to be reported.

(a) Each device manufacturer, importer, or distributor who initiates a correction or removal of a device that is not required to be reported to FDA under Sec. 806.10 shall keep a record of such correction or removal.

(b) Records of corrections and removals not required to be reported to FDA under Sec. 806.10 shall contain the following information:

(1) The brand name, common or usual name, classification, name and product code if known, and the intended use of the device.

(2) The model, catalog, or code number of the device and the manufacturing lot or serial number of the device or other identification number.

(3) A description of the event(s) giving rise to the information reported and the corrective or removal action that has been, and is expected to be taken.

(4) Justification for not reporting the correction or removal action to FDA, which shall contain conclusions and any followups, and be reviewed and evaluated by a designated person.

(5) A copy of all communications regarding the correction or removal.

(c) The manufacturer, importer, or distributor shall retain all records required under this section for a period of 2 years beyond the expected life of the device, even if the manufacturer, importer, or distributor has ceased to manufacture, import, or distribute the device. Records required to be maintained under paragraph (b) of this section must be transferred to the new manufacturer, importer, or distributor of the device and maintained for the required period of time.

Sec. 806.30 FDA access to records.

Each device manufacturer, importer, or distributor required under this part to maintain records concerning corrections or removals and every person who is in charge or custody of such records shall, upon request of an officer or employee designated by FDA and under section 704(e) of the act, permit such officer or employee at all reasonable times to have access to, and to copy and verify, such records and reports.

Sec. 806.40 Public availability of reports.

(a) Any report submitted under this part is available for public disclosure in accordance with part 20 of this chapter.

(b) Before public disclosure of a report, FDA will delete from the report:

(1) Any information that constitutes trade secret or confidential commercial or financial information under Sec. 20.61 of this chapter; and

(2) Any personnel, medical, or similar information, including the serial numbers of implanted devices, which would constitute a clearly unwarranted invasion of personal privacy under Sec. 20.63 of this chapter or 5 U.S.C. 552(b)(6); provided, that except for the information under Sec. 20.61 of this chapter or 5 U.S.C. 552(b)(4), FDA will disclose to a patient who requests a report all the information in the report concerning that patient.

Dated: May 9, 1997.
William B. Schultz,
Deputy Commissioner for Policy.

Please note that the FDA Modernization Act (FDAMA) of 1997 changed some of the elements of these regulations. FDA is expected to propose FDAMA changes to these MDR regulations by the end of 1998 or early in 1999.

ATTACHMENT C

DEPARTMENT OF HEALTH AND HUMAN SERVICES

FOOD AND DRUG ADMINISTRATION

21 CFR Part 803

Imports, Medical Devices, Reporting and Recordkeeping Requirements.

Therefore, under the Federal Food, Drug, and Cosmetic Act and under the authority delegated to the Commissioner of Food and Drugs, chapter I of title 21 of the Code of Federal Regulations is amended as follows:

1. Part 803 is revised to read as follows:

PART 803—MEDICAL DEVICE REPORTING

Subpart A—General Provisions
803.1 Scope.
803.3 Definitions.
803.9 Public availability of reports.
803.10 General description of reports required from user facilities and manufacturers.
803.11 Obtaining the forms.
803.12 Where to submit reports.
803.13 English reporting requirement.
803.14 Electronic reporting.
803.15 Requests for additional information.
803.16 Disclaimers.
803.17 Written MDR procedures.
803.18 Files.
803.19 Exemptions, variances, and alternative reporting requirements.

Subpart B--Generally Applicable Requirements for Individual Adverse Event Reports
803.20 How to report.
803.21 Reporting codes.
803.22 When not to file.

Subpart C—User Facility Reporting Requirements
803.30 Individual adverse event reports; user facilities.
803.32 Individual adverse event report data elements.
803.33 Semiannual reports.

Subpart D—[Reserved]

Subpart E—Manufacturer Reporting Requirements
803.50 Individual adverse event reports; manufacturers.
803.52 Individual adverse event report data elements.
803.53 Five-day reports.
803.55 Baseline reports.
803.56 Supplemental reports.
803.57 Annual certification.
803.58 Foreign manufacturers.
Authority: Secs. 502, 510, 519, 520, 701, 704 of the Federal Food, Drug, and Cosmetic Act (21 U.S.C. 352, 360, 360i, 360j, 371, 374).

Subpart A—General Provisions

Sec. 803.1 Scope.

(a) This part establishes requirements for medical device reporting. Under this part, device user facilities and manufacturers must report deaths and serious injuries to which a device has or may have caused or contributed, and must establish and maintain adverse event files. Manufacturers are also required to report certain device malfunctions and submit an annual report to FDA certifying that the correct number of medical device reports were filed during the previous 12-month period or, alternatively, that no reports were required during that same time period. These reports will assist FDA in protecting the public health by helping to ensure that devices are not adulterated or misbranded and are safe and effective for their intended use.

(b) This part supplements and does not supersede other provisions of this subchapter, including the provisions of part 820 of this chapter.

(c) References in this part to regulatory sections of the Code of Federal Regulations are to Chapter I of title 21, unless otherwise noted.

Sec. 803.3 Definitions.

(a) Act means the Federal Food, Drug, and Cosmetic Act.

(b) Ambulatory surgical facility (ASF) means a distinct entity that operates for the primary purpose of furnishing same day outpatient surgical services to patients. An ASF may be either an independent entity (i.e., not a part of a provider of services or any other facility) or operated by another medical entity (e.g., under the common ownership, licensure or control of an entity). An ASF is subject to this regulation regardless of whether it is licensed by a Federal, State, municipal, or local government or regardless of whether it is accredited by a recognized accreditation organization. If an adverse event meets the criteria for reporting, the ASF must report that event regardless of the nature or location of the medical service provided by the ASF.

(c) Become aware means that an employee of the entity required to report has acquired information reasonably suggesting a reportable adverse event has occurred. Device user facilities are considered to have "become aware" when medical personnel, as defined in paragraph (r) of this section, who are employed by or otherwise formally affiliated with the facility, acquire such information about a reportable event. Manufacturers are considered to have "become aware" of an event when:

(1) Any employee becomes aware of a reportable event that is required to be reported within 30 days, or that is required to be reported within 5 days pursuant to a written request from FDA under 803.53(b); and

(2) Any employee, who is a person with management or supervisory responsibilities over persons with regulatory, scientific, or technical responsibilities, or a person whose duties relate to the collection and reporting of adverse events, becomes aware that a reportable MDR

event or events, from any information, including any trend analysis, necessitate remedial action to prevent an unreasonable risk of substantial harm to the public health.

(d) Caused or contributed means that a death or serious injury was or may have been attributed to a medical device, or that a medical device was or may have been a factor in a death or serious injury, including events occurring as a result of:

(1) Failure;

(2) Malfunction;

(3) Improper or inadequate design;

(4) Manufacture;

(5) Labeling; or

(6) User error.

(e)

(1) Device family means a group of one or more devices manufactured by or for the same manufacturer and having the same:

(i) Basic design and performance characteristics related to device safety and effectiveness,

(ii) Intended use and function, and

(iii) Device classification and product code.

(2) Devices that differ only in minor ways not related to safety or effectiveness can be considered to be in the same device family. Factors such as brand name and common name of the device and whether the devices were introduced into commercial distribution under the same 510(k) or premarket approval application (PMA), may be considered in grouping products into device families.

(f) Device user facility means a hospital, ambulatory surgical facility, nursing home, outpatient diagnostic facility, or outpatient treatment facility as defined in paragraphs (l), (b), (s), (t), and (u), respectively, of this section, which is not a "physician's office," as defined in paragraph (w) of this section. School nurse offices and employee health units are not device user facilities.

(g) [Reserved]

(h) [Reserved]

(i) Expected life of a device (required on the manufacturer's baseline report) means the time that a device is expected to remain functional after it is placed into use. Certain implanted devices have specified "end of life" (EOL) dates. Other devices are not labeled as to their respective EOL, but are expected to remain operational through maintenance, repair, upgrades, etc., for an estimated period of time.

(j) FDA means the Food and Drug Administration.

(k) Five-day report means a medical device report that must be submitted by a manufacturer to FDA pursuant to Sec. 803.53, on FDA Form 3500A or electronic equivalent as approved under Sec. 803.14, within 5 work days.

(l) Hospital means a distinct entity that operates for the primary purpose of providing diagnostic, therapeutic (medical, occupational,\speech, physical, etc.), surgical and other patient services for specific and general medical conditions. Hospitals include general, chronic disease, rehabilitative, psychiatric, and other special-purpose facilities. A hospital may be either independent (e.g., not a part of a provider of services or any other facility) or may be operated by another medical entity (e.g., under the common ownership, licensure or control of another entity). A hospital is covered by this regulation regardless of whether it is licensed by a Federal, State, municipal or local government or whether it is accredited by a recognized accreditation organization. If an adverse event meets the criteria for reporting, the hospital must report that event regardless of the nature or location of the medical service provided by the hospital.

(m) Malfunction means the failure of a device to meet its performance specifications or otherwise perform as intended. Performance specifications include all claims made in the labeling for the device. The intended performance of a device refers to the intended use for which the device is labeled or marketed, as defined in Sec. 801.4 of this chapter.

(n) Manufacturer means any person who manufactures, prepares, propagates, compounds, assembles, or processes a device by chemical, physical, biological, or other procedure. The term includes any person who:

(1) Repackages or otherwise changes the container, wrapper or labeling of a device in furtherance of the distribution of the device from the original place of manufacture;

(2) Initiates specifications for devices that are manufactured by a second party for subsequent distribution by the person initiating the specifications;

(3) Manufactures components or accessories which are devices that are ready to be used and are intended to be commercially distributed and intended to be used as is, or are processed by a licensed practitioner or other qualified person to meet the needs of a particular patient; or

(4) Is the U.S. agent of a foreign manufacturer.

(o) Manufacturer report number means the number that uniquely identifies each individual adverse event report submitted by a manufacturer. This number consists of three parts as follows:

(1) The FDA registration number for the manufacturing site of the reported device. (If the manufacturing site does not have a registration number, FDA will assign a temporary number until the site is officially registered. The manufacturer will be informed of the temporary number.);

(2) The four-digit calendar year in which the report is submitted; and

(3) The five-digit sequence number of the reports submitted during the year, starting with 00001. (For example, the complete number will appear 1234567-1995-00001.)

(p) MDR means medical device report.

(q) MDR reportable event (or reportable event) means:

(1) An event about which user facilities become aware of information that reasonably suggests that a device has or may have caused or contributed to a death or serious injury; or

(2) An event about which manufacturers have received or become aware of information that reasonably suggests that one of their marketed devices:

(i) May have caused or contributed to a death or serious injury; or

(ii) Has malfunctioned and that the device or a similar device marketed by the manufacturer would be likely to cause or contribute to a death or serious injury if the malfunction were to recur.

(r) Medical personnel, as used in this part, means an individual who:

(1) Is licensed, registered, or certified by a State, territory, or other governing body, to administer health care;

(2) Has received a diploma or a degree in a professional or scientific discipline;

(3) Is an employee responsible for receiving medical complaints or adverse event reports; or

(4) Is a supervisor of such persons.

(s)

(1) Nursing home means an independent entity (i.e., not a part of a provider of services or any other facility) or one operated by another medical entity (e.g., under the common ownership, licensure, or control of an entity) that operates for the primary purpose of providing:

(i) Skilled nursing care and related services for persons who require medical or nursing care;

(ii) Hospice care to the terminally ill; or

(iii) Services for the rehabilitation of the injured, disabled, or sick.

(2) A nursing home is subject to this regulation regardless of whether it is licensed by a Federal, State, municipal, or local government or whether it is accredited by a recognized accreditation organization. If an adverse event meets the criteria for reporting, the nursing home must report that event regardless of the nature, or location of the medical service provided by the nursing home.

(t)

(1) Outpatient diagnostic facility means a distinct entity that:

(i) Operates for the primary purpose of conducting medical diagnostic tests on patients;

(ii) Does not assume ongoing responsibility for patient care; and

(iii) Provides its services for use by other medical personnel. (Examples include diagnostic radiography, mammography, ultrasonography, electrocardiography, magnetic resonance imaging, computerized axial tomography and in-vitro testing).

(2) An outpatient diagnostic facility may be either independent (i.e., not a part of a provider of services or any other facility) or operated by another medical entity (e.g., under the common ownership, licensure, or control of an entity). An outpatient diagnostic facility is covered by this regulation regardless of whether it is licensed by a Federal, State, municipal, or local government or whether it is accredited by a recognized accreditation organization. If an adverse event meets the criteria for reporting, the outpatient diagnostic facility must report that event regardless of the nature or location of the medical service provided by the outpatient diagnostic facility.

(u)

(1) Outpatient treatment facility means a distinct entity that operates for the primary purpose of providing nonsurgical therapeutic (medical, occupational, or physical) care on an outpatient basis or home health care

setting. Outpatient treatment facilities include ambulance providers, rescue services, and home health care groups. Examples of services provided by outpatient treatment facilities include: Cardiac defibrillation, chemotherapy, radiotherapy, pain control, dialysis, speech or physical therapy, and treatment for substance abuse.

(2) An outpatient treatment facility may be either independent (i.e., not a part of a provider of services or any other facility) or operated by another medical entity (e.g., under the common ownership, licensure, or control of an entity). An outpatient treatment facility is covered by this regulation regardless of whether it is licensed by a Federal, State, municipal, or local government or whether it is accredited by a recognized accreditation organization. If an adverse event meets the criteria for reporting, the outpatient treatment facility must report that event regardless of the nature or location of the medical service provided by the outpatient treatment facility.

(v) Patient of the facility means any individual who is being diagnosed or treated and/or receiving medical care at or under the control or authority of the facility. For the purposes of this part, the definition encompasses employees of the facility or individuals affiliated with the facility, who in the course of their duties suffer a device-related death or serious injury that has or may have been caused or contributed to by a device used at the facility.

(w) Physician's office means a facility that operates as the office of a physician or other health care professional (e.g., dentist, chiropractor, optometrist, nurse practitioner, school nurse offices, school clinics, employee health clinics, or free-standing care units) for the primary purpose of examination, evaluation, and treatment or referral of patients. A physician's office may be independent, a group practice, or part of a Health Maintenance Organization.

(x) [Reserved]

(y) Remedial action means, for the purposes of this subpart, any action other than routine maintenance or servicing, of a device where such action is necessary to prevent recurrence of a reportable event.

(z) [Reserved]

(aa)

(1) Serious injury means an injury or illness that:

(i) Is life-threatening;

(ii) Results in permanent impairment of a body function or permanent damage to body structure; or

(iii) Necessitates medical or surgical intervention to preclude permanent impairment of a body function or permanent damage to a body structure.

(2) Permanent means, for purposes of this subpart, irreversible impairment or damage to a body structure or function, excluding trivial impairment or damage.

(bb) Shelf life, as required on the manufacturer's baseline report, means the maximum time a device will remain functional from the date of manufacture until it is used in patient care. Some devices have an expiration date on their labeling indicating the maximum time they can be stored before losing their ability to perform their intended function.

(cc) [Reserved]

(dd)

(1) User facility report number means the number that uniquely identifies each report submitted by a user facility to manufacturers and FDA. This number consists of three parts as follows:

(i) The user facility's 10-digit Health Care Financing Administration (HCFA) number (if the HCFA number has fewer than 10 digits, fill the remaining spaces with zeros);

(ii) The four-digit calendar year in which the report is submitted; and

(iii) The four-digit sequence number of the reports submitted for the year, starting with 0001. (For example, a complete number will appear as follows: 1234560000-1995-0001.)

(2) If a facility has more than one HCFA number, it must select one that will be used for all of its MDR reports. If a facility has no HCFA number, it should use all zeros in the appropriate space in its initial report (e.g., 0000000000-1995-0001) and FDA will assign a number for future use. The number assigned will be used in FDA's record of that report and in any correspondence with the user facility. All zeros should be used subsequent to the first report if the user does not receive FDA's assigned number before the next report is submitted. If a facility has multiple sites, the primary site can report centrally and use one reporting number for all sites if the primary site provides the name, address and HCFA number for each respective site.

(ee) Work day means Monday through Friday, excluding Federal holidays.

Sec. 803.9 Public availability of reports.

(a) Any report, including any FDA record of a telephone report, submitted under this part is available for public disclosure in accordance with part 20 of this chapter.

(b) Before public disclosure of a report, FDA will delete from the report:

(1) Any information that constitutes trade secret or confidential commercial or financial information under Sec. 20.61 of this chapter;

(2) Any personal, medical, and similar information (including the serial number of implanted devices), which would constitute an invasion of personal privacy under Sec. 20.63 of this chapter. FDA will disclose to a patient who requests a report, all the information in the report concerning that patient, as provided in Sec. 20.61 of this chapter; and

(3) Any names and other identifying information of a third party voluntarily submitting an adverse event report.

(c) FDA may not disclose the identity of a device user facility which makes a report under this part except in connection with:

(1) An action brought to enforce section 301(q) of the act, including the failure or refusal to furnish material or information required by section 519 of the act;

(2) A communication to a manufacturer of a device which is the subject of a report required by a user facility under Sec. 803.30;

(3) A disclosure relating to a manufacturer or distributor adverse event report that is required under section 519(a) of the act; or

(4) A disclosure to employees of the Department of Health and Human Services, to the Department of Justice, or to the duly authorized committees and subcommittees of the Congress.

Sec. 803.10 General description of reports required from user facilities and manufacturers.

(a) Device user facilities. User facilities must submit the following reports, which are described more fully in subpart C of this part.

(1) User facilities must submit MDR reports of individual adverse events within 10 days after the user facility becomes aware of an MDR reportable event as described in Secs. 803.30 and 803.32.

(i) User facilities must submit reports of device-related deaths to FDA and to the manufacturer, if known.

(ii) User facilities must submit reports of device-related serious injuries to manufacturers, or to FDA, if the manufacturer is unknown.

(2) User facilities must submit semiannual reports as described in Sec. 803.33.

(b) [Reserved]

(c) Device manufacturers. Manufacturers must submit the following reports as described more fully in subpart E of this part:

(1) MDR reports of individual adverse events within 30 days after the manufacturer becomes aware of a reportable death, serious injury, or malfunction as described in Secs. 803.50 and 803.52.

(2) MDR reports of individual adverse events within 5 days of:

(i) Becoming aware that a reportable MDR event requires remedial action to prevent an unreasonable risk of substantial harm to the public health or,

(ii) Becoming aware of an MDR reportable event for which FDA has made a written request, as described in Sec. 803.53.

(3) Annual baseline reports as described in Sec. 803.55.

(4) Supplemental reports if they obtain information that was not provided in an initial report as described in Sec. 803.56.

(5) Annual certification to FDA of the number of MDR reports filed during the preceding year as described in Sec. 803.57.

Sec. 803.11 Obtaining the forms.

User facilities and manufacturers must submit all reports of individual adverse events on FDA Form 3500A (MEDWATCH form) or in an electronic equivalent as approved under Sec. 803.14. This form and all other forms referenced in this section can also be obtained from the Consolidated Forms and Publications Office, Washington Commerce Center, 3222 Hubbard Rd., Landover, MD 20785, or from the Division of Small Manufacturers Assistance, Office of Health and Industry Programs, Center for Devices and Radiological Health, 1350 Piccard Dr. (HFZ-220), Rockville, MD 20850, telephone facsimile (FAX) 301-443-8818. FDA Form 3500A may also be obtained from the Food and Drug Administration, MEDWATCH (HF-2), 5600 Fishers Lane, rm. 9-57, Rockville, MD 20850, 301-443-0117.

Sec. 803.12 Where to submit reports.

(a) Any written report or additional information required under this part shall be submitted to: Food and Drug Administration, Center for Devices and Radiological Health, Medical Device Reporting, PO Box 3002, Rockville, MD 20847-3002.

(b) Each report and its envelope shall be specifically identified, e.g., "User Facility Report," "SemiAnnual Report," "Manufacturer Report," "5-Day Report," "Baseline Report," etc.

(c) If an entity is confronted with a public health emergency, this can be brought to FDA's attention by contacting the FDA Emergency Operations Branch (HFC-162), Office of Regional Operations, at 301-443-1240, and should be followed by the submission of a FAX report to 301 443-3757.

(d) A voluntary telephone report may be submitted to, or information regarding voluntary reporting may be obtained from, the MEDWATCH hotline at 800-FDA-1088.

Sec. 803.13 English reporting requirement.

(a) All reports required in this part which are submitted in writing or electronic equivalent shall be submitted to FDA in English.

(b) All reports required in this part which are submitted on an electronic medium shall be submitted to FDA in a manner consistent with Sec. 803.14.

Sec. 803.14 Electronic reporting.

(a) Any report required by this part may be submitted electronically with prior written consent from FDA. Such consent is revocable. Electronic report submissions include alternative reporting media (magnetic tape, disc, etc.) and computer-to-computer communication.

(b) Any electronic report meeting electronic reporting standards, guidelines, or other procedures developed by the agency for MDR reporting will be deemed to have prior approval for use.

Sec. 803.15 Requests for additional information.

(a) FDA may determine that protection of the public health requires additional or clarifying information for medical device reports submitted to FDA under this part. In these instances, and in cases when the additional information is beyond the scope of FDA reporting forms or is not readily accessible, the agency will notify the reporting entity in writing of the additional information that is required.

(b) Any request under this section shall state the reason or purpose for which the information is being requested, specify the date that the information is to be submitted and clearly relate the request to a reported event. All verbal requests will be confirmed in writing by the agency.

Sec. 803.16 Disclaimers.

A report or other information submitted by a reporting entity under this part, and any release by FDA of that report or information, does not necessarily reflect a conclusion by the party submitting the report or by FDA that the report or information constitutes an admission that the device, or the reporting entity or its employees, caused or contributed to the reportable event. The reporting entity need not admit and may deny that the report or information submitted under this part constitutes an admission that the device, the party submitting the report, or employees thereof, caused or contributed to a reportable event.

Sec. 803.17 Written MDR procedures.

User facilities and manufacturers shall develop, maintain, and implement written MDR procedures for the following:

(a) Internal systems that provide for:

(1) Timely and effective identification, communication, and evaluation of events that may be subject to medical device reporting requirements;

(2) A standardized review process/procedure for determining when an event meets the criteria for reporting under this part; and

(3) Timely transmission of complete medical device reports to FDA and/or manufacturers;

(b) Documentation and recordkeeping requirements for:

(1) Information that was evaluated to determine if an event was reportable;

(2) All medical device reports and information submitted to FDA and manufacturers;

(3) Any information that was evaluated for the purpose of preparing the submission of semiannual reports or certification; and

(4) Systems that ensure access to information that facilitates timely followup and inspection by FDA.

Sec. 803.18 Files.

(a) User facilities and manufacturers shall establish and maintain MDR event files. All MDR event files shall be prominently identified as such and filed to facilitate timely access.

(b)

(1) For purposes of this part, "MDR event files" are written or electronic files maintained by user facilities and manufacturers. MDR event files may incorporate references to other information, e.g., medical records, patient files, engineering reports, etc., in lieu of copying and maintaining duplicates in this file. MDR event files must contain:

(i) Information in the possession of the reporting entity or references to information related to the adverse event, including all documentation of the entity's deliberations and decisionmaking processes used to determine if a device-related death, serious injury, or malfunction was or was not reportable under this part.

(ii) Copies of all MDR forms, as required by this part, and other information related to the event that was submitted to FDA and other entities (e.g., a distributor or manufacturer).

(2) User facilities and manufacturers shall permit any authorized FDA employee during all reasonable times to access, to copy, and to verify the records required by this part.

(c) User facilities shall retain an MDR event file relating to an adverse event for a period of 2 years from the date of the event. Manufacturers shall retain an MDR event file relating to an adverse event for a period of 2 years from the date of the event or a period of time equivalent to the expected life of the device, whichever is greater. MDR event files must be maintained for the time periods described in this paragraph even if the device is no longer distributed.

(d) [Reserved]

(e) The manufacturer may maintain MDR event files as part of its complaint file, under Sec. 820.198 of this chapter, provided that such records are prominently identified as MDR reportable events. A report submitted under this subpart A shall not be considered to comply with this part unless the event has been evaluated in accordance with the requirements of Secs. 820.162 and 820.198 of this chapter. MDR files shall contain an explanation of why any information required by this part was not submitted or could not be obtained. The results of the evaluation of each event are to be documented and maintained in the manufacturer's MDR event file.

Sec. 803.19 Exemptions, variances, and alternative reporting requirements.

(a) The following persons are exempt from the reporting requirements under this part.

(1) An individual who is a licensed practitioner who prescribes or administers devices intended for use in humans and who manufactures or imports devices solely for use in diagnosing and treating persons with whom the practitioner has a "physician- patient" relationship.

(2) An individual who manufactures devices intended for use in humans solely for such person's use in research or teaching and not for sale, including any person who is subject to alternative reporting requirements under the investigational device exemption regulations, parts 812 and 813 of this chapter, which require reporting of all adverse device effects.

(3) Dental laboratories, or optical laboratories.

(b) Manufacturers or user facilities may request exemptions or variances from any or all of the reporting requirements in this part. The request shall be in writing and include information necessary to identify the firm and device, a complete statement of the request for exemption, variance, or alternative reporting, and an explanation why the request is justified.

(c) FDA may grant in writing, to a manufacturer or user facility, an exemption, variance or alternative from, or to, any or all of the reporting requirements in this part and may change the frequency of reporting to quarterly, semi-annually, annually, or other appropriate time period. These modifications may be initiated by a request as specified in this section, or at the discretion of FDA. When granting such modifications, FDA may impose other reporting requirements to ensure the protection of public health.

(d) FDA may revoke or modify in writing an exemption, variance, or alternative reporting requirements if FDA determines that protection of the public health justifies the modification or a return to the requirements as stated in this part.

(e) Firms granted a reporting modification by FDA shall provide any reports or information required by that approval. The conditions of the approval will replace and supersede the reporting requirement specified in this part until such time that FDA revokes or modifies the alternative reporting requirements in accordance with paragraph (d) of this section.

Subpart B—Generally Applicable Requirements for Individual Adverse Event Reports

Sec. 803.20 How to report.

(a) Description of form. There are two versions of the MEDWATCH form for individual reports of adverse events. FDA Form 3500 is available for use by health professionals and consumers for the submission of voluntary reports regarding FDA-regulated products. FDA Form 3500A is the mandatory reporting form to be used for submitting reports by user facilities and manufacturers of FDA-regulated products. The form has sections that must be completed by all reporters and other sections that must be completed only by the user facility or manufacturer.

(1) The front of FDA Form 3500A is to be filled out by all reporters. The front of the form requests information regarding the patient, the event, the device and "initial reporter" (i.e., the first person or entity that submitted the information to the user facility, manufacturer, or distributor).

(2) The back part of the form contains sections to be completed by user facilities and manufacturers. User facilities must complete section F; device manufacturers must complete sections G and H. Manufacturers are not required to recopy information submitted to them on a Form 3500A unless the information is being copied onto an electronic medium. If the manufacturer corrects or supplies information missing from the other reporter's 3500A form, it should attach a copy of that form to the manufacturer's report form. If the information from the other reporter's 3500A form is complete and correct, the manufacturer can fill in the remaining information on the same form.

(b) Reporting standards.

(1) User facilities are required to submit MDR reports to:

(i) The device manufacturer and to FDA within 10 days of becoming aware of information that reasonably suggests that a device has or may have caused or contributed to a death; or

(ii) The manufacturer within 10 days of becoming aware of information that reasonably suggests that a device has or may have caused or contributed to a serious injury. Such reports shall be submitted to FDA if the device manufacturer is not known.

(2) [Reserved]

(3) Manufacturers are required to submit MDR reports to FDA:

(i) Within 30 days of becoming aware of information that reasonably suggests that a device may have caused or contributed to a death or serious injury; or

(ii) Within 30 days of becoming aware of information that reasonably suggests a device has malfunctioned and that device or a similar device marketed by the manufacturer would be likely to cause a death or serious injury if the malfunction were to recur; or

(iii) Within 5 days if required by Sec. 803.53.

(c) Information that reasonably suggests a reportable event occurred

(1) Information that reasonably suggests that a device has or may have caused or contributed to an MDR reportable event (i.e., death, serious injury, and, for manufacturers, a malfunction that would be likely to cause or contribute to a death or serious injury if the malfunction were to recur) includes any information, such as professional, scientific or medical facts and observations or opinions, that would reasonably suggest that a device has caused or may have caused or contributed to a reportable event.

(2) Entities required to report under this part do not have to report adverse events for which there is information that would cause a person who is qualified to make a medical judgment (e.g., a physician, nurse, risk manager, or biomedical engineer) to reach a reasonable conclusion that a device did not cause or contribute to a death or serious injury, or that a malfunction would not be likely to cause or contribute to a death or serious injury if it were to recur. Information which leads the qualified person to determine that a device-related event is or is not reportable must be contained in the MDR event files, as described in Sec. 803.18.

Sec. 803.21 Reporting codes.

(a) FDA has developed a MEDWATCH Mandatory Reporting Form Coding Manual for use with medical device reports. This manual contains codes for hundreds of adverse events for use with FDA Form 3500A. The coding manual is available from the Division of Small Manufacturer Assistance, Center for Devices and Radiological Health, 1350 Piccard Dr., Rockville, MD 20850, FAX 301-443-8818.

(b) FDA may use additional coding of information on the reporting forms or modify the existing codes on an ad hoc or generic basis. In such cases, FDA will ensure that the new coding information is available to all reporters

Sec. 803.22 When not to file.

(a) Only one medical device report from the user facility or manufacturer is required under this part if the reporting entity becomes aware of information from multiple sources regarding the same patient and same event.

(b) A medical device report that would otherwise be required under this section is not required if:

(1) The user facility or manufacturer determines that the information received is erroneous in that a device-related adverse event did not occur. Documentation of such reports shall be retained in MDR files for time periods specified in Sec. 803.18.

(2) The manufacturer determines that the device was manufactured by another manufacturer. Any reportable event information that is erroneously sent to a manufacturer shall be forwarded to FDA, with a cover letter explaining that the device in question was not manufactured by that firm.

Subpart C—User Facility Reporting Requirements

Sec. 803.30 Individual adverse event reports; user facilities.

(a) Reporting standard. A user facility shall submit the following reports to the manufacturer or to FDA, or both, as specified below:

(1) Reports of death. Whenever a user facility receives or otherwise becomes aware of information, from any source, that reasonably suggests that a device has or may have caused or contributed to the death of a patient of the facility, the facility shall as soon as practicable, but not later than 10 work days after becoming aware of the information, report the information required by Sec. 803.32 to FDA, on FDA Form 3500A, or an electronic equivalent as approved under Sec. 803.14, and if the identity of the manufacturer is known, to the device manufacturer.

(2) Reports of serious injury. Whenever a user facility receives or otherwise becomes aware of information, from any source, that reasonably suggests that a device has or may have caused or contributed to a serious injury to a patient of the facility, the facility shall, as soon as practicable but not later than 10 work days after becoming aware of the information, report the information required by Sec. 803.32, on FDA Form 3500A or electronic equivalent, as approved under Sec. 803.14, to the manufacturer of the device. If the identity of the manufacturer is not known, the report shall be submitted to FDA.

(b) Information that is reasonably known to user facilities. User facilities must provide all information required in this subpart C that is reasonably known to them. Such information includes information found in documents in the possession of the user facility and any information that becomes available as a result of reasonable followup within the facility. A user facility is not required to evaluate or investigate the event by obtaining or evaluating information that is not reasonably known to it.

Sec. 803.32 Individual adverse event report data elements. User facility reports shall contain the following information, reasonably known to them as described in 803.30(b), which corresponds to the format of FDA Form 3500A:

(a) Patient information (Block A) shall contain the following:

(1) Patient name or other identifier;

(2) Patient age at the time of event, or date of birth;

(3) Patient gender; and

(4) Patient weight.

(b) Adverse event or product problem (Block B) shall contain the following:

(1) Identification of adverse event or product problem;

(2) Outcomes attributed to the adverse event, e.g., death; or serious injury, that is:

(i) Life threatening injury or illness;

(ii) Disability resulting in permanent impairment of a body function or permanent damage to a body structure; or

(iii) Injury or illness that requires intervention to prevent permanent impairment of a body structure or function;

(3) Date of event;

(4) Date of report by the initial reporter;

(5) Description of event or problem, including a discussion of how the device was involved, nature of the problem, patient followup or required treatment, and any environmental conditions that may have influenced the event;

(6) Description of relevant tests including dates and laboratory data; and

(7) Description of other relevant history including pre- existing medical conditions.

(c) Device information (Block D) shall contain the following:

(1) Brand name;

(2) Type of device;

(3) Manufacturer name and address;

(4) Operator of the device (health professional, patient, lay user, other);

(5) Expiration date;

(6) Model number, catalog number, serial number, lot number, or other identifying number;

(7) Date of device implantation (month, day, year);

(8) Date of device explantation (month, day, year);

(9) Whether device was available for evaluation and whether device was returned to the manufacturer; if so, the date it was returned to the manufacturer; and

(10) Concomitant medical products and therapy dates. (Do not list products that were used to treat the event.)

(d) Initial reporter information (Block E) shall contain the following:

(1) Name, address, and telephone number of the reporter who initially provided information to the user facility, manufacturer, or distributor;

(2) Whether the initial reporter is a health professional;

(3) Occupation; and

(4) Whether initial reporter also sent a copy of the report to FDA, if known.

(e) User facility information (Block F) shall contain the following:

(1) Whether reporter is a user facility;

(2) User facility number;

(3) User facility address;

(4) Contact person;

(5) Contact person's telephone number;

(6) Date the user facility became aware of the event (month, day, year);

(7) Type of report (initial or followup (if followup, include report number of initial report));

(8) Date of the user facility report (month, day, year);

(9) Approximate age of device;

(10) Event problem codes—patient code and device code (refer to FDA "Coding Manual For Form 3500A");

(11) Whether a report was sent to FDA and the date it was sent (month, day, year);

(12) Location, where event occurred;

(13) Whether report was sent to the manufacturer and the date it was sent (month, day, year); and

(14) Manufacturer name and address; if available.

Sec. 803.33 Semiannual reports.

(a) Each user facility shall submit to FDA a semiannual report on FDA Form 3419, or electronic equivalent as approved by FDA under Sec. 803.14. Semiannual reports shall be submitted by January 1 (for reports made July through December) and by July 1 (for reports made January through June) of each year. The semiannual report and envelope shall be clearly identified and submitted to FDA with information that includes:

(1) User facility's HCFA provider number used for medical device reports, or number assigned by FDA for reporting purposes in accordance with Sec. 803.3(dd);

(2) Reporting year and period, e.g., January through June or July through December;

(3) Facility's name and complete address;

(4) Total number of reports attached or summarized;

(5) Date of the semiannual report and the lowest and highest user facility report number of medical device reports submitted during the report period, e.g., 1234567890-1995-0001 through 1000;

(6) Name, position title, and complete address of the individual designated as the facility contact person responsible for reporting to FDA and whether that person is a new contact for that facility; and

(7) Information for each reportable event that occurred during the semiannual reporting period including:

(i) User facility report number;

(ii) Name and address of the device manufacturer;

(iii) Device brand name and common name;

(iv) Product model, catalog, serial and lot number;

(v) A brief description of the event reported to the manufacturer and/or FDA; and

(vi) Where the report was submitted, i.e., to FDA, manufacturer, distributor, etc.

(b) In lieu of submitting the information in paragraph (a)(7) of this section, a user facility may submit a copy of FDA Form 3500A, or an electronic equivalent as approved under section 803.14, for each medical device report submitted to FDA and/or manufacturers by that facility during the reporting period.

(c) If no reports are submitted to either FDA or manufacturers during these time periods, no semiannual report is required.

Subpart D—[Reserved]

Subpart E—Manufacturer Reporting Requirements

Sec. 803.50 Individual adverse event reports; manufacturers.

(a) Reporting standards. Device manufacturers are required to report within 30 days whenever the manufacturer receives or otherwise becomes aware of information, from any source, that reasonably suggests that a device marketed by the manufacturer:

(1) May have caused or contributed to a death or serious injury; or

(2) Has malfunctioned and such device or similar device marketed by the manufacturer would be likely to cause or contribute to a death or serious injury, if the malfunction were to recur.

(b) Information that is reasonably known to manufacturers.—

(1) Manufacturers must provide all information required in this subpart E that is reasonably known to them. FDA considers the following information to be reasonably known to the manufacturer:

(i) Any information that can be obtained by contacting a user facility, distributor and/or other initial reporter;

(ii) Any information in a manufacturer's possession; or

(iii) Any information that can be obtained by analysis, testing or other evaluation of the device.

(2) Manufacturers are responsible for obtaining and providing FDA with information that is incomplete or missing from reports submitted by user facilities, distributors, and other initial reporters. Manufacturers are also responsible for conducting an investigation of each event, and evaluating the cause of the event. If a manufacturer cannot provide complete information on an MDR report, it must provide a statement explaining why such information was incomplete and the steps taken to obtain the information. Any required information not available at the time of the report, which is obtained after the initial filing, must be provided by the manufacturer in a supplemental report under Sec. 803.56.

Sec. 803.52 Individual adverse event report data elements.

Individual medical device manufacturer reports shall contain the following information, known or reasonably known to them as described in Sec. 803.50(b), which corresponds to the format of FDA Form 3500A:

(a) Patient information (Block A) shall contain the following:

(1) Patient name or other identifier;

(2) Patient age at the time of event, or date of birth;

(3) Patient gender; and

(4) Patient weight.

(b) Adverse event or product problem (Block B) shall contain the following:

(1) Adverse event or product problem;

(2) Outcomes attributed to the adverse event, e.g., death; or serious injury, that is:

(i) Life threatening injury or illness;

(ii) Disability resulting in permanent impairment of a body function or permanent damage to a body structure; or

(iii) Injury or illness that requires intervention to prevent permanent impairment of a body structure or function;

(3) Date of event;

(4) Date of report by the initial reporter;

(5) Description of the event or problem to include a discussion of how the device was involved, nature of the problem, patient followup or required treatment, and any environmental conditions that may have influenced the event;

(6) Description of relevant tests, including dates and laboratory data; and

(7) Other relevant patient history including pre-existing medical conditions.

(c) Device information (Block D) shall contain the following:

(1) Brand name;

(2) Type of device;

(3) Manufacturer name and address;

(4) Operator of the device (health professional, patient, lay user, other);

(5) Expiration date;

(6) Model number, catalog number, serial number, lot number or other identifying number;

(7) Date of device implantation (month, day, year);

(8) Date of device explantation (month, day, year);

(9) Whether the device was available for evaluation, and whether the device was returned to the manufacturer, and if so, the date it was returned to the manufacturer; and

(10) Concomitant medical products and therapy dates. (Do not list products that were used to treat the event.)

(d) Initial reporter information (Block E) shall contain the following:

(1) Name, address, and phone number of the reporter who initially provided information to the user facility, manufacturer, or distributor;

(2) Whether the initial reporter is a health professional;

(3) Occupation; and

(4) Whether the initial reporter also sent a copy of the report to FDA, if known.

(e) All manufacturers (Block G) shall contain the following:

(1) Contact office name and address and device manufacturing site;

(2) Telephone number;

(3) Report sources;

(4) Date received by manufacturer (month, day, year);

(5) Type of report being submitted (e.g., 5-day, initial, supplemental); and

(6) Manufacturer report number.

(f) Device manufacturers (Block H) shall contain the following:

(1) Type of reportable event (death, serious injury, malfunction, etc.);

(2) Type of followup report, if applicable (e.g., correction, response to FDA request, etc.);

(3) If the device was returned to the manufacturer and evaluated by the manufacturer, a summary of the evaluation. If no evaluation was performed, provide an explanation why no evaluation was performed;

(4) Device manufacture date (month, day, year);

(5) Was device labeled for single use;

(6) Evaluation codes (including event codes, method of evaluation, result, and conclusion codes) (refer to FDA "Coding Manual for Form 3500A");

(7) Whether remedial action was taken and type;

(8) Whether use of device was initial, reuse, or unknown;

(9) Whether remedial action was reported as a removal or correction under section 519(f) of the act (list the correction/removal report number); and

(10) Additional manufacturer narrative; and/or

(11) Corrected data, including:

(i) Any information missing on the user facility report or distributor report, including missing event codes, or information corrected on such forms after manufacturer verification;

(ii) For each event code provided by the user facility under Sec. 803.32(d)(10) or a distributor, a statement of whether the type of the event represented by the code is addressed in the device labeling; and

(iii) If any required information was not provided, an explanation of why such information was not provided and the steps taken to obtain such information.

Sec. 803.53 Five-day reports.

A manufacturer shall submit a 5-day report to FDA, on Form 3500A or electronic equivalent as approved by FDA under Sec. 803.14 within 5 workdays of:

(a) Becoming aware that a reportable MDR event or events, from any information, including any trend analysis, necessitates remedial action to prevent an unreasonable risk of substantial harm to the public health; or

(b) Becoming aware of an MDR reportable event for which FDA has made a written request for the submission of a 5-day report. When such a request is made, the manufacturer shall submit, without further requests, a 5-day report for all subsequent events of the same nature that involve substantially similar devices for the time period specified in the written request. The time period stated in the original written request can be extended by FDA if it is in the interest of the public health.

Sec. 803.55 Baseline reports.

(a) A manufacturer shall submit a baseline report on FDA Form 3417, or electronic equivalent as approved by FDA under Sec. 803.14 for a device when the device model is first reported under Sec. 803.50.

(b) Each baseline report shall be updated annually, on the anniversary month of the initial submission, after the initial baseline report is submitted. Changes to baseline information shall be reported in the manner described in Sec. 803.56 (i.e., include only the new, changed, or corrected information in the appropriate portion(s) of the report form). Baseline reports shall contain the following:

(1) Name, complete address, and registration number of the manufacturer's reporting site. If the reporting site is not registered, FDA will assign a temporary registration number until the reporting site officially registers. The manufacturer will be informed of the temporary registration number;

(2) FDA registration number of each site where the device is manufactured;

(3) Name, complete address, and telephone number of the individual who has been designated by the manufacturer as its MDR contact and date of the report. For foreign manufacturers, a confirmation that the individual submitting the report is the agent of the manufacturer designated under Sec. 803.58(a) is required;

(4) Product identification, including device family, brand name, generic name, model number, catalog number, product code and any other product identification number or designation;

(5) Identification of any device previously reported in a baseline report that is substantially similar (e.g., same device with a different model number, or same device except for cosmetic differences in color or shape) to the device being reported, including the identification of the previously reported device by model number, catalog number or other product identification, and the date of the baseline report for the previously reported device;

(6) Basis for marketing, including 510(k) premarket notification number or PMA number, if applicable, and whether the device is currently the subject of an approved post-market study under section 522 of the act;

(7) Date the device was initially marketed and, if applicable, the date on which the manufacturer ceased marketing the device;

(8) Shelf life, if applicable, and expected life of the device;

(9) The number of devices manufactured and distributed in the last 12 months and, an estimate of the number of devices in current use; and

(10) Brief description of any methods used to estimate the number of devices distributed and the method used to estimate the number of devices in current use. If this information was provided in a previous baseline report, in lieu of resubmitting the information, it may be referenced by providing the date and product identification for the previous baseline report.

Sec. 803.56 Supplemental reports.

When a manufacturer obtains information required under this part that was not provided because it was not known or was not available when the initial report was submitted, the manufacturer shall submit to FDA the supplemental information within 1 month following receipt of such information. In supplemental reports, the manufacturer shall:

(a) Indicate on the form and the envelope, that the reporting form being submitted is a supplemental report. If the report being supplemented is an FDA Form 3500A report, the manufacturer must select, in Item H-2, the appropriate code for the type of supplemental information being submitted;

(b) Provide the appropriate identification numbers of the report that will be updated with the supplemental information, e.g., original manufacturer report number and user facility report number, if applicable;

(c) For reports that cross reference previous reports, include only the new, changed, or corrected information in the appropriate portion(s) of the respective form(s).

Sec. 803.57 Annual certification.

All manufacturers, including U.S. agents of foreign manufacturers required to report under this section, shall submit a certification report to FDA, on FDA Form 3381, or electronic equivalent as approved under part 814 of this chapter. The date for submission of certification coincides with the date for the firm's annual registration, as designated in Sec. 807.21 of this chapter. The certification period will be the 12-month period ending 1 month before the certification date. The reports shall contain the following information:

(a) Name, address, telephone number, and FDA registration number or FDA-assigned identification number of the firm and whether the firm is a manufacturer;

(b) A statement certifying that:

(1) The firm listed in paragraph (a) of this section has filed reports for all reportable events required under this section during the previous 12-month period. The firm shall also provide a numerical summary of MDR reports that it submitted to FDA during the preceding year; or

(2) The firm listed in paragraph (a) of this section did not receive reportable events for any devices manufactured by the firm during the previous 12-month period.

(c) Certification shall be made by the president, chief executive officer, U.S.-designated agent of a foreign manufacturer, or other official most directly responsible for the firm's operations; and

(d) Name of the manufacturer and registration numbers submitted under paragraph (a) of this section shall be the same as those used in submitting the reports required by Secs. 803.52, 803.53 and 803.55. Multisite manufacturers who choose to certify centrally must identify the reporting sites, by registration number or FDA-assigned identification number and name covered by the certification, and provide the information required by paragraph (b) of this section for each reporting site.

Sec. 803.58 Foreign manufacturers.

(a) Every foreign manufacturer whose devices are distributed in the United States shall designate a U.S. agent to be responsible for reporting in accordance with Sec. 807.40 of this chapter. The U.S. designated agent accepts responsibility for the duties that such designation entails. Upon the effective date of this regulation, foreign manufacturers shall inform FDA, by letter, of the name and address of the U.S. agent designated under this sec-

tion and Sec. 807.40 of this chapter, and shall update this information as necessary. Such updated information shall be submitted to FDA, within 5 days of a change in the designated agent information.

(b) U.S.-designated agents of foreign manufacturers are required to:

(1) Report to FDA in accordance with Secs. 803.50, 803.52, 803.53, 803.55, and 803.56;

(2) Conduct, or obtain from the foreign manufacturer the necessary information regarding, the investigation and evaluation of the event to comport with the requirements of Sec. 803.50;

(3) Certify in accordance with Sec. 803.57;

(4) Forward MDR complaints to the foreign manufacturer and maintain documentation of this requirement;

(5) Maintain complaint files in accordance with Sec. 803.18; and

(6) Register, list, and submit premarket notifications in accordance with part 807 of this chapter.

ATTACHMENT D

TITLE 21—FOOD AND DRUGS

FOOD AND DRUG ADMINISTRATION, DEPARTMENT OF HEALTH AND HUMAN SERVICES

PART 807—ESTABLISHMENT REGISTRATION AND DEVICE LISTING FOR MANUFACTURERS AND DISTRIBUTORS OF DEVICES

Subpart A—General Provisions

Sec. 807.3 Definitions.

(a) Act means the Federal Food, Drug, and Cosmetic Act.

(b) Commercial distribution means any distribution of a device intended for human use which is held or offered for sale but does not include the following:

(1) Internal or interplant transfer of a device between establishments within the same parent, subsidiary, and/or affiliate company;

(2) Any distribution of a device intended for human use which has in effect an approved exemption for investigational use pursuant to section 520(g) of the act and part 812 of this chapter; or

(3) Any distribution of a device, before the effective date of part 812 of this chapter, that was not introduced or delivered for introduction into interstate commerce for commercial distribution before May 28, 1976, and that is classified into class III under section 513(f) of the act: Provided, That the device is intended solely for investigational use, and under section 501(f)(2)(A) of the act the device is not required to have an approved premarket approval application as provided in section 515 of the act.

(c) Establishment means a place of business under one management at one general physical location at which a device is manufactured, assembled, or otherwise processed.

(d) Manufacture, preparation, propagation, compounding, assembly, or processing of a device means the making by chemical, physical, biological, or other procedures of any article that meets the definition of device in section 201(h) of the act. These terms include the following activities:

(1) Repackaging or otherwise changing the container, wrapper, or labeling of any device package in furtherance of the distribution of the device from the original place of manufacture to the person who makes final delivery or sale to the ultimate consumer;

(2) Distribution of domestic or imported devices; or

(3) Initiation of specifications for devices that are manufactured by a second party for subsequent commercial distribution by the person initiating specifications.

(e) Official correspondent means the person designated by the owner or operator of an establishment as responsible for the following:

(1) The annual registration of the establishment;

(2) Contact with the Food and Drug Administration for device listing;

(3) Maintenance and submission of a current list of officers and directors to the Food and Drug Administration upon the request of the Commissioner;

(4) The receipt of pertinent correspondence from the Food and Drug Administration directed to and involving the owner or operator and/or any of the firm's establishments; and

(5) The annual certification of medical device reports required by Sec. 804.30 of this chapter or forwarding the certification form to the person designated by the firm as responsible for the certification.

(f) Owner or operator means the corporation, subsidiary, affiliated company, partnership, or proprietor directly responsible for the activities of the registering establishment.

(g) Distributor means any person who furthers the marketing of a device from the original place of manufacture, whether domestic or imported, to the person who makes final delivery or sale to the ultimate consumer or user, but does not repackage, or otherwise change the container, wrapper, or labeling of the device or device package.

(h) Any term defined in section 201 of the act shall have that meaning.

(i) Restricted device means a device for which the Commissioner, by regulation under Sec. 801.109 of this chapter or otherwise under section 520(e) of the act, has restricted sale, distribution, or use only upon the written or oral authorization of a practitioner licensed by law to administer or use the device or upon such other conditions as the Commissioner may prescribe.

(j) Classification name means the term used by the Food and Drug Administration and its classification panels to describe a device or class of devices for purposes of classifying devices under section 513 of the act.

(k) Representative sampling of advertisements means typical advertising material that gives the promotional claims made for the device.

(l) Representative sampling of any other labeling means typical labeling material (excluding labels and package inserts) that gives the promotional claims made for the device.

(m) Material change includes any change or modification in the labeling or advertisements that affects the identity or safety and effectiveness of the device. These changes may include, but are not limited to, changes in the common or usual or proprietary name, declared ingredients or components, intended use, contraindications, warnings, or instructions for use. Changes that are not material may include graphic layouts, grammar, or correction of typographical errors which do not change the content of the labeling, changes in lot number, and, for devices where the biological activity or known composition differs with each lot produced, the labeling containing the actual values for each lot.

(n) 510(k) summary (summary of any information respecting safety and effectiveness) means a summary, submitted under section 513(i) of the act, of the safety and effectiveness information contained in a premarket notification submission upon which a determination of substantial equivalence can be based. Safety and effectiveness information refers to safety and effectiveness data and information supporting a finding of substantial equivalence, including all adverse safety and effectiveness information.

(o) 510(k) statement means a statement, made under section 513(i) of the act, asserting that all information in a premarket notification submission regarding safety and effectiveness will be made available within 30 days of request by any person if the device described in the premarket notification submission is determined to be substantially equivalent. The information to be made available will be a duplicate of the premarket notification submission, including any adverse safety and effectiveness information, but excluding all patient identifiers, and trade secret or confidential commercial information, as defined in Sec. 20.61 of this chapter.

(p) Class III certification means a certification that the submitter of the 510(k) has conducted a reasonable search of all known information about the class III device and other similar, legally marketed devices.

(q) Class III summary means a summary of the types of safety and effectiveness problems associated with the type of device being compared and a citation to the information upon which the summary is based. The summary must be comprehensive and describe the problems to which the type of device is susceptible and the causes of such problems.

(r) U.S.-designated agent means the person, residing in the United States, designated and authorized by the owner or operator of a foreign manufacturer who exports devices into the United States and is responsible for:

(1) Submitting MDR reports,

(2) Submitting annual certifications,

(3) Acting as the official correspondent,

(4) Submitting registration information,

(5) Submitting device listing information, and

(6) Submitting premarket notifications on behalf of the foreign manufacturer.

[42 FR 42526, Aug. 23, 1977, as amended at 43 FR 37997, Aug. 25, 1978; 57 FR 18066, Apr. 28, 1992; 58 FR 46522, Sept. 1, 1993; 59 FR 64295, Dec. 14, 1994; 60 FR 63606, Dec. 11, 1995]

Effective Date Note: At 61 FR 38347, July 23, 1996, in Sec. 807.3, paragraph (r) was stayed indefinitely.

Subpart B—Procedures for Domestic Device Establishments

Sec. 807.20 Who must register and submit a device list.

(a) An owner or operator of an establishment not exempt under section 510(g) of the act or subpart D of this part who is engaged in the manufacture, preparation, propagation, compounding, assembly, or processing of a device intended for human use is required to register and to submit listing information for those devices in commercial distribution, except that listing information may be submitted by the parent, subsidiary, or affiliate company for all the domestic or foreign establishments under the control of one of these organizations when operations are conducted at more than one establishment and there exists joint ownership and control among all the establishments. The term "device" includes all in vitro diagnostic products and in vitro diagnostic biological products not subject to licensing under section 351 of the Public Health Service Act. An owner or operator is required to register its name, places of business, and all establishments and to list the devices whether or not the output of the establishments or any particular device so listed enters interstate commerce. The registration and listing requirements shall pertain to any person who:

(1) Initiates or develops specifications for a device that is to be manufactured by a second party for commercial distribution by the person initiating specifications;

(2) Manufactures for commercial distribution a device either for itself or for another person. However, a person who only manufactures devices according to another person's specifications, for commercial distribution by the person initiating specifications, is not required to list those devices.

(3) Repackages or relabels a device;

(4) Distributors;

(5) Manufactures components or accessories which are ready to be used for any intended health-related purpose and are packaged or labeled for commercial distribution for such health-related purpose, e.g., blood filters, hemodialysis tubing, or devices which of necessity must be further processed by a licensed practitioner or other qualified person to meet the needs of a particular patient, e.g., a manufacturer of ophthalmic lens blanks.

(6) Acts as the U.S.-designated agent as defined in Sec. 807.3(r).

(b) No registration or listing fee is required. Registration or listing does not constitute an admission or agreement or determination that a product is a device within the meaning of section 201(h) of the act.

(c) Distributors of domestic or imported devices must register and fulfill their listing obligations as described in Sec. 807.22(c) of this part. Distributors with multiple sites may submit one registration for all sites or submit a registration for each site. If a multisite distributor chooses to file one registration, the registration must be from the principal business establishment which maintains the MDR complaint files.

(d) Registration and listing requirements shall not pertain to any person who:

(1) Manufacturers devices for another party who both initiated the specifications and commercially distributes the device;

(2) Sterilizes devices on a contract basis for other registered facilities who commercially distribute the devices.

[42 FR 42526, Aug. 23, 1977, as amended at 43 FR 37997, Aug. 25, 1978; 58 FR 46522, Sept. 1, 1993; 60 FR 63606, Dec. 11, 1995]

Effective Date Note: At 61 FR 38347, July 23, 1996, in Sec. 807.20, paragraph (a)(6) was stayed indefinitely.

Sec. 807.21 Times for establishment registration and device listing.

(a) An owner or operator of an establishment who has not previously entered into an operation defined in Sec. 807.20 shall register within 30 days after entering into such an operation and submit device listing information at that time. An owner or operator of an establishment shall update its registration information annually within 30 days after receiving registration forms from FDA. FDA will mail form FDA-2891a to the owners or operators of registered establishments according to a schedule based on the first letter of the name of the owner or operator.

The schedule is as follows:

First letter of owner or operator name	Date FDA will mail forms
A, B, C, D, E............	March.
F, G, H, I, J, K, L, M............	June.
N, O, P, Q, R............	August.
S, T, U, V, W, X, Y, Z............	November.

(b) Owners or operators of all registered establishments shall update their device listing information every June and December or, at their discretion, at the time the change occurs.

[58 FR 46522, Sept. 1, 1993]

Sec. 807.22 How and where to register establishments and list devices.

(a) The first registration of a device establishment shall be on Form FDA-2891 (Initial Registration of Device Establishment). Forms are available upon request from the Office of Compliance, Center for Devices and Radiological Health (HFZ-307), Food and Drug Administration, 2098 Gaither Rd., Rockville, MD 20850, or from Food and Drug Administration district offices. Subsequent annual registration shall be accomplished on Form FDD-2891a (Annual Registration of Device Establishment), which will be furnished by FDA to establishments whose registration for that year was validated under Sec. 807.35(a). The forms will be mailed to the owner or operators of all establishments via the official correspondent in accordance with the schedule as described in Sec. 807.21(a). The completed form shall be mailed to the address designated in this paragraph 30 days after receipt from FDA.

(b) The initial listing of devices and subsequent June and December updatings shall be on form FD-2892 (Medical Device Listing). Forms are obtainable upon request as described in paragraph (a) of this section. A separate form FD-2892 shall be submitted for each device or device class listed with the Food and Drug Administration. Devices having variations in physical characteristics such as size, package, shape, color, or composition should be considered to be one device: Provided, The variation does not change the function or intended use of the device. In lieu of form FD-2892, tapes for computer input or hard copy computer output may by submitted if equivalent in all elements of information as specified in form FD-2892. All formats proposed for use in lieu of form FD-2892 require initial review and approval by the Food and Drug Administration.

(c) The listing obligations of the distributor are satisfied as follows:

(1) The distributor is not required to submit a form FDA-2892 for those devices for which such distributor did not initiate or develop the specifications for the device or repackage or relabel the device. However, the distributor shall submit, for each device, the name and address of the manufacturer. Distributors shall also be pre-pared to submit, when requested by FDA, the proprietary name, if any, and the common or usual name of each device for which they are the distributors; and

(2) The distributor shall update the information required by paragraphs (c)(1) of this section at the intervals specified in Sec. 807.30.

[43 FR 37997, Aug. 25, 1978, as amended at 58 FR 46522, Sept. 1, 1993; 60 FR 63606, Dec. 11, 1995]

Sec. 807.25 Information required or requested for establishment registration and device listing.

(a) Form FD-2891 and Form FD-2891(a) are the approved forms for initially providing the information required by the act and for providing annual registration, respectively. The required information includes the name and street address of the device establishment, including post office ZIP Code, all trade names used by the establishment, and the business trading name of the owner or operator of such establishment.

(b) The owner or operator shall identify the device activities of the establishment such as manufacturing, repackaging, or distributing devices.

(c) Each owner or operator is required to maintain a listing of all officers, directors, and partners for each establishment he registers and to furnish this information to the Food and Drug Administration upon request.

(d) Each owner or operator shall provide the name of an official correspondent who will serve as a point of contact between the Food and Drug Administration and the establishment for matters relating to the registration of device establishments and the listing of device products. All future correspondence relating to registration, including requests for the names of partners, officers, and directors, will be directed to this official correspondent. In the event no person is designated by the owner or operator, the owner or operator of the establishment will be the official correspondent.

(e) The designation of an official correspondent does not in any manner affect the liability of the owner or operator of the establishment or any other individual under section 301(p) or any other provision of the act.

(f) Form FD-2892 is the approved form for providing the device listing information required by the act. This required information includes the following:

(1) The identification by classification name and number, proprietary name, and common or usual name of each device being manufactured, prepared, propagated, compounded, or processed for commercial distribution that has not been included in any list of devices previously submitted on form FD-2892.

(2) The Code of Federal Regulations citation for any applicable standard for the device under section 514 of the act or section 358 of the Public Health Service Act.

(3) The assigned Food and Drug Administration number of the approved application for each device listed that is subject to section 505, 507, or 515 of the act.

(4) The name, registration number, and establishment type of every domestic or foreign device establishment under joint ownership and control of the owner

or operator at which the device is manufactured, repackaged, or relabeled.

(5) Whether the device, as labeled, is intended for distribution to and use by the general public.

(6) Other general information requested on form FD-2892, i.e., (i) if the submission refers to a previously listed device, as in the case of an update, the document number from the initial listing document for the device, (ii) the reason for submission, (iii) the date on which the reason for submission occurred, (iv) the date that the form FD-2892 was completed, (v) the owner's or operator's name and identification number.

(7) Labeling or other descriptive information (e.g., specification sheets or catalogs) adequate to describe the intended use of a device when the owner or operator is unable to find on the Food and Drug Administration list in the device listing package, an appropriate classification name for the device.

[42 FR 42526, Aug. 23, 1977, as amended at 43 FR 37998, Aug. 25, 1978; 58 FR 46523, Sept. 1, 1993]

Sec. 807.26 Amendments to establishment registration.
Changes in individual ownership, corporate or partnership structure, or location of an operation defined in Sec. 807.3(c) shall be submitted on Form FD-2891(a). This information shall be submitted within 30 days of such changes. Changes in the names of officers and/or directors of the corporation(s) shall be filed with the establishment's official correspondent and shall be provided to the Food and Drug Administration upon receipt of a written request for this information.

Sec. 807.30 Updating device listing information.
(a) Form FD-2892 shall be used to update device listing information. The preprinted original document number of each form FD-2892 on which the device was initially listed shall appear in block 2 on the form subsequently used to update the listing information for the device and on any correspondence related to the device.

(b) An owner or operator shall update the device listing information during each June and December or, at its discretion, at the time the change occurs. Conditions that require updating and information to be submitted for each of these updates are as follows:

(1) If an owner or operator introduces into commercial distribution a device identified with a classification name not currently listed by the owner or operator, then the owner or operator must submit form FD-2892 containing all the information required by Sec. 807.25(f).

(2) If an owner or operator discontinues commercial distribution of all devices in the same device class, i.e., with the same classification name, the owner or operator must submit form FD-2892 containing the original document number of the form FD-2892 on which the device class was initially listed, the reason for submission, the date of discontinuance, the owner or operator's name and identification number, the classification name and number, the proprietary name, and the common or usual name of the discontinued device.

(3) If commercial distribution of a discontinued device identified on a form FD-2892 filed under paragraph (b)(2) of this section is resumed, the owner or operator must submit on form FD-2892 a notice of resumption containing: the original document number of the form initially used to list that device class, the reason for submission, date of resumption, and all other information required by Sec. 807.25(f).

(4) If one or more classification names for a previously listed device with multiple classification names has been added or deleted, the owner or operator must supply the original document number from the form FD-2892 on which the device was initially listed and a supplemental sheet identifying the names of any new or deleted classification names.

(5) Other changes to information on form FD-2892 will be updated as follows:

(i) Whenever a change occurs only in the owner or operator name (block 6) or number (block 7), e.g., whenever one company's device line is purchased by another owner or operator, it will not be necessary to supply a separate form FD-2892 for each device. In such cases, the new owner or operator must follow the procedures in Sec. 807.26 and submit a letter informing the Food and Drug Administration of the original document number from form FD-2892 on which each device was initially listed for those devices affected by the change in ownership.

(ii) The owner or operator must also submit update information whenever changes occur to the responses to the questions in blocks 12, 12a, 13, 13a, and 14 on form FD-2892, or whenever establishment registration numbers, establishment names, and/or activities are added to or deleted from blocks 15, 16, and 17 of form FD-2892. The owner or operator must supply the original document number from the form FD-2892 on which the device was initially listed, the reason for submission, and all other information required by Sec. 807.25(f).

(6) Updating is not required if the above information has not changed since the previously submitted list. Also, updating is not required if changes occur in proprietary names, in common or usual names (blocks 10 and 11 of form FD-2892), or to supplemental lists of unclassified components or accessories.

[43 FR 37998, Aug. 25, 1978]

Sec. 807.31 Additional listing information.
(a) Each owner or operator shall maintain a historical file containing the labeling and advertisements in use on the date of initial listing, and in use after October 10, 1978, but before the date of initial listing, as follows:

(1) For each device subject to section 514 or 515 of the act that is not a restricted device, a copy of all labeling for the device;

(2) For each restricted device, a copy of all labeling and advertisements for the device;

(3) For each device that is neither restricted nor subject to section 514 or 515 of the act, a copy of all labels, package inserts, and a representative sampling of any other labeling.

(b) In addition to the requirements set forth in paragraph (a) of this section, each owner or operator shall maintain in the historical file any labeling or advertisements in which a material change has been made anytime after initial listing.

(c) Each owner or operator may discard labeling and advertisements from the historical file 3 years after the date of the last shipment of a discontinued device by an owner or operator.

(d) Location of the file:

(1) Currently existing systems for maintenance of labeling and advertising may be used for the purpose of maintaining the historical file as long as the information included in the systems fulfills the requirements of this section, but only if the labeling and advertisements are retrievable in a timely manner.

(2) The contents of the historical file may be physically located in more than one place in the establishment or in more than one establishment provided there exists joint ownership and control among all the establishments maintaining the historical file. If no joint ownership and control exists, the registered establishment must provide the Food and Drug Administration with a letter authorizing the establishment outside its control to maintain the historical file.

(3) A copy of the certification and disclosure statements as required by part 54 of this chapter shall be retained and physically located at the establishment maintaining the historical file.

(e) Each owner or operator shall be prepared to submit to the Food and Drug Administration, only upon specific request, the following information:

(1) For a device subject to section 514 or 515 of the act that is not a restricted device, a copy of all labeling for the device.

(2) For a device that is a restricted device, a copy of all labeling for the device, a representative sampling of advertisements for the device, and for good cause, a copy of all advertisements for a particular device. A request for all advertisements will, where feasible, be accompanied by an explanation of the basis for such request.

(3) For a device that is neither a restricted device, nor subject to section 514 of 515 of the act, the label and package insert for the device and a representative sampling of any other labeling for the device.

(4) For a particular device, a statement of the basis upon which the registrant has determined that the device is not subject to section 514 or 515 of the act.

(5) For a particular device, a statement of the basis upon which the registrant has determined the device is not a restricted device.

(6) For a particular device, a statement of the basis for determining that the product is a device rather than a drug.

(7) For a device that the owner or operator has manufactured for distribution under a label other than its own, the names of all distributors for whom it has been manufactured.

[43 FR 37999, Aug. 25, 1978, as amended at 51 FR 33033, Sept. 18, 1986; 63 FR 5253, Feb. 2, 1998]

Effective Date Note: At 63 FR 5253, Feb. 2, 1998, Sec. 807.31 was amended by adding new paragraph (d)(3), effective Feb. 2, 1999.

Sec. 807.35 Notification of registrant.

(a) The Commissioner will provide to the official correspondent, at the address listed on the form, a validated copy of Form FD-2891 or Form FD-2891(a) (whichever is applicable) as evidence of registration. A permanent registration number will be assigned to each device establishment registered in accordance with these regulations.

(b) Owners and operators of device establishments who also manufacture or process blood or drug products at the same establishment shall also register with the Center for Biologics Evaluation and Research and Center for Drug Evaluation and Research, as appropriate. Blood products shall be listed with the Center for Biologics Evaluation and Research, Food and Drug Administration, pursuant to part 607 of this chapter; drug products shall be listed with the Center for Drug Evaluation and Research, Food and Drug Administration, pursuant to part 207 of this chapter.

(c) Although establishment registration and device listing are required to engage in the device activities described in Sec. 807.20, validation of registration and the assignment of a device listing number in itself does not establish that the holder of the registration is legally qualified to deal in such devices and does not represent a determination by the Food and Drug Administration as to the status of any device.

[42 FR 42526, Aug. 23, 1977, as amended at 43 FR 37999, Aug. 25, 1978; 53 FR 11252, Apr. 6, 1988]

Sec. 807.37 Inspection of establishment registration and device listings.

(a) A copy of the forms FD-2891 and FD-2891a filed by the registrant will be available for inspection in accordance with section 510(f) of the act, at the Center for Devices and Radiological Health (HFZ-342), Food and Drug Administration, Department of Health and Human Services, 1390 Piccard Dr., Rockville, MD 20850. In addition, there will be available for inspection at each of the Food and Drug Administration district offices the same information for firms within the geographical area of such district office. Upon request, verification of registration number or location of a registered establishment will be provided.

(b)(1) The following information filed under the device listing requirements will be available for public disclosure:

(i) Each form FD-2892 submitted;

(ii) All labels submitted;

(iii) All labeling submitted;

(iv) All advertisements submitted;

(v) All data or information that has already become a matter of public knowledge.

(2) Requests for device listing information identified in paragraph (b)(1) of this section should be directed to the Center for Devices and Radiological Health (HFZ-342), Food and Drug Administration, Department of Health and Human Services, 1390 Piccard Dr., Rockville, MD 20850.

(3) Requests for device listing information not identified in paragraph (b)(1) of this section shall be submitted and handled in accordance with part 20 of this chapter.

[43 FR 37999, Aug. 25, 1978, as amended at 53 FR 11252, Apr. 6, 1988; 55 FR 11169, Mar. 27, 1990]

Sec. 807.39 Misbranding by reference to establishment registration or to registration number.

Registration of a device establishment or assignment of a registration number does not in any way denote approval of the establishment or its products. Any representation that creates an impression of official approval because of registration or possession of a registration number is misleading and constitutes misbranding.

Subpart C—Registration Procedures for Foreign Device Establishments

Sec. 807.40 Establishment registration and device listing for U.S. agents of foreign manufacturers of devices.

(a) Each foreign device manufacturer who exports devices into the

United States shall designate a person as their U.S.-designated agent, who is responsible for:

(1) Submitting MDR reports,

(2) Submitting annual certifications,

(3) Acting as the official correspondent,

(4) Submitting registration information,

(5) Submitting device listing information, and

(6) Submitting premarket notifications.

(b) The foreign manufacturer shall provide FDA with a statement of authorization for their U.S.-designate to perform MDR reporting duties under part 803 of this chapter, and to register, list, and submit premarket notifications under this part. The foreign manufacturer must provide this statement of authorization along with the name, address, and telephone number of the person initially designated, or any subsequent person designated as the U.S.-designated agent, within 5 days of the initial or subsequent designation. Information shall be sent to the Center for Devices and Radiological Health, Medical Device Reporting, Food and Drug Administration, P.O. Box 3002, Rockville, MD 20847-3002.

(c) The U.S.-designated agent of a foreign device manufacturer that exports devices into the United States is required to register the foreign manufacturer's establishments or places of business, and to list the foreign manufacturer's devices, in accordance with subpart B of this part, unless exempt under subpart D of this part, and to submit premarket notifications in accordance with subpart E of this part. The information submitted shall be in the English language.

[60 FR 63606, Dec. 11, 1995]

Effective Date Note: At 61 FR 38347, July 23, 1996, Sec. 807.40 was stayed indefinitely.

Subpart D—Exemptions

Sec. 807.65 Exemptions for device establishments.

The following classes of persons are exempt from registration in accordance with Sec. 807.20 under the provisions of section 510(g) (1), (2), and (3) of the act, or because the Commissioner has found, under section 510(g)(4) of the act, that such registration is not necessary for the protection of the public health:

(a) A manufacturer of raw materials or components to be used in the manufacture or assembly of a device who would otherwise not be required to register under the provisions of this part.

(b) A manufacturer of devices to be used solely for veterinary purposes.

(c) A manufacturer of general purpose articles such as chemical reagents or laboratory equipment whose uses are generally known by persons trained in their use and which are not labeled or promoted for medical uses.

(d) Licensed practitioners, including physicians, dentists, and optometrists, who manufacture or otherwise alter devices solely for use in their practice.

(e) Pharmacies, surgical supply outlets, or other similar retail establishments making final delivery or sale to the ultimate user. This exemption also applies to a pharmacy or other similar retail establishment that purchases a device for subsequent distribution under its own name, e.g., a properly labeled health aid such as an elastic bandage or crutch, indicating "distributed by" or "manufactured for" followed by the name of the pharmacy.

(f) Persons who manufacture, prepare, propagate, compound, or process devices solely for use in research, teaching, or analysis and do not introduce such devices into commercial distribution.

(g) [Reserved]

(h) Carriers by reason of their receipt, carriage, holding or delivery of devices in the usual course of business as carriers.

(i) Persons who dispense devices to the ultimate consumer or whose major responsibility is to render a service necessary to provide the consumer (i.e., patient, physician, layman, etc.) with a device or the benefits to be derived from the use of a device; for example, a hearing aid dispenser, optician, clinical laboratory, assembler of diagnostic x-ray systems, and personnel from a hospital, clinic, dental laboratory, orthotic or prosthetic retail facility, whose primary responsibility to the ultimate consumer is to dispense or provide a service through the use of a previously manufactured device.

(j) Distributors of cigarettes or smokeless tobacco as defined in part 897 of this chapter.

[42 FR 42526, Aug. 23, 1977, as amended at 58 FR 46523, Sept. 1, 1993; 61 FR 44615, Aug. 28, 1996]

Subpart E—Premarket Notification Procedures

Sec. 807.81 When a premarket notification submission is required.

(a) Except as provided in paragraph (b) of this section, each person who is required to register his establishment pursuant to Sec. 807.20 must submit a premarket notification submission to the Food and Drug Administration at least 90 days before he proposes to begin the introduction or delivery for introduction into interstate commerce for commercial distribution of a device intended for human use which meets any of the following criteria:

(1) The device is being introduced into commercial distribution for the first time; that is, the device is not of the same type as, or is not substantially equivalent to, (i) a device in commercial distribution before May 28, 1976, or (ii) a device introduced for commercial distribution after May 28, 1976, that has subsequently been reclassified into class I or II.

(2) The device is being introduced into commercial distribution for the first time by a person required to register, whether or not the device meets the criteria in paragraph (a)(1) of this section.

(3) The device is one that the person currently has in commercial distribution or is reintroducing into commercial distribution, but that is about to be significantly changed or modified in design, components, method of manufacture, or intended use. The following constitute significant changes or modifications that require a premarket notification:

(i) A change or modification in the device that could significantly affect the safety or effectiveness of the device, e.g., a significant change or modification in design, material, chemical composition, energy source, or manufacturing process.

(ii) A major change or modification in the intended use of the device.

(b) A premarket notification under this subpart is not required for a device for which a premarket approval application under section 515 of the act, or for which a petition to reclassify under section 513(f)(2) of the act, is pending before the Food and Drug Administration.

(c) In addition to complying with the requirements of this part, owners or operators of device establishments that manufacture radiation-emitting electronic products, as defined in Sec. 1000.3 of this chapter, shall comply with the reporting requirements of part 1002 of this chapter.

Sec. 807.85 Exemption from premarket notification.

(a) A device is exempt from the premarket notification requirements of this subpart if the device intended for introduction into commercial distribution is not generally available in finished form for purchase and is not offered through labeling or advertising by the manufacturer, importer, or distributor thereof for commercial distribution, and the device meets one of the following conditions:

(1) It is intended for use by a patient named in the order of the physician or dentist (or other specially qualified person); or

(2) It is intended solely for use by a physician or dentist (or other specially qualified person) and is not generally available to, or generally used by, other physicians or dentists (or other specially qualified persons).

(b) A distributor who places a device into commercial distribution for the first time under his own name and a repackager who places his own name on a device and does not change any other labeling or otherwise affect the device shall be exempted from the premarket notification requirements of this subpart if:

(1) The device was in commercial distribution before May 28, 1976; or

(2) A premarket notification submission was filed by another person.

Sec. 807.87 Information required in a premarket notification submission.

Each premarket notification submission shall contain the following information:

(a) The device name, including both the trade or proprietary name and the common or usual name or classification name of the device.

(b) The establishment registration number, if applicable, of the owner or operator submitting the premarket notification submission.

(c) The class in which the device has been put under section 513 of the act and, if known, its appropriate panel; or, if the owner or operator determines that the device has not been classified under such section, a statement of that determination and the basis for the person's determination that the device is not so classified.

(d) Action taken by the person required to register to comply with the requirements of the act under section 514 for performance standards.

(e) Proposed labels, labeling, and advertisements sufficient to describe the device, its intended use, and the directions for its use. Where applicable, photographs or engineering drawings should be supplied.

(f) A statement indicating the device is similar to and/or different from other products of comparable type in commercial distribution, accompanied by data to support the statement. This information may include an identification of similar products, materials, design considerations, energy expected to be used or delivered by the device, and a description of the operational principles of the device.

(g) Where a person required to register intends to introduce into commercial distribution a device that has undergone a significant change or modification that could significantly affect the safety or effectiveness of the device, or the device is to be marketed for a new or different indication for use, the premarket notification submission must include appropriate supporting data to show that the manufacturer has considered what consequences and effects the change or modification or new use might have on the safety and effectiveness of the device.

(h) A 510(k) summary as described in Sec. 807.92 or a 510(k) statement as described in Sec. 807.93.

(i) A financial certification or disclosure statement or both, as required by part 54 of this chapter.

(j) For submissions claiming substantial equivalence to a device which has been classified into class III under section 513(b) of the act:

(1) Which was introduced or delivered for introduction into interstate commerce for commercial distribution before December 1, 1990; and

(2) For which no final regulation requiring premarket approval has been issued under section 515(b) of the act, a summary of the types of safety and effectiveness problems associated with the type of devices being compared and a citation to the information upon which the summary is based (class III summary). The 510(k) submitter shall also certify that a reasonable search of all information known or otherwise available about the class III device and other similar legally marketed devices has been conducted (class III certification), as described in Sec. 807.94. This information does not refer to information that already has been submitted to the Food and Drug Administration (FDA) under section 519 of the act. FDA may require the submission of the adverse safety and effectiveness data described in the class III summary or citation.

(k) A statement that the submitter believes, to the best of his or her knowledge, that all data and information submitted in the premarket notification are truthful and accurate and that no material fact has been omitted.

(l) Any additional information regarding the device requested by the Commissioner that is necessary for the Commissioner to make a finding as to whether or not the device is substantially equivalent to a device in commercial distribution. A request for additional information will advise the owner or operator that there is insufficient information contained in the original premarket notification submission for the Commissioner to make this determination and that the owner or operator may either submit the requested data or a new premarket notification containing the requested information at least 90 days before the owner or operator intends to market the device, or submit a premarket approval application in accordance with section 515 of the act. If the additional information is not submitted within 30 days following the date of the request, the Commissioner will consider the premarket notification to be withdrawn.

(Information collection requirements in this section were approved by the Office of Management and Budget (OMB) and assigned OMB control number 0910-0281)

[42 FR 42526, Aug 23, 1977, as amended at 57 FR 18066, Apr. 28, 1992; 59 FR 64295, Dec. 14, 1994; 63 FR 5253, Feb. 2, 1998]

Effective Date Note: At 63 FR 5253, Feb. 2, 1998, Sec. 807.87 was amended by redesignating paragraphs (i) through (k) as paragraphs (j) through (l), respectively, and by adding a new paragraph (i), effective Feb. 2, 1999.

Sec. 807.90 Format of a premarket notification submission.

Each premarket notification submission pursuant to this part shall be submitted in accordance with this section. Each submission shall:

(a)(1) For devices regulated by the Center for Devices and Radiological Health, be addressed to the Food and Drug Administration, Center for Devices and Radiological Health (HFZ-401), 1390 Piccard Dr., Rockville, MD 20850.

(2) For devices regulated by the Center for Biologics Evaluation and Research, be addressed to the Food and Drug Administration, Center for Biologics Evaluation and Research, Division of Product Certification (HFB-240), 8800 Rockville Pike, Bethesda, MD 20892.

(3) All inquiries regarding a premarket notification submission should be in writing and sent to one of the addresses above.

(b) Be bound into a volume or volumes, where necessary.

(c) Be submitted in duplicate on standard size paper, including the original and two copies of the cover letter.

(d) Be submitted separately for each product the manufacturer intends to market.

(e) Designated "510(k) Notification" in the cover letter.

[42 FR 42526, Aug. 23, 1977, as amended at 53 FR 11252, Apr. 6, 1988; 55 FR 11169, Mar. 27, 1990]

Sec. 807.92 Content and format of a 510(k) summary.

(a) A 510(k) summary shall be in sufficient detail to provide an understanding of the basis for a determination of substantial equivalence. FDA will accept summaries as well as amendments thereto until such time as FDA issues a determination of substantial equivalence. All 510(k) summaries shall contain the following information:

(1) The submitter's name, address, telephone number, a contact person, and the date the summary was prepared;

(2) The name of the device, including the trade or proprietary name if applicable, the common or usual name, and the classification name, if known;

(3) An identification of the legally marketed device to which the submitter claims equivalence. A legally marketed device to which a new device may be compared for a determination regarding substantial equivalence is a device that was legally marketed prior to May 28, 1976, or a device which has been reclassified from class III to class II or I (the predicate), or a device which has been found to be substantially equivalent through the 510(k) premarket notification process;

(4) A description of the device that is the subject of the premarket notification submission, such as might be found in the labeling or promotional material for the device, including an explanation of how the device functions, the scientific concepts that form the basis for the device, and the significant physical and performance characteristics of the device, such as device design, material used, and physical properties;

(5) A statement of the intended use of the device that is the subject of the premarket notification submission, including a general description of the diseases or conditions that the device will diagnose, treat, prevent, cure, or mitigate, including a description, where

appropriate, of the patient population for which the device is intended. If the indication statements are different from those of the legally marketed device identified in paragraph (a)(3) of this section, the 510(k) summary shall contain an explanation as to why the differences are not critical to the intended therapeutic, diagnostic, prosthetic, or surgical use of the device, and why the differences do not affect the safety and effectiveness of the device when used as labeled; and

(6) If the device has the same technological characteristics (i.e., design, material, chemical composition, energy source) as the predicate device identified in paragraph (a)(3) of this section, a summary of the technological characteristics of the new device in comparison to those of the predicate device. If the device has different technological characteristics from the predicate device, a summary of how the technological characteristics of the device compare to a legally marketed device identified in paragraph (a)(3) of this section.

(b) 510(k) summaries for those premarket submissions in which a determination of substantial equivalence is also based on an assessment of performance data shall contain the following information:

(1) A brief discussion of the nonclinical tests submitted, referenced, or relied on in the premarket notification submission for a determination of substantial equivalence;

(2) A brief discussion of the clinical tests submitted, referenced, or relied on in the premarket notification submission for a determination of substantial equivalence. This discussion shall include, where applicable, a description of the subjects upon whom the device was tested, a discussion of the safety or effectiveness data obtained from the testing, with specific reference to adverse effects and complications, and any other information from the clinical testing relevant to a determination of substantial equivalence; and

(3) The conclusions drawn from the nonclinical and clinical tests that demonstrate that the device is as safe, as effective, and performs as well as or better than the legally marketed device identified in paragraph (a)(3) of this section.

(c) The summary should be in a separate section of the submission, beginning on a new page and ending on a page not shared with any other section of the premarket notification submission, and should be clearly identified as a "510(k) summary."

(d) Any other information reasonably deemed necessary by the agency.

[57 FR 18066, Apr. 28, 1992, as amended at 59 FR 64295, Dec. 14, 1994]

Sec. 807.93 Content and format of a 510(k) statement.

(a)(1) A 510(k) statement submitted as part of a premarket notification shall state as follows:

I certify that, in my capacity as (the position held in company by person required to submit the premarket notifica-

tion, preferably the official correspondent in the firm), of (company name), I will make available all information included in this premarket notification on safety and effectiveness within 30 days of request by any person if the device described in the premarket notification submission is determined to be substantially equivalent. The information I agree to make available will be a duplicate of the premarket notification submission, including any adverse safety and effectiveness information, but excluding all patient identifiers, and trade secret and confidential commercial information, as defined in 21 CFR 20.61.

(2) The statement in paragraph (a)(1) of this section should be signed by the certifier, made on a separate page of the premarket notification submission, and clearly identified as "510(k) statement."

(b) All requests for information included in paragraph (a) of this section shall be made in writing to the certifier, whose name will be published by FDA on the list of premarket notification submissions for which substantial equivalence determinations have been made.

(c) The information provided to requestors will be a duplicate of the premarket notification submission, including any adverse information, but excluding all patient identifiers, and trade secret and confidential commercial information as defined in Sec. 20.61 of this chapter.

[59 FR 64295, Dec. 14, 1994]

Sec. 807.94 Format of a class III certification.

(a) A class III certification submitted as part of a premarket notification shall state as follows:

I certify, in my capacity as (position held in company), of (company name), that I have conducted a reasonable search of all information known or otherwise available about the types and causes of safety or effectiveness problems that have been reported for the (type of device). I further certify that I am aware of the types of problems to which the (type of device) is susceptible and that, to the best of my knowledge, the following summary of the types and causes of safety or effectiveness problems about the (type of device) is complete and accurate.

(b) The statement in paragraph (a) of this section should be signed by the certifier, clearly identified as "class III certification," and included at the beginning of the section of the premarket notification submission that sets forth the class III summary.

[59 FR 64296, Dec. 14, 1994]

Sec. 807.95 Confidentiality of information.

(a) The Food and Drug Administration will disclose publicly whether there exists a premarket notification submission under this part:

(1) Where the device is on the market, i.e., introduced or delivered for introduction into interstate commerce for commercial distribution;

(2) Where the person submitting the premarket notification submission has disclosed, through advertising

or any other manner, his intent to market the device to scientists, market analysts, exporters, or other individuals who are not employees of, or paid consultants to, the establishment and who are not in an advertising or law firm pursuant to commercial arrangements with appropriate safeguards for secrecy; or

(3) Where the device is not on the market and the intent to market the device has not been so disclosed, except where the submission is subject to an exception under paragraph (b) or (c) of this section.

(b) The Food and Drug Administration will not disclose publicly the existence of a premarket notification submission for a device that is not on the market and where the intent to market the device has not been disclosed for 90 days from the date of receipt of the submission, if:

(1) The person submitting the premarket notification submission requests in the submission that the Food and Drug Administration hold as confidential commercial information the intent to market the device and submits a written certification to the Commissioner:

(i) That the person considers his intent to market the device to be confidential commercial information;

(ii) That neither the person nor, to the best of his knowledge, anyone else, has disclosed through advertising or any other manner, his intent to market the device to scientists, market analysts, exporters, or other individuals, except employees of, or paid consultants to, the establishment or individuals in an advertising or law firm pursuant to commercial arrangements with appropriate safeguards for secrecy;

(iii) That the person will immediately notify the Food and Drug Administration if he discloses the intent to market the device to anyone, except employees of, or paid consultants to, the establishment or individuals in an advertising or law firm pursuant to commercial arrangements with appropriate safeguards for secrecy;

(iv) That the person has taken precautions to protect the confidentiality of the intent to market the device; and

(v) That the person understands that the submission to the government of false information is prohibited by 18 U.S.C. 1001 and 21 U.S.C. 331(q); and

(2) The Commissioner agrees that the intent to market the device is confidential commercial information.

(c) Where the Commissioner determines that the person has complied with the procedures described in paragraph (b) of this section with respect to a device that is not on the market and where the intent to market the device has not been disclosed, and the Commissioner agrees that the intent to market the device is confidential commercial information, the Commissioner will not disclose the existence of the submission for 90 days from the date of its receipt by the agency. In addition, the Commissioner will continue not to disclose the existence of such a submission for the device for an additional time when any of the following occurs:

(1) The Commissioner requests in writing additional information regarding the device pursuant to Sec.

807.87(h), in which case the Commissioner will not disclose the existence of the submission until 90 days after the Food and Drug Administration's receipt of a complete premarket notification submission;

(2) The Commissioner determines that the device intended to be introduced is a class III device and cannot be marketed without premarket approval or reclassification, in which case the Commissioner will not disclose the existence of the submission unless a petition for reclassification is submitted under section 513(f)(2) of the act and its existence can be disclosed under Sec. 860.5(d) of this chapter; or

(d) FDA will make a 510(k) summary of the safety and effectiveness data available to the public within 30 days of the issuance of a determination that the device is substantially equivalent to another device. Accordingly, even when a 510(k) submitter has complied with the conditions set forth in paragraphs (b) and (c) of this section, confidentiality for a premarket notification submission cannot be granted beyond 30 days after FDA issues a determination of equivalency.

(e) Data or information submitted with, or incorporated by reference in, a premarket notification submission (other than safety and effectiveness data that have not been disclosed to the public) shall be available for disclosure by the Food and Drug Administration when the intent to market the device is no longer confidential in accordance with this section, unless exempt from public disclosure in accordance with part 20 of this chapter. Upon final classification, data and information relating to safety and effectiveness of a device classified in class I (general controls) or class II (performance standards) shall be available for public disclosure. Data and information relating to safety and effectiveness of a device classified in class III (premarket approval) that have not been released to the public shall be retained as confidential unless such data and information become available for release to the public under Sec. 860.5(d) or other provisions of this chapter.

[42 FR 42526, Aug. 23, 1977, as amended at 53 FR 11252, Apr. 6, 1988; 57 FR 18067, Apr. 28, 1992; 59 FR 64296, Dec. 14, 1994]

Sec. 807.97 Misbranding by reference to premarket notification.

Submission of a premarket notification in accordance with this subpart, and a subsequent determination by the Commissioner that the device intended for introduction into commercial distribution is substantially equivalent to a device in commercial distribution before May 28, 1976, or is substantially equivalent to a device introduced into commercial distribution after May 28, 1976, that has subsequently been reclassified into class I or II, does not in any way denote official approval of the device. Any representation that creates an impression of official approval of a device because of complying with the premarket notification regulations is misleading and constitutes misbranding.

Sec. 807.100 FDA action on a premarket notification.

(a) After review of a premarket notification, FDA will:

(1) Issue an order declaring the device to be substantially equivalent to a legally marketed predicate device;

(2) Issue an order declaring the device to be not substantially equivalent to any legally marketed predicate device;

(3) Request additional information; or

(4) Withhold the decision until a certification or disclosure statement is submitted to FDA under part 54 of this chapter.

(5) Advise the applicant that the premarket notification is not required. Until the applicant receives an order declaring a device substantially equivalent, the applicant may not proceed to market the device.

(b) FDA will determine that a device is substantially equivalent to a predicate device using the following criteria:

(1) The device has the same intended use as the predicate device; and

(2) The device:

(i) Has the same technological characteristics as the predicate device; or

(ii)(A) Has different technological characteristics, such as a significant change in the materials, design, energy source, or other features of the device from those of the predicate device;

(B) The data submitted establishes that the device is substantially equivalent to the predicate device and contains information, including clinical data if deemed necessary by the Commissioner, that demonstrates that the device is as safe and as effective as a legally marketed device; and

(C) Does not raise different questions of safety and effectiveness than the predicate device.

(3) The predicate device has not been removed from the market at the initiative of the Commissioner of Food and Drugs or has not been determined to be misbranded or adulterated by a judicial order.

[57 FR 58403, Dec. 10, 1992, as amended at 63 FR 5253, Feb. 2, 1998]

Effective Date Note: At 63 FR 5253, Feb. 2, 1998, Sec. 807.100 was amended by redesignating paragraph (a)(4) as paragraph (a)(5) and by adding a new paragraph (a)(4), effective Feb. 2, 1999.

References and List
of FDA Offices

REFERENCES

FEDERAL FOOD, DRUG, AND COSMETIC ACT, AS AMENDED, 21 USC '321 ET SEQ. MAJOR AMENDMENTS INCLUDE THE FOLLOWING:

1. Medical Device Amendments of 1976.
2. Safe Medical Devices Act of 1990 (SMDA).
3. The FDA Export Reform and Enhancement Act of 1996.
4. The FDA Modernization Act of 1997.

FEDERAL FOOD, DRUG, AND COSMETIC ACT, SPECIFICALLY:

1. Section 501 Adulterated Drugs and Devices
2. Section 503 Exemptions and Consideration for Certain Drugs, Devices, and Biological Products
3. Section 510 Registration of Producers of Drugs and Devices
4. Section 513 Classification of Devices Intended for Human Use
5. Section 514 Performance Standards
6. Section 515 Premarket Approval
7. Section 516 Banned Devices
8. Section 519 Records and Reports on Devices
9. Section 520 General Provisions Respecting Control of Devices Intended for Human Use
10. Section 522 Postmarket Surveillance
11. Section 555 Corrective Actions, Cessation of Dissemination
12. Section 563 Classification of Products
13. Section 704 Inspections
14. Section 801 Imports and Exports

FDA REGULATIONS

1. Code of Federal Regulations, Title 21, Part 11 Electronic Records; Electronic Signatures.
2. Code of Federal Regulations, Title 21, Parts 800 1299, and specifically, 21 CFR 801 Labeling.
3. Code of Federal Regulations, Title 21, Parts 800 1299, and specifically, 21 CFR 803 Medical Device Reporting.
4. Code of Federal Regulations, Title 21, Parts 800 1299, and specifically, 21 CFR 807 Establishment Registration and Device Listing for Manufacturers and Distributors of Devices.
5. Code of Federal Regulations, Title 21, Parts 800 1299, and specifically, 21 CFR 809 In Vitro Diagnostic Device Requirements.
6. Code of Federal Regulations, Title 21, Parts 800 1299, and specifically, 21 CFR 814 Premarket Approval of Medical Devices.
7. Code of Federal Regulations, Title 21, Parts 800 1299, and specifically, 21 CFR 820 Quality System Regulations.

8. Code of Federal Regulations, Title 21, Parts 800 1299, and specifically, 21 CFR 821 Medical Device Tracking Requirements.
9. Code of Federal Regulations, Title 21, Parts 800 1299, and specifically, 21 CFR 860 Medical Device Classification Procedures.
10. Code of Federal Regulations, Title 21, Parts 800 1299, and specifically, 21 CFR 861 Procedures for Performance Standards Development.
11. Code of Federal Regulations, Title 21, Parts 800 1299, and specifically, 21 CFR 862 Clinical Chemistry and Clinical Toxicology Devices.
12. Code of Federal Regulations, Title 21, Parts 800 1299, and specifically, 21 CFR 864 Hematology and Pathology Devices.
13. Code of Federal Regulations, Title 21, Parts 800 1299, and specifically, 21 CFR 866 Immunology and Microbiology Devices.
14. Code of Federal Regulations, Title 21, Parts 800 1299, and specifically, 21 CFR 895 Banned Devices.

FDA DOCUMENTS

Quality System Regulation

Quality Systems Regulation Manual, A Small Entity Compliance Guide for Medical Device Manufacturers, 1st Edition, 1997.

Computers and Software

1. FDA Glossary of Computerized System and Software Development Terminology, August 1995, ORA.
2. Guidance for the Content and Review of 510(k) Notifications for Picture Archiving and Communications Systems (PACS) and Related Devices, draft August 1993.
3. Guideline for the Validation of Blood Establishment Computer Systems, version 1.0, October 1994, CBER.
4. Guide to the Inspections of Software Development Activities (The Software Life Cycle) draft, November 1995, ORA.
5. Guidance for FDA Reviewers and Industry, Guidance for the Content of Premarket Submissions for Software Contained in Medical Devices, May 29, 1998.
6. Guidance for Industry, Computerized Systems Used in Clinical Trials, Draft Guidance, June 18, 1997.
7. Guidance for Industry, General Principles of Software Validation, Draft Guidance, Version 1.1, June 9, 1997, CDRH.
8. Guidance for OfftheShelf Software Use in Medical Devices, Draft Document, August 17, 1998, CDRH.

9. Guidance Concerning Conversion to FDAReviewed Software Products, November 13, 1995, CBER.
10. Application of the Medical Device GMPs to Computerized Devices and Manufacturing Processes, Medical Device GMP Guidance for FDA Investigators, November, 1990.
11. FDA/NLM Software Policy Workshop, September 3–4, 1996.

Design Controls
1. Do It by Design: An Introduction to Human Factors in Medical Devices, 1996, CDRH.
2. Design Control Guidance for Medical Device Manufacturers, March 11, 1997, CDRH.
3. Design Control Inspectional Strategy Report Evaluation, October 23, 1997, CDRH.

Inspections
1. Guide to Inspections of Medical Device Manufacturers, December 1997, ORA.
2. QSIT (Quality System Inspection Technique) Inspection Handbook, October 1998 Draft, ORA.

International Standards
1. Draft Global Harmonization Task Force Study Group 3, Process Validation Guidance, June 1, 1998. FDA recognizes many international standards. For a complete listing, visit CDRH's website at www.fda.gov/cdrh/stdsprog.html.

Labeling
1. Medical Device Labeling: Suggested Format and Content, Draft, April 25, 1997, CDRH.

Medical Device Reporting
1. Medical Device Reporting: An Overview, April, 1996, CDRH.
2. Medical Device Reporting for Manufacturers, Draft, May 4, 1996, FDA.

Premarket Notifications or 510(k)s
1. Premarket Notification 510(k): Regulatory Requirements for Medical Devices, HHS Publication FDA 95-4158, August 1995, CDRH.
2. Deciding When to Submit a 510(k) for a Change to an Existing Device, January 10, 1997, CDRH.
3. Background Information On Reclassification And 515(i) Submission, October 27, 1997, CDRH.
4. Determination of Intended Use for 510(k) Devices Guidance for Industry and CDRH Staff, January 30, 1998, CDRH.
5. A New 510(k) Paradigm: Alternate Approaches to Demonstrating Substantial Equivalence in Premarket Notifications, June 13, 1997, CDRH.

Process Control
1. Guideline on the General Principles of Process Validation, ORA

Product Development Protocol
1. Contents of a Product Development Protocol, Guidance for Industry (Draft), April 23, 1998, CDRH.

Registration and Listing
1. Instructions for Completion of Medical Device Registration and Listing Forms FDA 2891, 2891a and 2892, July 1997, CDRH.

ISO 9000 STANDARDS

1. ANSI/ISO/ASQC Q9001-1994, Quality Systems—Model for Quality Assurance in Design, Development, Production, Installation, and Servicing.
2. ANSI/ISO/ASQC Q9002-1994, Quality Systems—Model for Quality Assurance in Production, Installation, and Servicing.
3. ANSI/ISO/ASQC Q9000-3-1991, Quality Management and Quality Assurance Standards - Guidelines for the Application of ANSI/ISO/ASQC 9001 to the Development, Supply, and Maintenance of Software.
4. ANSI/ISO/ASQC Q10011-1-1994, Guidelines for Auditing Quality Systems—Auditing.
5. ANSI/ISO/ASQC Q10011-2-1994, Guidelines for Auditing Quality Systems—Qualification Criteria for Quality System Auditors.
6. ANSI/ISO/ASQC Q10011-3-1994, Guidelines for Auditing Quality Systems—Management of Audit Programs.

ADDITIONAL REFERENCES

1. AAMI Quality System Standards Handbook for Medical Devices, Association for the Advancement of Medical Instrumentation, Arlington, VA 1997.
2. EU Directive Handbook, Allen R. Bailey and Melinda C. Bailey, St. Lucie Press, Boca Raton, FL 1997.
3. Good Computer Validation Practices, Teri Stokes, et. al., Interpharm Press, Inc., 1994.
4. Guide To Medical Device Regulation, Mark A. Heller, Esq., Thompson Publishing Group, Washington, D.C.
5. The FDA and Worldwide Quality System Requirements Guidebook for Medical Devices, Kimberly A. Trautman, ASQC Quality Press, 1997.
6. The ISO 9000 Handbook, 2nd Edition, edited by Robert W. Peach, CEEM Information Services, Fairfax, VA 1994.

LIST OF FDA OFFICES

FDA Main Office
Food and Drug Administration
5600 Fishers Lane
Rockville, Maryland 20857

District Offices Addresses
Atlanta
60 Eighth Street N.E.
Atlanta, Georgia 30309
telephone: (404) 347-3162; fax: (404) 347-4206

Baltimore
900 Madison Avenue
Baltimore, Maryland 21201
t: (410) 962-4040; f: (410) 962-2307

Boston
One Montvale Avenue, 4th Floor
Stoneham, Massachusetts 02180
t: (617) 279-1675, ext. 178; f: (617) 279-1742

Buffalo
599 Delaware Avenue
Buffalo, New York 14202
t: (716) 551-4461, ext. 3116; f: (716) 551-4470

Chicago
300 S. Riverside Plaza
Suite 550 South
Chicago, Illinois 60606
t: (312) 353-5863, ext. 171; f: (312) 886-3280

Cincinnati
1141 Central Parkway
Cincinnati, Ohio 45202-1097
t: (513) 684-3501, ext. 160; f: (513) 684-2905

Dallas
3310 Live Oak Street
Dallas, Texas 75204
t: (214) 655-5317; f: (214) 655-5331

Denver
Denver Federal Center
Building 20
6th and Kipling Streets
Denver, Colorado 80225-0087
(mail to: P.O. Box 25087, Denver, CO 80225-0087)
t: (303) 236-3041; f: (303) 236-3099

Detroit
1560 East Jefferson Avenue
Detroit, Michigan 48207-3179
t: (313) 226-6260, ext. 105; f: (313) 226-3076

Florida
7200 Lake Ellenor Drive
Suite 120
Orlando, Florida 32809
t: (407) 648-6823; f: (407) 648-6881

Kansas City
11630 West 80th Street
Lenexa, Kansas 66214-3338
(mail to: P.O. Box 15905, Lenexa, KS 66285-5905)
t: (913) 752-2101; f: (913) 752-2111

Los Angeles
19900 MacArthur Boulevard
Suite 300
Irvine, California 92715
t: (714) 798-7755; f: (714) 798-7771

Minneapolis
240 Hennepin Avenue
Minneapolis, Minnesota 55401
t: (612) 334-4100, ext. 154; f: (612) 334-4134

Nashville
297 Plus Park Boulevard
Nashville, Tennessee 37217
t: (615) 781-5388; f: (615) 781-5383

New Jersey
Waterview Corporate Center
10 Waterview Boulevard, 3rd Floor
Parsippany, New Jersey 07054
t: (201) 331-2902; f: (201) 331-2969

New Orleans
4298 Elysian Fields Avenue
New Orleans, Louisiana 70122
t: (504) 589-7166; f: (504) 589-6360

New York
850 Third Avenue
Brooklyn, New York 11232
t: (718) 965-5300, ext. 5707; f: (718) 965-5117

Philadelphia
900 U.S. Customhouse
2nd and Chestnut Streets
Philadelphia, Pennsylvania 19106
t: (215) 597-4390, ext. 4410; f: (215) 597-8212

Seattle
22201 23rd Drive, S.E.
Bothell, Washington 98041-3012
(mail to: P.O. Box 3012, Bothell, WA 98041-3012)
t: (206) 483-4971; f: (206) 483-4996

San Francisco
1431 Harbor Bay Parkway
Alameda, California 94502-7070
t: (510) 337-6820; f: (510) 337-6703

San Juan
466 Fernandez Juncos Avenue
San Juan, Puerto Rico 00901-3223
t: (809) 729-6894; f: (809) 729-6809

International communications may be expedited by sending them to: International Affairs Staff (HFY-50) Food and Drug Administration 5600 Fishers Lane Rockville, Maryland 20857 t: (301) 443-4480; f: (301) 443-7539

Acronym List

483—FDA Form 483, Inspectional Observations

510(k)—From Section 510(k) of the Federal Food, Drug and Cosmetic Act, a submission to FDA for a new device review. See Glossary, Premarket notification.

- A -

AAMI—Association for the Advancement of Medical Instrumentation

ANSI—American National Standards Institute

ASQ—American Society for Quality, formerly ASQC (American Society for Quality Control), U.S. counterpart to ISO

- C -

CASE—Computer-Aided Software Engineering

CBER—Center for Biologics Evaluation and Research (of the FDA)

CDRH—Center for Devices and Radiological Health (of the FDA)

CE—Communaute Europeene, the approval mark of the European Community (EC)

CEC—Commission of the European Communities

CEI—Commission Electrotechnique Internationale or Commission Electrotechnique Internationale

CEN—European Committee for Standardization (European Standards Committee)

CENELEC—Comite Europeen de Normalisation Electrotechnique (European Committee for Electrotechnical Standardization)

CENLECT/TC62—CENELEC Technical Committee for Medical Devices

CFR—Code of Federal Regulations

CGMP or cGMP—Current Good Manufacturing Practice(s)

CHPR—Canadian Health Protectorate Branch (Canadian equivalent of the FDA)

CSA—Canadian Standards Association

- D -

DHF—Design History File

DHSS—Department of Health and Human Services

DHR—Device History Record

DMR—Device Master Record

DSMA—Division of Small Manufacturers Assistance (of the FDA)

- E -

EC—European Community

EIR—Establishment Inspection Report, see Glossary

EMC—Electro Magnetic Compatibility

EN—European Standard

EN46000—European Quality System Standard for Medical Devices

EPROM—Acronym for Erasable Programmable Read-only Memory

- F -

FDA—Food and Drug Administration

FD&C Act—The Food, Drug, and Cosmetic Act (of 1938)

FDAMA—The Food and Drug Administration Modernization Act (of 1997)

FOIA—Freedom of Information Act

FMEA—Failure Mode and Effects Analysis

FMECA—Failure Mode, Effects and Criticality Analysis

FR—Federal Register

FTA—Fault Tree Analysis

- G -

GMP—Good Manufacturing Practice(s)

- H -

HA—Hazard Analysis

HACCP—Hazard Analysis and Critical Control Points

HHS—U.S. Department of Health and Human Services

HIMA—Health Industry Manufacturers Association

- I -

IEC—International Electrotechnical Commission or Commission Electrotechnique Internationale

IEC/TC 62—IEC Technical Committee for Electrical Equipment in Medical Practice

ID—Identification

IDE—Investigational Device Exemption

IEEE—Institute of Electrical and Electronic Engineers

IQ—Installation Qualification

IRB—Institutional Review Board

ISO—The International Organization for Standardization based in Geneva, Switzerland. ISO is a created acronym taken from the Greek word, isos, meaning "equal."

ISO 9000—A group of generic international standards for quality management, quality assurance and implementation of a quality system.

ISO 9001—A specific generic international conformance standard to which a firm, involved with design, development, production, installation and servicing, may comply with and be found compliant.

ISO 9002—A specific generic international conformance standard to which a firm, involved with production, installation and servicing, may comply with and be found compliant.

ISO 9003—A specific generic international conformance standard to which a firm, involved with final inspection and test activity, may comply with and be found compliant.

ISO 9004—A specific generic international conformance standard for Quality Management and Quality System Elements Guideline.

ISO 10011—A specific generic international conformance standard for Quality Assurance Auditing Guideline.

ISO 10013—A specific generic international conformance standard for Quality Manuals.

ISO 13485—A specific generic international conformance standard that combines ISO 9000 and EN46000.

ISO 14000—Refers to a specific generic international conformance standard for Environmental Control Systems.

ISO/TC—ISO Technical Committee

IVD—In Vitro Diagnostics

- M -

MDR—Medical Device Report(ing)

MVaP—Master Validation Plan

MVeP—Master Verification Plan

- N -

NAI—No Action Indicated. A conclusion made by the FDA's Inspection Branch following an FDA inspection on the level of action taken against a firm, this classification indicates that no apparent corrective action is required.

NIH—National Institutes of Health

NIST—National Institute of Standards and Technology

- O -

OAI—Official Action Indicated. A conclusion made by the FDA's Inspection Branch following an FDA inspection on the level of action taken against a firm, this classification indicates that regulatory action, Warning Letter, other administrative action and firm corrective action is required. Copy of Report is supplied to the FDA's appropriate compliance branch.

OC—Office of Compliance (of FDA)

OC—Office of the Commissioner (of FDA)

ODE—Office of Device Evaluation (of FDA)

OEA—Office of External Affairs (of FDA)

OELPS—Office of Establishment Licensing and Product Surveillance (of FDA)

OO—Office of Operations (of FDA)

ORA—Office of Regulatory Affairs (of FDA)

OSR—Office of Standards and Regulations (of FDA)

OST—Office of Science and Technology (of FDA)

- P -

PAI—Pre-Approval Inspection

PDP—Product Development Protocol

PMA—Premarket approval—see Glossary

PQ—Process/Performance Qualification

- Q -

QA—Quality Assurance

QC—Quality Control

QS—Quality System—see Glossary

QSR—Quality System Regulation

- R -

RA—Risk Analysis

RAB—Registration Accreditation Board, the U.S. ISO 9000 accreditation body

- S -

SDS—System Design Specification

Sec.—Section(s) of Federal Regulations or United States Code

secs—Sections of United States Code

SMDA—Safe Medical Devices Act (of 1990)

SOP or SOPs—Standard Operating Procedure(s)

- T -

TQ—Total Quality

TQM—Total Quality Management

- U -

U.S.—United States

U.S.C. or USC—United States Code

- V -

V&V—Verification and Validation

VV&T—Verification, Validation and Testing

Glossary

Absurd conditions are those testing activities that are performed even though there is little likelihood the conditions will occur during normal medical device use.*

Accessory is any finished unit distributed separately but intended to be attached to or used in conjunction with another finished device.*

Act means the Federal Food, Drug, and Cosmetic Act, as amended (secs. 201-903, 52 Stat. 1040 et seq., as amended (21 U.S.C. 321-394)). Note: Also referred to as the FD&C Act.

Adulterated (device) means any device found, in whole, part, or its container, to consist of any filthy, putrid, or decomposed substance; does not conform with an applicable performance standard; does not have a required premarket approval; is a banned device; is manufactured, packaged, stored or installed in a manner in violation of applicable regulations; or fails to comply with an applicable exemption for an investigational use device.*

Become aware means that an employee of the entity required to report has acquired information reasonably suggesting a reportable adverse event has occurred. Device user facilities are considered to have "become aware" when medical personnel, who are employed by or otherwise formally affiliated with the facility, acquire such information about a reportable event. Manufacturers are considered to have "become aware" of an event when:

(1) Any employee becomes aware of a reportable event that is required to be reported within 30 days, or that is required to be reported within 5 days pursuant to a written request from FDA under 803.53(b); and

(2) Any employee, who is a person with management or supervisory responsibilities over persons with regulatory, scientific, or technical responsibilities, or a person whose duties relate to the collection and reporting of adverse events, becomes aware that a reportable MDR event or events, from any information, including any trend analysis, necessitate remedial action to prevent an unreasonable risk of substantial harm to the public health.*

Beta testing is testing of a finished medical device performed at a user's facility.*

Bottom-up inspection was FDA's standard inspection process for routine good manufacturing practice (GMP) inspections prior to 1998. Investigators were taught to start inspections by investigating one or more instances of quality problems, such as complaints or recalls, as a strategy to evaluate each manufacturer's GMP compliance.*

Caused or contributed means that a death or serious injury was or may have been attributed to a medical device, or that a medical device was or may have been a factor in a death or serious injury, including events occurring as a result of:

(1) Failure;

(2) Malfunction;

(3) Improper or inadequate design;

(4) Manufacture;

(5) Labeling; or

(6) User error.*

Class I medical devices are subject only to FDA's general controls because they are the least complicated and present the least risk. FDA's general controls are thought to provide reasonable assurance of these devices' safe and effective use.*

Class II medical devices are more complicated and present greater risks than Class I devices. Class II devices are subject to FDA's general controls and, because those controls are insufficient to provide reasonable assurance of their safety and effectiveness, any specific performance standard, postmarket surveillance, patient registry, guidelines, and premarket notification requirements promulgated by FDA. See Premarket Notification, below.*

Class III medical devices are devices that cannot be classified as Class I or Class II because general controls and special controls are insufficient to provide reasonable assurance of their safety and effectiveness and the device is represented to be used in supporting or sustaining human life and the device presents a potential unreasonable risk of illness or injury. See Premarket Approval, below.*

Complaint means any written, electronic, or oral communication that alleges deficiencies related to the identity, quality, durability, reliability, safety, effectiveness, or performance of a device.

Component means any raw material, substance, piece, part, software, firmware, labeling, or assembly which is intended to be included as part of the finished, packaged, and labeled device.

Control chart is a graphic representation of any characteristic of a process or any process output documenting individually plotted statistical values, a central line, and one or two control limits used to assess the state of control and maintain statistical control of any process or output.*

Controlled document means a document subject to procedural control as well as review and approval by an appropriate individual or group.*

Control number means any distinctive symbols, such as a distinctive combination of letters or numbers, or both, from which the history of the manufacturing, packaging, labeling, and distribution of a unit, lot, or batch of finished devices can be determined.

Correction means the repair, modification, adjustment, relabeling, destruction, or inspection (including patient monitoring) of a device without its physical removal from its point of use to some other location.*

Design History File means a compilation of records which describe the complete design history of a finished device.

Design input means the physical and performance requirements of a device that are used as a basis for device design.

Design output means the results of a design effort at each design phase and at the end of the total design effort. The total finished design output consists of the device, its packaging and labeling, the associated specifications and drawings, and the production and quality assurance specifications and procedures. The finished design output will be the basis for the device master record.

Design review means a documented, comprehensive, systematic examination of a design to evaluate the adequacy of the design requirements, to evaluate the capability of the design to meet these requirements, and to identify problems and propose the development of solutions.

Design risk analysis is the ongoing investigation of available information to identify hazards, potential failures, their causes or mechanisms, and degree of risk to ensure these risks are addressed during the design process or any subsequent design review and change.

Design validation means establishing by objective evidence that device specifications conform with user needs and intended use(s).

Device means an instrument, apparatus, implement, machine, contrivance, implant, in vitro reagent, or other similar or related article, including any component, part, or accessory, which is—
  (1) recognized in the official National Formulary, the United States Pharmacopoeia, or any supplement to them,
  (2) intended for use in the diagnosis of disease or other conditions, or in the cure, mitigation, treatment, or prevention of disease, in man or other animals, or
  (3) intended to affect the structure or any function of the body of man or other animals, and which does not achieve its primary intended purposes through chemical action within or on the body of man or other animals and which is not dependent upon being metabolized for the achievement of its primary intended purposes. [Title 21, USC, Section 201 (h)]*

Device history record (DHR) means a compilation of records containing the production history of a finished device.

Device master record (DMR) means a compilation of records containing the procedures and specifications for a finished device.

Directions for use provides directions under which the practitioner or layman (e.g., patient or unlicensed health care provider), as appropriate, can use the device safely and for the purposes for which it is intended. Directions for use also include indications for use and appropriate contraindications, warnings, precautions and adverse reaction information. Directions for use requirements applicable to prescription and over-the-counter devices appear throughout 21 CFR Part 801.*

Documentation means any records, written, electronic or automated, that provide information describing, defining, specifying, reporting, certifying, or auditing any manufacturer's FDA regulatory activities, requirements, verifications or validations.*

Establish means define, document (in writing or electronically), and implement.

Establishment Inspection Report (EIR) is the report completed by the FDA investigators after the inspection that is completed and forwarded to their district office. This report is lengthy and provides details of the firm, its management, products, the inspection, investigator's findings, and concerns related to the "objectionable conditions or practices" that were identified in the 483 as "observations."*

Expected life of a device (required on the manufacturer's baseline report) means the time that a device is expected to remain functional after it is placed into use. Certain implanted devices have specified "end of life" (EOL) dates. Other devices are not labeled as to their respective EOL, but are expected to remain operational through maintenance, repair, upgrades, etc., for an estimated period of time.*

Failure Mode and Effects Analysis (FMEA) is an inductive technique that assesses the frequency and consequence of individual fault modes related to product functions and components.*

Failure Mode, Effects and Criticality Analysis (FMECA) is a FMEA process that includes an assessment of the criticality of identified fault modes.*

Fault Tree Analysis (FTA) is a systematic inductive technique that diagrams information on a system and can be used to assess a system's known, probable, or potential failures.*

Federal Register is the legal newspaper published every business day by the National Archives and Records Administration (NARA). It contains federal agency regulations; proposed rules and notices; and executive orders, proclamations, and other presidential documents. The *Federal Register* informs citizens of their rights and obligations and provides access to a wide range of federal benefits and opportunities for funding. NARA's Office of the *Federal Register* prepares the *Federal Register* for publication in partnership with the Government Printing Office (GPO), which distributes it in paper, on microfiche, and on the worldwide web.*

Finished device means any device or accessory to any device that is suitable for use or capable of functioning, whether or not it is packaged, labeled, or sterilized.

Five-day report means a medical device report that must be submitted by a manufacturer to FDA pursuant to 803.53, on FDA Form 3500A or electronic equivalent as approved under 803.14, within 5 work days.*

Form FDA 482, Notice of Inspection is the form FDA presents to firms immediately prior to an inspection. Typically the form is presented to the senior management individual available at the firm.*

Form FDA 483, Inspectional Observations is the form FDA presents to inspected firms at the end of each inspection. Typically the form is presented to the senior management individual available at the firm.*

General Controls include an establishment's FDA registration (Form FDA 2891), product listing (Form FDA 2892), compliance with FDA's good manufacturing practice regulations, now called Quality System Regulations, and adverse event reporting or FDA's Medical Device Reporting regulations.*

Guidelines establish principles or practices of general applicability and do not include decisions or advice on particular situations. Guidelines relate to performance characteristics, pre-clinical and clinical test procedures, manufacturing practices, product standards, scientific protocols, compliance criteria, ingredient specifications, labeling, or other technical or policy criteria. Guidelines state procedures or standards of general applicability that are not legal requirements but are acceptable to FDA for a subject matter which falls within the laws administered by the Commissioner.*

Human factors are those design activities that address the human interface, e.g., the device and user performance, and the user's training in the operation, maintenance and installation of a medical device.*

Installation qualification (IQ) means establishing by objective evidence that all key aspects of the process, process equipment, and ancillary system installation adhere to the approved design criteria and that the recommendations of the manufacturer of the equipment are suitably considered.*

Intended use is the objective intent of the manufacturer or person(s) legally responsible for the labeling of devices and includes labeling claims, advertising matter, oral or written statements by such firms or their representatives.*

ISO The International Organization for Standardization (ISO) is based in Geneva, Switzerland. ISO is a created acronym taken from the Greek word *isos*, meaning "equal."*

ISO 9000 A group of generic international standards for quality management, quality assurance, and implementation of a quality system.*

ISO 9001 A specific generic international conformance standard to which a firm involved with design, development, production, installation and servicing may comply and be found compliant.*

Label is a display of written, printed or graphic matter upon the immediate container of any article. [Act, section 201(k).]*

Labeling includes all labels and other written, printed or graphic matter (1) upon any article or any of its containers

or wrappers, or (2) accompanying such article. [Act, section 201(m).]*

Lead auditor is the individual responsible for auditing management and finalization of audit findings and reports.*

Lot or batch means one or more components or finished devices that consist of a single type, model, class, size, composition, or software version that are manufactured under essentially the same conditions and that are intended to have uniform characteristics and quality within specified limits.

Malfunction means the failure of a device to meet its performance specifications or otherwise perform as intended. Performance specifications include all claims made in the labeling for the device. The intended performance of a device refers to the intended use for which the device is labeled or marketed, as defined in § 801.4.*

Management with executive responsibility means those senior employees of a manufacturer who have the authority to establish or make changes to the manufacturer's quality policy and quality system.

Manufacturer means any person who designs, manufactures, fabricates, assembles, or processes a finished device. Manufacturer includes but is not limited to those who perform the functions of contract sterilization, installation, relabeling, remanufacturing, repacking, or specification development, and initial distributors of foreign entities performing these functions.

Manufacturing material means any material or substance used in or used to facilitate the manufacturing process, a concomitant constituent, or a byproduct constituent produced during the manufacturing process, which is present in or on the finished device as a residue or impurity not by design or intent of the manufacturer.

Master verification or validation plan is a document that identifies all responsibilities, expectations, systems, and subsystems involved with a specific verification or validation activity and the qualification approaches that ensure verification or total system validation.*

MDR means medical device report or medical device reporting.*

MDR reportable event (or reportable event) means:
(1) An event about which user facilities become aware of information that reasonably suggests that a device has or may have caused or contributed to a death or serious injury; or
(2) An event about which manufacturers have received or become aware of information that reasonably suggests that one of their marketed devices:
  (i) May have caused or contributed to a death or serious injury; or
  (ii) Has malfunctioned and that the device or a similar device marketed by the manufacturer would be likely to cause or contribute to a death or serious injury if the malfunction were to recur.*

MedWatch Report refers to Form FDA 3500A, required for MDR filings.*

Miranda Warning is the statement U.S. police officers must make to inform anyone taken into custody that they have a right to counsel and to remain silent and that the courts will provide a lawyer for those who cannot afford to pay for such representation.*

Misbranded means a device's labeling provides false or misleading information in any particular.*

Misleading mean that labeling is deceptive if it creates or leads to a false impression in the mind of a reader.*

Nonconformity means the nonfulfillment of a specified requirement.

Operational qualification (OQ) means establishing by objective evidence parameters that result in product that meets all predetermined requirements.*

Pareto analysis is the use of a Pareto bar chart with problems prioritized in descending order of importance, providing users with information on the state of control associated with these problems.*

Performance qualification (PQ) means establishing by objective evidence that the process, under anticipated conditions, including worst case conditions, consistently produces a product that meets all predetermined requirements.*

Permanent means irreversible impairment or damage to a body structure or function, excluding trivial impairment or damage.*

Predicate device is a medical device legally marketed prior to May 28, 1976, the date of The Medical Device Amendments of 1976 enactment. A predicate device is required for all Class I or Class II medical devices.*

Premarket approval (PMA) is a process by which Class III medical devices are approved to enter into interstate commerce. Typically a PMA requires detailed labeling that identifies the intended use of the device, clinical and nonclinical studies documenting safety and effectiveness, and a detailed summary of the medical device's design, development, verification, validation, manufacturing, and distribution.*

Premarket notification or 510(k) is a process by which a submitter notifies the FDA at least 90 days prior to the introduction of any appropriate device (some Class I and most Class II devices) into interstate commerce. The submission must include a product classification based on safety and effectiveness. Based on the information submitted, the FDA determines whether the product is substantially equivalent to a legally marketed predicate device. When FDA makes that finding, the submitter is notified and may market the device. These submissions are called 510(k)s because the report submission requirement is identified in the Act under section 510(k).*

Process is a combination of people, equipment, machines, tools, including software, raw materials, methods, and an environment that results in a specific product or service.*

Process validation means establishing by objective evidence that a process consistently produces a result or product meeting its predetermined specifications.

Product means components, manufacturing materials, in-process devices, finished devices, and returned devices.

Quality means the totality of features and characteristics that bear on the ability of a device to satisfy fitness-for-use, including safety and performance.

Quality audit means an established systematic, independent examination of a manufacturer's quality system that is performed at defined intervals and at sufficient frequency to determine whether both quality system activities and the results of such activities comply with quality system procedures, that these procedures are implemented effectively, and that these procedures are suitable to achieve quality system objectives.

Quality policy means the overall quality intentions and direction of an organization with respect to quality, as established by management with executive responsibility.

Quality system means the organizational structure, responsibilities, procedures, processes, and resources for implementing quality management. [Note: Quality system includes all activities previously referred to by FDA as "quality assurance."]

Quality System Inspection Technique (QSIT) is FDA's latest inspection strategy. QSIT involves what FDA calls "top-down" inspections of the four major subsystems of each device manufacturer's quality system: their management controls, design controls, corrective and preventive actions, and production and process controls.*

Record means any written, electronic or automated document, including books, manuals, papers, photographs, and machine-readable materials, which contain specifications, procedures, work instructions, protocols, standards, methods, plans, files, notes, reviews, analyses, corrections or changes, checklists, reports, training materials or instructions, regardless of their physical form or characteristics, made during the design, development, change, testing, manufacture, review, approval, labeling, packaging, promotion, shipment, distribution, service or support of any regulated medical device.*

Redact means to blot out, line out, obliterate, and render unreadable.*

Regulations are the FDA's implementation of federal law. Regulations require preannouncement, publishing in the *Federal Register,* a public comment period and review of that comment prior to finalization.*

Remedial action means any action other than routine maintenance or servicing, of a device where such action is necessary to prevent recurrence of a reportable event.*

Removal means the physical removal of a device from its point of use to some other location for repair, modification, adjustment, relabeling, destruction, or inspection.*

Reprocessing means all or part of a manufacturing operation which is intended to correct nonconformance in a component or finished device before distribution.

Requirements are documented functions, conditions or capabilities that a medical device must meet or possess to satisfy user's needs, standards or regulatory expectations.*

Rework means action taken on a nonconforming product so that it will fulfill the specified DMR requirements before it is released for distribution.

Risk analysis is the ongoing investigation of available information to identify hazards and estimate their risk.*

Risk management is the systematic application of management policies, procedures, and practices to identification, analyses, control, and monitoring of risks.*

Risk to health means

(1) A reasonable probability that use of, or exposure to, the product will cause serious adverse health consequences or death; or

(2) That use of, or exposure to, the product may cause temporary or medically reversible adverse health consequences, or an outcome where the probability of serious adverse health consequences is remote.*

Root cause is the most basic cause of any undesirable condition or problem, which when eliminated or mitigated will prevent or significantly reduce the effect of the condition or problem.*

Serious injury means an injury or illness that:

(i) Is life-threatening;

(ii) Results in permanent impairment of a body function or permanent damage to body structure; or

(iii) Necessitates medical or surgical intervention to preclude permanent impairment of a body function or permanent damage to a body structure.*

Situation I conditions are those conditions that provide evidence "that the manufacturing process is producing nonconforming and/or defective finished devices." Under Situation I conditions, inspectors identify "system-wide deficiencies" and are instructed to terminate the routine inspection and issue an FDA Form 483 list of observations. These inspections usually result in a Warning Letter.*

Situation II conditions are those conditions that do not meet the description of Situation I. Inspectors are instructed to complete the inspection and issue an FDA Form 483 list of observations.*

Specification means any requirement with which a product, process, service, or other activity must conform.

Statistic is any value calculated from or based upon sampling data used to assess a process or the sampled output of a process.*

Statistical Process Control (SPC) is the use of statistical techniques to analyze any process or the outputs of any process to provide information on the state of control of the process or output and improve the capability of the process or improve the quality of the output.*

Table-top inspection is an inspection strategy of reviewing a firm's written procedures and, perhaps, records from a fixed location such as an office or table-top and not performing audits of practices and records at the location in which they are created or implemented.*

Test plan is a step-by-step plan to be followed during the verification or validation of a product or process.*

Top-down Inspection is FDA's newest inspection strategy. Inspectors are taught to evaluate device manufacturers' "quality systems," starting with the firm's quality policy, quality system procedures, and quality plan and to "touch bottom" by sampling each firm's quality system records.*

Track I inspection is a limited inspection of a manufacturer's quality system performed by FDA every two years.*

Track II inspection is a complete audit of a manufacturer's quality system performed by FDA every four years.*

Trends are patterns identified on a control chart that demonstrate the continued rise or fall of a series of data points.*

Validation means confirmation by examination and provision of objective evidence that the particular requirements for a specific intended use can be consistently fulfilled.

Verification means confirmation by examination and provision of objective evidence that specified requirements have been fulfilled.*

Warning Letter is an administrative action typically issued to firms with Situation I conditions identified on their Form FDA 483 observations. Warning Letters require a written response from the firm within 15 working days.*

*Definitions without an asterisk are quoted from the FDA's Quality System Regulations.

Index

Page numbers in italic indicate figures. Page numbers followed by "t" indicate tables.

ABOUT THE AUTHOR

The author is president of Oracle Consulting Group, 5398 Golder Ranch Road, Suite 1, Tucson, Arizona 85739. Oracle Consulting Group is a consulting firm specializing in quality system implementation and Food and Drug Administration (FDA) medical device compliance, including submission of premarket notifications.

Mr. Harnack served as a Captain in the U.S. Army and was a Laboratory Officer, MSC, USA, at Darnall Army Hospital, Ft. Hood, Texas. He has held positions with a variety of manufacturers of in-vitro diagnostic, medical device, and clinical software products. Included in those positions were senior management positions in sales and marketing, including Vice-President, and Director of Sales and Marketing.

Mr. Harnack has assisted in or directed the compliance efforts pertaining to FDA oversight of in-vitro diagnostic firms, regulated medical device manufacturers, and regulated software manufacturers, including their medical device labeling, quality assurance, and good manufacturing practices (GMP) regulations, now called Quality System Regulations.

Mr. Harnack was the Director of Quality Assurance and Regulatory Affairs, a manufacturer of clinical information system software during the period that the FDA identified one of their stand-alone software products as a regulated "medical device" and imposed device regulations.

Mr. Harnack's consulting clients include a variety of U.S. and foreign medical device manufacturers, clinical information system software manufacturers, institutional members of America's Blood Centers (ABC), a software testing firm, and a legislative consulting firm.

Mr. Harnack is a registered Medical Technologist (MT) ASCP, and a member of the American Society for Quality (ASQ), the Regulatory Affairs Professional Society (RAPS), American Association of Blood Banks (AABB), and the American Society for Training and Development (ASTD). In August 1995, Mr. Harnack successfully completed an ISO 9000 Lead Auditor Training Course accredited by the Registrar Accreditation Board of the ASQ.

COMMENT AND CORRECTION FORM

Oracle Consulting Group encourages any reader to provide their comments and corrections to assist in making future editions of **Mastering and Managing the FDA Maze—Medical Device Overview** a better desk reference. Please feel free to make as many copies of this form as necessary to provide those comments and corrections to our offices. You may also provide comments and corrections by E-mail to *<author@fdamaze.com>*

Optional Information:

Name:_____ Title:_____

Organization:_____

Address:_____

Phone:_____ FAX:_____ E-mail:_____

Comment(s) **[Please provide Chapter and page number]:**

Correction(s) **[Please provide Chapter and page number]:**

Thank you for your information